What contemporaries say ab

"This is more than an authoritative his
has written an ode to science that draw
colorful characters, reversals of fortune, ... and tragedies. Carefully researched and substantive insights into the origins of the field and its evolution are punctuated with engaging personal anecdotes that only he could share. A great read for anyone interested in science and scientists."

– **W. Ian Lipkin, M.D.** (Director, Center for Infection and Immunity, Professor of Epidemiology and Neurology, Mailman School of Public Health, Columbia University, New York City, New York, USA)

"Calisher's book conveys the value of collegial, collaborative, apolitical research and should be an inspiration to the reader. He presents a readily understandable history of the field and makes a convincing, but often ignored case, for investing in field work and in training of the next generation of young scientists. I highly recommend this book for established scientists, students, administrators, and anyone else who might want an enlightening and enjoyable read."

– **Stephen Higgs Ph.D., F.R.E.S., F.A.S.T.M.H.** (Editor-in-Chief, Vector-Borne & Zoonotic Diseases; Biosecurity Research Institute, Associate Vice President for Research, University Distinguished Professor, Kansas State University, Manhattan, Kansas, USA)

"In this book Calisher shares with us his own multi-colored view of the personalities and discoveries of microbe hunters. He does this from a unique vantage point, his own participation in a rich web of highly individualistic colleagues. This borderless camaraderie of scientists serves to further the advance of human joy and culture. They also serve humanity by their achievements."

– **Erling Norrby, M.D., Ph.D.** (Professor, Center for the History of Science, The Royal Swedish Academy of Sciences, Stockholm, Sweden)

"This remarkable book records Charlie Calisher's lifetime career among fellow arbovirologists and the viruses they study, and is an authoritative account of the subject and its history. Many books record, somewhat autobiographically, the peculiar obsessions of eminent scientists, but I know of no other written by such a scientist, who is also a witty raconteur, and who has made it a lifetime habit to travel the world to meet and enjoy the company of all others with the same obsession. This book is a marvelous collection of facts and stories covering all these and more facets of Charlie's broad interests and therefore will be of great interest to a wide range of readers: not only those working on arboviruses and other viruses, but also epidemiologists, historians of science and society, etc. and those wanting a well-furnished mind."

– **Adrian J. Gibbs, Ph.D.** (Emeritus Faculty, Australian National University, Canberra, Australia)

APRIL clayton

What contemporaries say about *Lifting the Impenetrable Veil...*

"Calisher has a keen eye for the strengths and foibles of human nature as well as an encyclopedic knowledge of the field in which he has worked for over half a century. Lifting The Impenetrable Veil *is a compulsively readable memoir of striking comprehension, humor, and wisdom."*

– **John Booss, M.D.** (Departments of Neurology and Laboratory Medicine, Yale University School of Medicine; former National Program Director, Neurology Service, Department of Veterans Affairs, New Haven, Connecticut, USA)

"Current virological research is becoming increasingly driven by new technologies. It is useful to reflect on how we came to be where we are today. Charlie Calisher documents the history of virological exploration and viral haemorrhagic fever research with amusing anecdotes and personal memories. This book will captivate experienced virologists and educate the young. Start reading it and you won't want to stop."

– **Ernest A. Gould, Ph.D.** (Visiting Professor, Aix-Marseille University, Marseille, France)

"This book captures in splendid detail achievements of scientists, past and present, belonging to the special multi-disciplinary fraternity that study arboviruses and hemorrhagic fever viruses. It is replete with personal anecdotes, occasional humor and, most importantly, Charlie Calisher's special perspective on the progress and current status of this exciting area of infectious disease research. This book will be of interest not only to scientists in the field but to those with a more casual interest in these fascinating agents."

– **Harvey Artsob, Ph.D.** (former Director, Zoonotic Diseases and Special Pathogens Program, National Microbiology Laboratory, Public Health Agency of Canada)

"What gives this book its unique and special flair is the personal perspective, narrated with nostalgia, humor, and a clear respect for those who paved the way. The anecdotal stories are priceless gems that give the reader a true sense of the people involved in these adventures. Even if the reader has never met any of these individuals, by the end of the book, they feel a personal connection to these scientists and their passion for arbovirology. This book is essential for any virologist with a love of history."

– **Ann Powers, Ph.D.** (Chief, Alphavirus Laboratory, Division of Vector-Borne Diseases, National Center for Emerging and Zoonotic Infectious Diseases, Centers for Disease Control and Prevention, Fort Collins, Colorado, USA)

"This is a delightful book, well-written and humorous, that can be read by both the lay public and the molecular biologist with an understanding and interest in the unfolding panoply of a fascinating and important branch of microbiology."

– **C.J. Peters, M.D.** (Professor of Pathology, Microbiology and Immunology, W.H.O. Collaborating Center for Tropical Diseases, University of Texas Medical Branch, Galveston, Texas, USA)

Lifting the Impenetrable Veil: From Yellow Fever to Ebola Hemorrhagic Fever and SARS

Printed in the United States of America
First Edition June 2013
Revised March 2014

Cover concept: Charles H. Calisher
Layout and electronic pre-press: Gail Blinde, Fort Collins, Colorado

Funded in part by Yale School of Public Health, New Haven, Connecticut

history; science; arboviruses; viruses; virology; epidemiology; public health

ISBN-13: 978-0-615-82773-5

Rockpile Press, Fort Collins, Colorado 80524

Lifting the Impenetrable Veil: From Yellow Fever to Ebola Hemorrhagic Fever and SARS

Charles H. Calisher, Ph.D.

Professor, Arthropod-borne and Infectious Diseases Laboratory, Department of Microbiology, Immunology and Pathology, College of Veterinary Medicine and Biomedical Sciences, Colorado State University, 3195 Rampart Rd., Delivery Code 1690, Foothills Campus, Fort Collins, CO 80523-1690. E-mail: calisher@ cybersafe.net

"To do science is to search for repeated patterns, not simply to accumulate facts."

– Robert A. MacArthur (1972) Geographical ecology: patterns in the distribution of species. New York: Harper and Row

ROCKPILE PRESS
Fort Collins, Colorado

TABLE OF CONTENTS

Page

FOREWORD

Charles Calisher has written a very personal history of the subject he loves so much – arbovirology (and hemorrhagic fever virology). Although he has used chronological and geographic perspectives, the heart of his book lies in his personal perspective, his memory-based view of the people who developed the field, especially the people who advanced the field throughout the middle years of the twentieth century.

With the discovery of the major arbovirus pathogens in the course of adventuresome field expeditions and the biological characterization of these viruses in laboratories during this era, the field and lab workers became a community, a community separate from the nearby larger and associated communities of the infectious disease, microbiology and public health scientists – and even rather separate from the rest of the field of virology. This community seemed to be populated by more than the expected number of colorful and unique characters. It became a very closely knit community, held together by lifelong friendships and personal trust, a sharing of risk (since many of the viruses posed real dangers to the scientists who worked with them), and in many instances an intent to advance the public health and welfare. Charlie has been in the middle of this community for more than 50 years, mostly while at the Centers for Disease Control in Fort Collins, Colorado and later at Colorado State University. In one way or another, all of the players in arbovirology came into his life, those from the older generation who had done their great work before his time to those of the following generation, his peers.

Throughout this era, incredible change in the science took place, shifting from an early emphasis on exploring the planet to define the diversity of its arbovirus fauna, and to explore the connection of viruses to human and animal diseases. Emphasis moved from natural history, with its biologic, diagnostic, epidemiologic, ecologic and whole-organism experimental tacks to the emerging molecular approaches: molecular biology, molecular epidemiology, and molecular ecology. During the span of Charlie's career, the dominance of field work and the lab work to support it gave way to molecular technologies, "rationally designed" experimentation, and an emphasis on "counter-measures" such as vaccines. Within this era there were also political winds mandating change: the erosion of support for and senescence of overseas laboratories supporting field research in the tropics, the concern about bioterrorism, the select agent and biosafety rules, and the increasing difficulty in exchanging materials critical for field research. These changes and the passage of time, have, of course, repopulated the community with scientists with their own friendships, adventures, discoveries, and stories.

Charlie has produced a work that may be seen as a link between the people comprising these "two" generations. He has done this at an auspicious time: many of the people he has written about are retiring or otherwise passing from the scene. This book will serve to remind or inform the current and next generations of arbovirologists of their roots. As always, a generation that fails to understand and appreciate its forebears is doomed to repeat its follies. We live in a world with repeated surprises resulting from new understandings of virus evolution and the complex interactions of viruses, environment, host, and vector, thus posing the question: given our current approach to the science and its funding, are we about to lose something important for the future of the discipline of arbovirology? This question might profitably be kept in mind by the reader, who will find in this book a story of a wonderful era, filled with wonderful people and a rich panoply of discovery. It is a story not otherwise told, a story that might only be told in this way by Charlie Calisher.

Thomas P. Monath, M.D., FACP, FASTMH
Harvard, Massachusetts, USA

Frederick A. Murphy, D.V.M., Ph.D.
Professor, Department of Pathology
University of Texas Medical Branch
Galveston, Texas, USA

2013

DEDICATION

This book is dedicated to all the people not mentioned in this text: disease victims, laboratory technicians, photographers, climatologists, ornithologists, mammalogists, entomologists, veterinarians, physicians, glassware washers, secretaries, journal editors, shipping clerks, property owners, students, taxpayers, and scores of others who did not realize how helpful they were.

PREFACE

For many years I collected viruses, publications, adventures, and stories about arbovirology, mostly for my own amusement. When I shared the stories with younger scientists, they would ask me when I was planning to write a history of the field; I wasn't planning to do that. Nonetheless, when it was clear that no one else was preparing to gather in one place the important discoveries, original thinking, and useful methods devised by the people who built the history of this field or who, often at great risk to themselves, described the nature of the endeavors and of its critical integrative nature, I decided to have a go at it. It has been a daunting and humbling task.

A title being needed to fill the first blank page, I settled on "LIFTING THE IMPENETRABLE VEIL", a phrase taken from a letter written by Walter Reed to his wife in 1900, when he realized he and his colleagues had shown that yellow fever was caused by a virus transmitted by mosquitoes.

> "We have lifted the impenetrable veil that surrounded the causation of this most wonderful, dreadful pest of humanity... the prayer that has been mine for twenty years, that I might be permitted in some way or at some time to do something good to alleviate human suffering has been granted! A thousand Happy New Years." – Walter Reed, in a letter to his wife.

(http://www.rootsweb.ancestry.com/~vaggsv/dr_walter_reed.htm)

It probably is worth relating here how I found myself as an employee at CDC. After I read a 1964 paper in *Science* on Venezuelan equine encephalitis virus in Florida, I wrote to Telford Work, not only an author of that paper but head of arbovirologic studies at the CDC. Much to my chagrin, he did not reply. As I had just been liberated from graduate school and needed some time to ponder the rest of my life, I chose to drive south from Washington, D.C. to visit Ocracoke Island, North Carolina. I had been there previously and knew the weather was decent and the fishing was good at that time of year. Taking some borrowed camping gear, my English cocker spaniel, and a few clothes, off I went in my convertible, a red Austin-Healy Sprite, appropriate for someone who thought he was at the top of the world. Arriving there late in an afternoon, I erected and arranged my tent on the beach but then realized I had made no plans to eat and, given that there were no restaurants nearby, I decided to just read and then go to sleep when it got dark. Two fellows approached my tent and asked me whether I had previously camped and whether I had actually set up a tent in the past. I told them I had camped but had never before set up a tent and asked them why they wanted to know. They told me I had the triangular tent upside down and that the vent was on the ground, when it should have been at the top. Taking pity on me, they invited me to join them and their families for dinner. After they reorganized my tent, we ate, drank some beer and exchanged backgrounds and jokes. They were a marvelous, fun-loving, and generous bunch. One of the men said he worked for the Federal Aviation Administration, the other, James L. Goddard, said he worked at CDC. When I told him I had written to Telford Work and that he had not replied, he suggested that, should I find myself in Atlanta, I might consider dropping by and he would try to connect me with Work.

Because of the acute racial problems in the southern United States at the time and because my mother had been born in Alabama, I asked her what in the world was going on down there. She responded to me that "There are a few nasty people everywhere." I decided to extend my trip a bit and drive around, to see for myself what was happening.

Three young civil rights workers had been murdered in Mississippi the month before, so I knew the situation was not safe. Nonetheless, I drove from Okracoke Island to Florida, Alabama, and then Mississippi, where I stopped in a bar during a rainstorm to get something to eat. Another customer approached my table and asked me whether that was my car with Maryland license plates in the parking lot. When I told him it was, he hit me on the head with a beer bottle, creating quite a laceration. I'd seen enough; not a large sample but an adequate one. Bleeding profusely, I drove directly to Atlanta, about 480 km (300 mi.), to Grady Memorial Hospital, where they put in some stitches, after which I found a motel room.

The next morning I called CDC and asked for Jim Goddard. I was told he would see me immediately, so I drove there, wearing shorts, no socks under my sneakers, and an undershirt with a pack of cigarettes rolled into a sleeve, as was the style then and, leaving my dog in the car and parking in a "No parking" zone, I started the rest of my life.

Jim Goddard turned out not only to work at CDC but was its Director, a uniformed member of the Commissioned Corps of the United States Public Health Service, and Assistant Surgeon General of the United States. He invited me into his office, which had maps on the walls with pins stuck in them, signifying locations where CDC employees were and for what reasons. After we chatted for a while and after a brief wait, Telford Work came to the office. Goddard left us to our conversation and, after a long discussion, I was offered a job. I wonder what my life would have been like had I erected that tent properly.

Goddard invited me to stay the night with his kind family. He asked whether I played bridge. It seems that one of the three others who played bridge with him on a regular basis had had a conflict and they needed a fourth. I agreed to join them, although I was a bit hesitant about that, not knowing how expert the others were. In the evening the two others appeared and we began with introductions. One was J. Donald Millar, M.D. and the other was Donald A. Henderson, M.D., "D.A." as he is called. We played a bit and between hands I asked what they did at CDC. D.A. said, "We are epidemiologists and we are planning to eradicate smallpox." I had a vague idea as to what an epidemiologist did but my first reaction to his statement was that he was trying to pull the leg of a very young and inexperienced guy. All I said was, "Right". I recall that when I left Atlanta it occurred to me that they might not have been joking with me and, if that was the case, CDC was definitely where I wanted to be. They were not joking, as history has shown.

This is a convenient point to mention hiring practices at CDC and elsewhere many years ago. Early on, it was CDC's institutional philosophy to hire people who appeared to show promise. A young physician or Ph.D. who impressed someone at a meeting might be hired and placed in a rotation including bacteriology, virology, mycology, and parasitology laboratories. If he (mostly men at the time) discovered that he was keen on one of those areas of research, he then would be assigned there, possibly making a career at CDC, possibly spending a year or three and then leaving to establish his own laboratory elsewhere in government or at a university or commercial enterprise. People were not hired to fill a position. When that is the policy, as it is today, those who want or need a job will apply; such a policy becomes a gamble on the part of the hiring organization. The Rockefeller Foundation had a policy similar to that of CDC's, which is why so many of its employees were or became world-class and accomplished investigators.

When I was transferred to CDC's Division of Vector-Borne Infectious Diseases in Fort Collins, Colorado in 1973, it was under the leadership of Thomas Monath, who also had been at CDC, Atlanta, and I was able to continue and expand my interests and goals, thanks to him; one could make a nice career by simply following Tom's secondary, and therefore rejected, ideas. It was because I had been the Director of the World Health Organization's Collaborating Centre for Arbovirus Reference and Research in the Americas while I was at CDC that I had multiple opportunities to visit laboratories through the Americas, in Europe, Africa, Asia, and Australia, and to meet the people who worked in those laboratories; they became not only my scientific associates but my friends, for which I will be grateful until I die, or forever, whichever comes first.

After retiring from CDC in 1992, I joined the faculty at Colorado State University, working for Barry J. Beaty, as swell a guy, as decent a human being, and as good a scientist as I have known. Barry, now University Distinguished Professor at Colorado State University and a member of the United States National Academy of Sciences, has "retired". As for so many of us, retirement has meant that he can do pretty much what he wants, which is to stay involved in matters arbovirus, contribute ideas to students and others, and cut his work week from 80 hours to only 60. The sign on his door remains on his door: "Beatings will continue until morale improves". Coming from a small town in Wisconsin, Barry's language is interspersed with the expressions and wisdom of mid-America, such as "do-better talks" and "handier than pockets in your underwear". Monday morning staff meetings were never boring.

At Colorado State University I learned even more about arboviruses and other viruses and was able to focus on a few of the important ones, including the rodent-borne non-arbovirus Sin Nombre hantavirus, an etiologic agent of hantavirus pulmonary syndrome. This got me out of the laboratory and into the field. Collaborative studies of hantaviruses with investigators at CDC/Atlanta, who provided funding and general aims, and people at other institutions with the same interests, including Ho-Wang Lee, Republic of Korea National Academy of Sciences, James N. Mills, CDC, Clarence James ("C.J.") Peters, CDC, and others were extremely fruitful and I was introduced to non-virologists who knew more about rodents, habitat characterization, and ecology in general than I had realized was known: Richard (Rick) J. Douglass and Amy J. Kuenzi, Montana Tech of Montana State University, and the late Terry L. Yates, University of New Mexico among them.

The people mentioned herein, and those not mentioned, individually and in concert made countless significant and innovative contributions, helping to build our understanding of these viruses, brick by brick, often with the sweat of their brows and under less than ideal conditions. This book is about not only the science of arbovirology but the interrelations of arbovirologists. It describes a tangled web of collaborations, cooperation, and partnerships, efforts by a group of dedicated people who were and are fascinated by the diseases, the viruses, and the epidemiologic and ecologic complications they comprise.

It is important to point out that this book has a bias; it is North American-centric, the reason being that I am much more knowledgeable about arbovirologic studies in North America than anywhere else. If I have omitted the names and accomplishments of key investigators or have not cited critical discoveries by our colleagues elsewhere, I take full responsibility and apologize for such unacceptable and personally embarrassing oversights.

This book is a love story and a history lesson; either is valuable for anyone.

Charles H. Calisher, Ph.D.

INTRODUCTION

What is arbovirology?

Figure 1.William C. Reeves (1916 - 2004)
(image courtesy of Archives of Virology)

William C. Reeves (Figure 1) wrote of the invention of the word "arbovirus", which came from discussions at a 1958 Lisbon, Portugal meeting of people interested in arthropod-borne viruses.

"As the day ended, someone suggested the meeting should select a name for this field of study and for the specific viruses that were included. I thought, 'Oh boy, now we will really have some turmoil.' Then, someone got the floor and I was stunned to hear him say, 'Bill, tell us about the derivation of terms used for these viruses in your laboratory.' I did and ended with 'Arborviruses'. Immediately, someone made a motion that this meeting and the WHO should accept that name and make it official worldwide. I held my breath and saw a hand wave. It was Dr. Anatol

> Smirodintsev from Russia. I thought, 'Here we go—Russia vs. the U.S.A.' Anatol said, 'The proposed name "arborviruses" has nothing to do with trees but "arbor" does.' I said, 'What if we take out the second 'r' and call it "Arbovirus"?' He said, 'I like it. Accept that change and move for its acceptance by this group and after it's approved I also move that we terminate this meeting.' It was approved with no further discussion."

> Colonel Ed Buescher, later to become the head of Walter Reed Army Institute of Research in Washington, D.C., as sort of a practical joke, named two newly discovered Malaysian viruses "Getah" and "Bebaru", which are Malaysian names for certain trees found there, i.e., pokok getah, a rubber tree, and pokok bebaru, a hibiscus tree, respectively.

Nowadays, arboviruses (arthropod-borne viruses) are defined as viruses maintained in nature by transmission between susceptible vertebrate hosts by hematophagous (blood-feeding) arthropods (jointed-legged insects such as mosquitoes, psychodids, ceratopogonids, etc.), and ticks (arachnids). Transmission here indicates "biological transmission", meaning that the viruses replicate in the arthropod host, rather than "mechanical transmission", as when introduced from the arthropod's mouth parts without replication in the vector. Once established, arbovirology, the study of arboviruses, not only has had a defined history but a remarkable one, fueled by the interests and, yes, the peculiarities of the people who established and defined the field. Although each of these investigators, working in the hot sun or in the freezing cold, under the glare of media attention or in isolation, with only their intellects and fascinations to prod them along, has provided a piece or many pieces of the seemingly endless puzzle, it is the totality of their work that is so remarkable, a work of fascination and love on the part of many.

Arboviruses are not members of a single taxonomic class of viruses. Rather, they are included in a single category of viruses by virtue of their biological characteristics – where they are found and what they do. Complicating this picture, there are arboviruses that are related, one way or another, to viruses that are not transmitted by arthropods. There also are viruses that replicate in and are transmitted by arthropods and replicate in vertebrates, but do not do so as a part of their natural cycles and are not dependent on vertebrates for persistence in nature. It seems reasonable to include in this brief summary the recently recognized flaviviruses that replicate in and are transmitted by arthropods to their progeny but which do not replicate in vertebrates; they therefore are not arboviruses. The key phrase in all this is "biological transmission" but there are many permutations of the basic definition that create shades of the original meaning. For example, simply because a virus replicates in a hematophagous arthropod does not mean that that arthropod transmits the virus to a vertebrate host when it feeds on that host.

In the early days, arbovirologists, the people who studied these viruses, often were frustrated in their attempts to understand many of the numerous facets of virus transmission. Gradually, it came to be recognized that the mechanisms by which arboviruses are transmitted are deeply embedded in the socio-cultural and environmental characteristics of the affected population. Religious, ethnic, and social customs can affect virus transmission. So can weather patterns, the types and diversity of other vertebrates in the area, arthropod occurrence, blood-feeding proclivities, availability of arthropod breeding and resting sites, arthropod prevalence (and which arthropods they are), the birds and mammals, amphibians and reptiles, and other vertebrates of the area, and the viruses themselves, all have the potential to affect virus transmission.

Arboviruses are peculiar in the sense that they can and must replicate in hosts of two very different types; arthropods, which are poikilothermic (have body temperatures that vary with the ambient temperature), and vertebrates, which are homeothermic (maintain their body temperature at a roughly constant level, regardless of the ambient temperature). Many of the diseases arbovirologists study are so medically important that a deeper understanding of arthropod life cycles is a necessity. With such a broad understanding of natural conditions, one can begin to make sense of this epidemiologic mosaic because each and all facets play discrete roles in the natural cycles of the viruses and, with knowledge of the entirety of this complex picture, we can begin to consider interrupting those cycles, thereby reducing the incidences or even the occurrences of these many and various diseases.

By unquestionably collegial means, veterinarians, and physicians made discoveries and advances in arbovirology either by discovering the diseases or by researching other diseases caused by other viruses. People from other disciplines contributed – entomologists, immunologists, laboratory diagnosticians, electron microscopists, molecular biologists, wildlife biologists including mammalogists, ornithologists, herpetologists, and ecologists, and many other specialists of one sort or another. Nonetheless, these specialists soon realized that if they were to hope to understand the natural history of a particular arbovirus, they must expand their horizons more than a little – what was needed was a broad-based integrative approach.

Arthropods share a basic body arrangement: a rigid cuticle, composed largely of chitin and proteins, which form an exoskeleton that may or may not be further hardened with calcium carbonate. Arthropods have segmented bodies and various patterns of segment fusion, which form specialized and coordinated units (heads, abdomens, and so on). The word "arthropod" means "jointed foot", a word coined to describe invertebrate animals (insects, arachnids, crustaceans) that have such segmented bodies and jointed appendages, a chitinous exoskeleton molted at intervals, and a dorsal anterior brain connected to a ventral chain of ganglia. Arthropods can be found in the depths of the oceans and on high mountains. They vary in size from king crab to microscopic forms.

There are at least a million species of arthropods, possibly 10 or more million species. Three-fourths of all currently known living and fossil organisms are arthropods, of which mosquitoes and ticks are of greatest interest to arbovirologists because they take blood meals from vertebrates and therefore can become infected with viruses circulating in the blood and potentially pass that virus to other vertebrates, including humans and the animals on which we depend or otherwise care about. The study of insects is called "entomology", a specialty in itself. Identification of arthropods to the level of species is an onerous task, one that requires great skill and considerable experience.

An entomologist alone cannot solve the intellectual and practical problems associated with viral diseases transmitted by arthropods. These require medical specialists, laboratorians, virologists, and others pooling their knowledge and experiences. Complicating such studies are the dangers inherent in being exposed to or handling these viruses. Members of the scientific community have learned the hard way that exposure to such disease agents, whether in the field or the laboratory can be fatal. When viruses not transmitted by arthropods were first recognized to cause frightening diseases, such as those causing Argentine hemorrhagic fever, Bolivian hemorrhagic fever, Lassa fever, Marburg hemorrhagic fever, and Ebola hemorrhagic fever, it was arbovirologists and their colleagues and students who established the original safety standards which now are used to avert unnecessary illnesses and deaths of the people who were investigating those epidemics and who worked with the viruses.

A very brief history of infectious diseases

Each field of study has a history, some lengthy, others relatively brief. Understanding the history of a particular discipline provides insights into the field itself, how thinking evolved and how problems and difficulties were solved and ultimately mastered. Things that we take for granted today, such as cell cultures, antibiotics and biosafety cabinets, were unavailable when arbovirology was young and yet the earliest workers in this field were able to isolate and work with what are today regarded as some of the world's deadliest pathogens.

Long ago, people responsible for the health of plants and animals described illnesses we easily recognize today. At the time, the causes of these diseases were unknown, of course, because the "germ theory" had not yet been conceived. In historical times it was thought that diseases were generated spontaneously (microorganisms and viruses were unrecognized at that time). Here is a cursory overview showing how the germ theory evolved from discoveries made over many centuries:

In 36 B.C.E. Marcus Terentius Varro, citing the Atharva-Veda in his treatise *On Agriculture*, warns of establishing homes near swamps "because there are bred certain minute creatures which cannot be seen by the eyes, which float in the air and enter the body through the mouth and nose and there cause serious diseases."

In *The Canon of Medicine* in 1020, Avicenna (Abu Ali ibn Sina) suggests that body secretions may be contaminated by foreign bodies. Avicenna recognized the contagious nature of tuberculosis and of other infectious diseases and introduced quarantine as a means of limiting the spread of infectious diseases.

Quarantine was first introduced in Ragusa (now Dubrovnik, Croatia) in 1377 in the form of a 40-day detention (from Latin *quaranta* for "forty" and the 17th century Venetian dialect *quaranta giorni* or *quarantena* for "40-day period") in ports where ships arrived from locales affected with plague.

In the 14th century, when bubonic plague ("the Black Death") reached the Iberian Peninsula, then under Arab control, Ibn Khatima suggested that infectious diseases are caused by microorganisms that somehow enter the human body. Another 14th century physician in Andalusia, Ibn al-Khatib, wrote a treatise called *On the Plague,* in which he stated:

> "The existence of contagion is established by experience, investigation, the evidence of the senses and trustworthy reports. These facts constitute a sound argument. The fact of infection becomes clear to the investigator who notices how he who establishes contact with the afflicted gets the disease, whereas he who is not in contact remains safe, and how transmission is affected through garments, vessels and earrings."

Veronese physician, Girolamo Fracastoro proposed in 1546 that epidemic diseases are caused by transferable seed-like entities that can transmit infection by direct or indirect contact, or even without contact, over long distances. It was another hundred years before some of the real culprits, microorganisms, were seen.

Microorganisms (which he called "animalcules") and other living entities were first observed directly in 1668 by Anton van Leeuwenhoek, the "Father of Microbiology". He was a Dutch fabric merchant whose hobby was making lenses and, eventually, microscopes. He needed lenses to count the number of threads per centimeter in fabrics, but he became fascinated with looking at entities that could not be seen without a lens. In the mid-1660s, van Leeuwenhoek was able to visualize bee mouth parts and stingers using one of his crude microscopes. Until 1668, it was thought that various "vermin", i.e., maggots, worms, insects, frogs, and other small creatures, arose by spontaneous generation. However, Italian physician Francesco Redi had read the speculation of English physician William Harvey, who had doubted that spontaneous generation occurred and that such life forms might arise from seeds or eggs too small to be seen with the naked eye. In 1668, Redi proved that spontaneous generation did not occur by demonstrating that the presence of maggots in putrefying meat does not result from spontaneous generation but from eggs laid on the meat by flies.

The Italian Agostino Bassi first asserted a germ theory of disease, a hypothesis he based on observations he had made regarding lethal and epidemic muscardine, a fungal disease of silkworms. In 1835 he speculated that the deaths of the insects were caused by a contagious, living agent visible to the naked eye as powdery spore masses; this fungus was named *Beauveria bassiana*. When in 1854 English physician John Snow famously showed that the cholera outbreak in London of that year could be traced to water from the Broad Street pump, the germ theory was acknowledged as probably correct.

In 1875 Robert Koch (Figure 2), a German researcher, developed proofs for the germ theory, and it finally was accepted as fact. Koch's

Figure 2. Robert Koch (1843 - 1910) (image courtesy of the Robert Koch-Institut, Berlin)

four postulates were: (1) the microorganism must be found in abundance in all organisms suffering from the disease, but not in healthy organisms, (2) they must be isolated from a diseased organism and grown in pure culture, (3) the cultured microorganism must cause disease when introduced into a healthy organism, and (4) the microorganism must be re-isolated from the inoculated, diseased experimental host and identified as being identical to the original specific causative agent. Koch's third postulate was found wanting because of the existence of infected but asymptomatic hosts. Nonetheless, "germs" had been shown to cause disease. This became the basis for the adaptation of good hygienic practices, public sanitation, epidemiology, antibiotic treatments, vaccines, and much more. These findings and thoughts revolutionized the study of diseases and served as the basis for establishment of new fields of study and treatment.

Although many studies had been done with microorganisms, bacteria, fungi and parasites, viruses had not yet been recognized, even though their effects were well documented. Until methods for amplifying viruses were developed, Koch's first and second postulates could not be proven for viruses. It was, and still is, immoral (and illegal in most countries) to attempt to prove his other postulates in humans. Clearly, new and different methods were needed in order to study viruses.

Not all discoveries and ideas need be of equal importance to be useful. However, small or large, they become part of the scientific record and of the totality of an area of study. Once, nearly 35 years ago, when I was in the midst of studies of the antigenic relationships among a group of viruses not known to cause disease, I called Robert Shope, M.D. (Figure 3), who always had a positive response to everything; I needed such a response. I told him that I was wondering whether what I was doing was valuable and what I should do with the rest of my life. His words have stayed with me since:

Figure 3. Robert E. Shope (1930 - 2004)
(image courtesy of John Glowczwski, University of Texas Medical Branch, Galveston)

> "I have no idea. No one can predict the long-term value of research. Sometimes what appears to be invaluable isn't and other times a small discovery is recognized years later as being the key element in an unexpected breakthrough. I suggest you just go home, come back tomorrow and get back to work."

This book is the story of the people whose discoveries and painstaking research laid the foundation for the study of arboviruses and the human history of the viruses with which they worked. In another attempt to at least partially summarize the sequence of events, a set of historical slides and innovative educational tables has been made available to the public by Frederick A. Murphy, D.V.M., Ph.D., (Figure 4) University of Texas Medical Branch, Department of Pathology, Galveston, who conceived, designed and thoroughly researched this remarkable historical and teaching tool.

Figure 4. Frederick Aloysius Murphy (1934 -)
(image courtesy of Frederick Murphy)

http://www.utmb.edu/pathology/faculty/murphy/murphy_bio.htm

Titled by Murphy "The Foundations of Medical and Veterinary Virology: Discoverers and Discoveries, Inventors and Inventions, Developers and Technologies", these images and notes provide the reader with historic references, as well as a sense of sequence and contexts, so that it becomes clearer as to who did what, and after which who did what else.

For those who would like further information regarding the history of virology, here are a few sources in addition to the references provided in the *Suggested Readings* section of this book: (1) A.P. Waterson and Lise Wilkinson's classic book, An Introduction To The History Of Virology [Cambridge University Press, 1978]; (2) Frank Fenner and Adrian Gibbs' series, Portraits of Viruses: A History of Virology [Karger, 1988]; (3) Alfred Grafe's book, A History of Experimental Virology [Springer-Verlag, 1991]; (4) Brian Mahy and Dmitri Lvov's book, Concepts in Virology—From Ivanovsky to the Present [Harwood, 1993]; (5) Hilary Koprowski and Michael Oldstone's book, Microbe Hunters—Then and Now [Medi-Ed Press, 1996]; (6) Charles Calisher and Marian Horzinek's book, Virology: The First 100 Years. [Springer-Verlag, 1999]; (7) Michael Oldstone and Arnold Levine's article, Virology in the Next Millennium [Cell 100:139-142, 2000]; and (8) especially Arnold Levine and Lynn Enquist's chapter in Fields VIROLOGY, Fifth Edition, entitled History of Virology [Lippincott Williams & Wilkins, 2006].

CHAPTER 1

From unsubstantiated opinions to scientific discipline

In 1796 Edward Jenner used cowpox virus (now recognized as a member of the family *Poxviridae,* genus *Orthopoxvirus*) to immunize people against the related smallpox virus (variola virus). Although a major clinically and epidemiologically significant step forward in terms of preventing disease, this development did not greatly improve our understanding of viruses themselves.

In ancient times, when identified at all, illnesses were identified by people with experience in such things. Nonetheless, it cannot be said that they were knowledgeable or that their diagnoses were accurate. These healers or shamans were more than likely basing their diagnoses and treatments on their personal or cultural traditions and experiences, much as is too often done today. Still, some people, perhaps many, somehow survived both the diseases and the treatments themselves, which often were harsh. Questions of legality, propriety, and accuracy rarely arose. One called in the healer who, with various poultices, salves, herbs, solutions, and the like, "cast out the evil spirits causing the disease" and then waited, hoping for the best.

Diseases such as smallpox, leprosy, typhoid fever, tuberculosis, syphilis, malaria, and plagues of one sort or another affecting people or animals were well known even in biblical times and perhaps before, but their causes were not. The populace was at the mercy of the unknown. About the time of the birth of Jesus of Nazareth, Susruta, a practitioner of Ayurvedic medicine, an ancient system of health care native to the Indian subcontinent, and Lucius Junius Moderatus Columella, a Roman agriculturalist, independently wrote of the spread of fevers (most of which likely were due to malaria) by biting flies (probably mosquitoes).

Until relatively recently (fewer than 150 years ago), physicians and others had no accurate idea about either the cause (a virus) or the vector (mosquito) of yellow fever. An 1817 report by physician William Fergusson, in which green wood was considered a possible source of the many illnesses on board his ship, never mentioned mosquitoes (and certainly never mentioned viruses). That report is worth reading to help us realize realize how little was known of infectious diseases at the time.

The beginning of virology as a field of endeavor could be attributed to Adolph Mayer, who in 1879 recognized a disease of tobacco plants in the Netherlands and named it "tobacco mosaic disease". He described that disease in infected plants in 1886 and showed that it could be transmitted to healthy plants by rubbing their leaves with leaf sap from an infected tobacco plant. He demonstrated that heating the sap to 80°C for several hours eliminated the "infectious substance" and reasonably but erroneously concluded that the cause might be a bacterium. As tobacco mosaic virus and other viruses were discovered and their properties elucidated, it became increasingly clear that there likely were more than a few of these disease agents.

Agostino Bassi (1835), John Snow (1854), Robert Koch and Louis Pasteur (Figure 5) (1875-1878) were first to assert, support, and popularize the germ theory. Pasteur had established the microbiological/virological/infectious disease sciences, first in 1857 by discovering that fermentations of wine, beer, and cheese were microbially produced.

Figure 5. Louis Pasteur (1822 - 1895)
(image courtesy of the Pasteur Institute)

In 1865 he extended the concept to infectious diseases of silkworms and between 1877 and 1895 he extended the concept to human and animal diseases. His early infectious disease work had focused on septic war wounds but he then turned to anthrax and other bacterial diseases and to rabies. In each instance, he moved from studies aimed at discovering the causative agent to the development of specific intervention. In 1885, Pasteur famously gave the first rabies vaccine to a boy, Joseph Meister, who had been bitten severely by a rabid dog, an act which has been celebrated as the beginning of the modern era of infectious disease science aimed at disease prevention and control. Pasteur was joined by Koch, who discovered the causative (bacterial) agents of tuberculosis and cholera and who contributed so much to the development of laboratory methods in bacteriology. Koch also worked on several diseases which others eventually showed were caused by viruses. As a result of the work of Pasteur, Koch and others, the identification of the causative agents of many important human diseases proceeded quickly thereafter at the turn of the twentieth century.

In 1875 a paper by Louis Daniel Beauperthuy suggested that "the cause of illness is not an ideal miasmatic agent, insensitive to our means of research: they are agents readily imperceptible to simple observation but visible when examined under a microscope." So much for "miasmas" and other pollutants! Here was a publication alluding to a germ theory. Although he has been mostly overlooked, Beauperthuy should be recognized for his contributions regarding microbial origins of infectious diseases, a fact accepted after Beauperthuy's death when work by Walter Reed and his group and by Pasteur and Koch proved it correct.

Figure 6. Dimitri Iosifovich Ivanovsky (1864 - 1920)
(image courtesy D.I. Ivanovsky Institute, Moscow, Russia)

Researchers now knew that microorganisms were associated with certain diseases and that those organisms could be visualized by microscopy or proven to be present using other means, such as with filters or by dilution. This remarkable deduction revolutionized medicine and its associated fields. However, until tools and methods were developed, it was not possible to prove the existence of viruses, which were impossible to visualize by light microscopy, so virus diseases and their causes remained unexplained.

Using the filter invented by Charles Chamberland, a colleague of Louis Pasteur, Dimitri Iosifovich Ivanovsky (Figure 6), a Russian biologist at the University of St. Petersburg passed extracts from infected tobacco plants and was able to transmit what was called tobacco mosaic (light and dark green mottling of the leaves) disease. As the pores in these filters were known not to allow (large) bacteria to pass through, Ivanovsky recognized that whatever had come through the filter was either smaller than a large bacterium or a toxin produced by bacteria, or that the filter might have had small cracks in it that allowed bacteria to pass through. He had discovered the first virus but did not recognize that he had done so.

Independent of Ivanovsky's discovery, Martinus Beijerinck (Figure 7), worked on tobacco mosaic disease in Delft, South Holland, and published his findings in 1898. The infection, wrote Beijerinck is not caused by microbes but by a "fluid infectious principle", a virus (*virus* is Latin for poison). Beijerinck found the following:

- the virus multiplies only in living tissues.
- the infectious agent can diffuse through agar gels.
- the virus is inactivated by boiling but can be dried or precipitated with ethanol and still retain its infectious properties.

Figure 7. Martinus Willem Beijerinck (1851 - 1931)
(image courtesy of Lesley Robertson, Delft School of Microbiology Archive, Department of Biotechnology, Delft University of Technology, the Netherlands)

This is not the first time that the word "virus" had been used in association with a disease. The word "virus" had been used by Aulus Cornelius Celsus in the first century C.E. In A.D. 50, Celsus stated that "Rabies is caused by a virus." Celsus, by the way, was the first person to record the cardinal signs of inflammation: rubor (redness), calor (heat), dolor (pain), and tumor (swelling).

Also in 1898, Friedrich Loeffler (Figure 8), at a laboratory on the Island of Reims in eastern Germany, and Paul Frosch (Figure 9), from Robert Koch's Institute of Infectious Diseases in Berlin, discovered that foot-and-mouth disease of livestock is caused by a virus. Who, then, was the first to discover and recognize a virus? Although Ivanovski clearly was the first to show that the agent causing tobacco mosaic disease passed through a bacteria-retaining filter, all his publi-

Figure 8. Friedrich Löeffler (1852 - 1915)
(image courtesy of the archive, Friedrich Löeffler Institute, Insel Riems)

Figure 9. Paul Frosch (1860 - 1928)
(image courtesy of the Robert Koch-Institut, Berlin)

cations show that he did not grasp the significance of his observation. Beijerinck realized he was dealing with something different from a microbe, but he thought that the virus was an infectious liquid and not a particle. It was Loeffler and Frosch who correctly concluded that the virus causing foot-and-mouth disease was a small particle that passed through a Chamberland filter, but which was retained by a finer filter. They examined two possible hypotheses: whatever passed through the filter was either a soluble toxin or a particle so small it could pass through filters that would retain bacteria.

Marc van Regenmortel asserts that Loeffler and Frosch should be considered the founders of virology because in order to make a discovery, it is not sufficient to make a novel observation (i.e., the filterability of an infectious agent) and, in addition, it is also necessary to interpret the observation correctly. Good science does not consist only in making new observations or collecting new data but it requires also unbiased, imaginative thinking which enables the scientist to arrive at the correct interpretation of his experimental findings. Loeffler and Frosch's interpretation of their filtration experiments was the closest to the modern concept of a virus, so they should be acknowledged as the founders of virology.

Figure 10. Sir Arnold Theiler (1867 - 1936)
(image courtesy of Daan Verwoerd, University of Pretoria, Union of South Africa)

Both Ivanovsky and Beijerinck, through meticulous experimentation, discovered tobacco mosaic virus but did not recognize the novel characteristics of that virus. So Loeffler and Frosch were credited with the first discovery of a virus , discovery of the first vertebrate virus, and discovery the first picornavirus (family *Picornaviridae*), foot-and-mouth disease virus. In that same remarkable year of 1898, Giuseppe Sanarelli of the University of Bologna reported his discovery of myxoma virus, the first recognized poxvirus (family *Poxviridae*)

Before the end of the 19th century J. M'Fadyean, T. Edgington, and Arnold Theiler (Figure 10) discovered an African horse sickness virus, which we now know to be the first recognized orbivirus (family *Reoviridae*). Had they had the tools and procedures we have now, surely these brilliant investigators would have been able to elucidate much of the natural cycle of African horse sickness viruses.

Most often, the vectors of African horse sickness viruses are midges of the genus *Culicoides.* Zebras and African donkeys (*Equus asinus*) rarely display clinical symptoms, despite high virus titers in their bloods. The disease in horses manifests itself in any of four different forms: pulmonary, cardiac, mild, and mixed. African horse sickness was first recognized in southern Africa in the early 18th century when imported European horses became ill and died. That must have been difficult to understand at the time because native equids (zebras and donkeys) grazing nearby remained asymptomatic. This disease is the most lethal infectious disease of horses. Horses are the most susceptible hosts, with as many as 95% of susceptible animals dying, but mules (50% case-fatality), donkeys (10% case-fatality), and dogs also are affected. The causative agents of this disease, however, were not determined until long after the illness itself was recognized, and the reason for its irregular occurrence, about every 10 to 15 years, had been a mystery. It was shown that the arthropod vectors of the nine viruses which can cause this disease were culicoids, biting midges, also called "no-see-ums". In South Africa these culicoids feed on a variety of vertebrates, including zebras of the three species (*Equus quagga, E. grevyi,* and *E. zebra*). Apparently, zebras are resistant to the disease, but the viruses replicate in them, so that they serve as a virus reservoir. Horses, however, which are not native to southern Africa and have not developed a resistance to these viruses, become clinically affected. Why outbreaks of this disease occur in individuals of one species of equid (horses) and not in another (zebras) and why outbreaks occur at all has not been definitively determined. Recently, Baylis and colleagues found a strong association between the timing of these epizootics and the warm (El Niño) phase of the El Niño/ Southern Oscillation. They suggested that the association is mediated by the combination of rainfall and drought brought to South Africa by this climatologic phenomenon.

In the late 19th century, Patrick Manson (Figure 11), Charles Laveran (Figure 12), Ronald Ross (Figure 13) and Giovanni Grassi accumulated sufficient evidence to prove that malaria was caused by a protozoan parasite of mosquitoes. They discovered that other parasites were the etiologic agents of filariasis and trypanosomiasis and hypothesized that the arthropods were fundamental to their transmission cycles. These findings were seminal in terms of understanding parasitic diseases and also suggested the possibility that mosquitoes were

Figure 11. Patrick Manson (1844 - 1922)
(image courtesy of the National Library of Medicine)

Figure 12. Charles Louis Alphonse Laveran (1845 - 1922)
(image courtesy of the Rockefeller Archive Center)

Figure 13. Ronald Ross (1857 - 1932)
(image courtesy of the National Library of Medicine)

Figure 14. Carlos Juan Finlay (1833 - 1915)
(image courtesy of the National Library of Medicine)

Figure 15. (standing l. to r.) Henry Rose Carter, M.D. (1852 – 1925), Juan Guiteras; (seated l. to r.) Mrs. Gorgas, General William Crawford Gorgas (image courtesy of the National Library of Medicine)

the vectors of other agents of diseases. This new knowledge certainly influenced Carlos Finlay (Figure 14), Henry Rose Carter (Figure 15), Walter Reed (Figure 16), James Carroll (Figure 17), Aristides Agramonte (Figure 18), and Jesse Lazear (Figure 19) in their investigations of the causal agent as well as the arthropod vector of yellow fever and their acceptance of the validity and significance of Carter's hypothesis of an "extrinsic incubation period" in mosquitoes. Eventually these discoveries led to the implementation of biological control of the vec-

Figure 16. Walter Reed (1851 - 1902)
(image courtesy of the National Library of Medicine)

Figure 17. James Carroll (1854 - 1907)
(image courtesy of Historical Collections and Services, Claude Moore Health Sciences Library, University of Virginia)

Figure 18. Aristides Agramonte (1868 - 1931)
(image courtesy of the National Library of Medicine)

Figure 19. Jesse William Lazear (1866 - 1900)
(image courtesy of the National Library of Medicine)

tor and the development of a vaccine by Max Theiler (Figure 20) and others. These were the first steps taken towards combating vector-borne diseases, laying the groundwork for the entire field of arbovirology, which developed and began to flourish soon after.

Figure 20. Max Theiler (1899 - 1972) (image courtesy of the Rockefeller Archive Center)

These and other discoveries, coming in rapid succession at about the turn of the 20th century, changed the thinking of researchers world-wide and energized their enthusiasms and efforts. Before the discovery of the cause of African horse sickness and its transmissibility to dogs, diseases of animals were thought to be of parasitic or bacterial origin. The recognition that African horse sickness is caused by filterable agents opened yet another door to further research. Although many diseases of great importance to farmers, plant pathologists, veterinarians, and others were discovered by the 1890s, no human virus had yet been found. Yet the discovery of the viral cause of yellow fever was not far off.

CHAPTER 2

Yellow fever: the "King of terrors"

To say that yellow fever has been and remains a serious disease of humans in Africa and South America is an enormous understatement. Yellow fever was the first human infectious hemorrhagic fever to be recognized. The clinical features of yellow fever had been described for hundreds of years, superbly and inclusively summarized in the landmark book "Yellow Fever", edited by George K. Strode of the Rockefeller Foundation. Signs and symptoms of the illness usually develop within 3-6 days after the patient has been fed upon by an infected mosquito. This acute disease, which is of brief duration and varying severity, may comprise three stages, infection, remission, and intoxication, although clear demarcations between these stages are not always seen. In the first stage, headache, fever, muscle, and joint aches, loss of appetite, vomiting, and jaundice occur. The "yellow" in the name reflects the color of the skin in patients with jaundice (*jaune* is French for yellow), also known as icterus. This coloration, which also occurs in the membranes over the white of the eyes (the sclera) and other mucous membranes, is caused by an overabundance of bilirubin in the blood, the result of liver cell damage and the resulting inability of the liver to break down old red blood cells to recycle the iron in them. Although the presence of Councilman bodies (eosinophilic irregular spherical masses found in the livers of patients with yellow fever) was at one time considered pathognomonic for this disease, it is now recognized that they are present in livers of patients suffering from other viral causes of hepatitis. These bodies, which are degenerated hepatocytes, were first described by the pathologist William Thomas Councilman (1854-1933), who had been trained in Europe, worked for William Henry Welch at Johns Hopkins University (who himself trained Walter Reed and others), and eventually became Shattuck Professor at Harvard University Medical School.

In the second stage, which may occur 3 to 4 days after onset of the illness, symptoms may subside and the patient may go into apparent remission. Most patients who recover do so at this time. However, if a third stage occurs, it does so within 24 hours, and the patient becomes "intoxicated". At this point, although virus is not detected in the blood, neutralizing antibodies are found, fever rises, pulse slows, moderate jaundice may be observed, vomiting is persistent, and the vomitus contains blood blackened by gastric juices, i.e., black vomit (*vomito negro* in Spanish).

In a small proportion of patients, albuminuria is present and the patient becomes oliguric and "toxic" due to multi-organ dysfunction or failure. At this stage, when heart, liver, and kidneys fail, bleeding (hemorrhaging) is seen, brain abnormalities become apparent and the patient might die or remain in this condition 3 to 4 days to 2 weeks, after which he will remain quite ill for many months and then recover or die, usually of cardiac failure. The seriousness of this disease manifests in the final days by patient delirium, seizures, coma, shock, and death. Yellow fever is a catastrophic disease of immense significance, both medical and historical.

Because there are no known descriptions of a disease compatible with yellow fever in ancient times, it is thought to be of relatively recent origin. A disease that might have been yellow fever was described in the 6th century in Europe. The term *yellow fever* first appeared in 1750 in *Natural History of Barbados* by Griffin Hughes.

In an effort to weaken Spain's hold on the Americas, British and American colonial troops attacked the Spanish colony of Cuba in 1762, in the Battle of Havana. They succeeded at a price. Many members of the British expeditionary force died of yellow fever; after that experience, the disease was clearly recognized.

During the next nearly 150 years, epidemics of yellow fever struck coastal and island communities throughout the Caribbean area; an estimated 10 percent of the indigenous population died as a result. Slavery had been abolished in the French colonies after the French Revolution but in 1802 Napoleon Bonaparte forced through a law revoking this act and reinstating slavery. Numerous slave insurrections occurred in Haiti. Napoleon responded by sending an army of 25,000 French soldiers to the colony. Under the command of his brother-in-law, Victor Leclerc, they arrested the native black patriot-liberator, Francois Dominique Toussaint Louverture. In mid-May a yellow fever epidemic broke out in the largest cities of Haiti; by the first week of June, thousands of French soldiers had died. The epidemic continued into January 1803, by which time essentially all of Leclerc's troops, as well as Leclerc himself, had died. Napoleon, belatedly responding to Leclerc's request for reinforcements, sent more troops but only a few thousand of the 50,000 French soldiers sent to Haiti survived the disease.

Haitian resistance to French rule was fierce and in late 1803 French troops withdrew from Haiti. This incident alone forever changed the political scene in the Western Hemisphere. Haiti was forced to pay France for what it considered its loss of slaves and real property and Haiti still suffers from the events of those days. Single cases, small and large outbreaks, and epidemics of yellow fever continued to occur not only in the Caribbean area but in South America and Africa but they were poorly documented. Nothing was possible then in the way of control of or even of definitive diagnosis of the illness.

In 1805 President Thomas Jefferson wrote to C.F. Volney, a.k.a. Constantin François de Chasseboeuf, the French philosopher, about a plan to prevent outbreaks of yellow fever.

> "I have supposed it practicable to prevent its generation by building our cities on a more open plan. Take, for instance, the checkerboard for a plan. Let the black squares only be building squares, and the white ones be left open, in turf and trees. Every square of houses will be surrounded by four open squares, and every house will front an open square. The atmosphere of such a town would be like that of the country, insusceptible of the miasmas which produce yellow fever. I have proposed that the enlargements of the city of New Orleans … shall be on this plan."

Jefferson further suggested that "all the diseases plaguing Europe" were due to congestion and lack of fresh air. No mention of an infectious agent was made or considered. His and recommendations by others were of little or no avail without knowledge of the cause of the disease and the origins of that cause. Those who suggested that yellow fever was somehow associated with mosquitoes were ridiculed, and worse.

Mobile, Alabama, physician Josiah Clark Nott described yellow fever epidemics in an 1848 publication the *New Orleans Medical and Surgical Journal:*

> "When Yellow Fever shakes off its mild endemic form and assumes that of a great Epidemic, as it did here in 1839, it comes robed in majesty and power – all febrile diseases disappear before it, or are compelled to wear its livery – the peculiar characteristics of the disease stand out boldly and, with few exceptions, all difficulty of diagnosis vanishes – patients are stricken down by hundreds with attacks varying from the mildest to the most malignant and yet all wholly unlike periodic fevers – in the same family and house one will be so lightly attacked as scarcely to lie down, while another is dying with all the horrors of black-vomit; and what is particularly worthy of note, the light cases pass off spontaneously in two or three

days without a dose of quinine, and afford protection against the disease in after years!"

Note that Nott's writings preceded by many decades Pasteur's earliest work and the acceptance of the germ theory.

Figure 21. Louis-Daniel Beauperthuy (1807 - 1871)
(image courtesy of the National Library of Medicine)

Born on Guadalupe and educated at the University of Paris, Louis Daniel Beauperthuy (Figure 21) worked as a museum naturalist, then practiced medicine in Venezuela and was the first to suggest that mosquitoes somehow were involved in the natural cycle of yellow fever transmission. His wide interests in tropical medicine motivated him to make clinical observations on yellow fever, leprosy, cholera, malaria, dysentery, syphilis, and many other diseases and conditions.

During a yellow fever epidemic in his home town of Cumaná in 1853, Beauperthuy connected mosquitoes with the disease. His published comments included observations that mosquitoes were possible carriers of yellow fever, though he thought these mosquitoes were carrying the infection from decomposing material in swamps. He showed that the absence of mosquitoes precluded the occurrence of yellow fever and formulated methods to eliminate the disease by killing mosquitoes or by preventing them from feeding on healthy people. He also suggested that yellow fever is not contagious, i.e., not transmitted directly from person to person. For these and other reasonable views, he was considered insane by many (unqualified) members of the medical community. Beauperthuy was quoted as saying:

> "But rubbish! The small amount of sulphuretted hydrogen or marsh gas which might arise from a marsh could not possibly hurt a fly, much less a man. It is not that, it is a mosquito called in Cumana the 'Zancudo bobo', the striped-legged domestic mosquito."

Presumably, that mosquito was *Aedes aegypti,* now recognized as the principal vector of yellow fever and dengue viruses. (The mosquito he described could also have been the yellow fever-irrelevant salt marsh mosquito, *Aedes taeniorhynchus*). It is remarkable that all this came from a single physician working in geographic isolation, without academic collaborators, and with no institutional support. Whether this or that physician, chemist or other scientist was first to make a discovery matters, however, only to historians. The discovery is what is important, of course. Nonetheless, to this day scientists and historians in Cuba, Venezuela and elsewhere vehemently debate who did exactly what and, therefore, who made the greatest original contributions to our understanding and control of yellow fever. An example of these polemics can be seen in a paper by Quevedo et al.

Yellow fever struck residents of the Mississippi Valley in 1878 and more than 20,000 of them died, more than 5,000 in Memphis alone. Khaled Bloom's book "The Mississippi Valley's Great Yellow Fever Epidemic of 1878" documents the origin of the epidemic, the efforts to curtail it, the political fallout from failure to control it, and the damage done to both humans and economies. The disease came to be known as the "King of Terrors" or "Yellow Jack" (Figure 22), named for the yellow flag flown over cities and ships with yellow fever patients, or hoisted on a ship to request pratique, a license given to a ship to enter port on assurance from the captain that it is free of a contagious disease, or to warn of a disease on board. Intermittent yellow fever epidemics occurred in the United States in New Orleans and surrounding areas of Louisiana (Figure 23), Galveston, Savannah (Figure 24), Charleston (South Carolina), Norfolk, Baltimore, Philadelphia, New York City, Boston, even as far north as Halifax, Canada.

During and after the 1878 epidemic, many hypotheses regarding the origin and treatment of yellow fever were developed, among them that:

- African-Americans were carriers of the disease because of the observation that many of them did not become ill (they were immune, because of prior infections)
- Sewers or waterfront landfills of garbage or "diffusible miasmas in the atmosphere" were its source

Figure 22. Frank Leslie's Illustrated Newspaper, Sept. 1878
(image courtesy of Thomas P. Monath)

Figure 23. Yellow fever hospital, Franklin, Louisiana
(image courtesy of the National Library of Medicine)

- Disinfection by application of carbolic acid and other stinking compounds would rid the cities of whatever was causing this plague
- Paving the streets, or cutting down forests to allow wind to clear the air, or erecting an awning over the entire waterfront to reduce air temperature might work.

Coincidentally, in 1878 Patrick Manson proved that *Culex* species mosquitoes served as "true vectors" of the filarial worm, *Wuchereria bancrofti,* the cause of Bancroftian filariasis, also called "elephantiasis". By "true vectors", he meant that a period of time is required for the parasite to develop in the mosquito before the mosquito can transmit it. Manson is considered by many to be the father of tropical medicine. He was the first to demonstrate that a parasite that causes a human disease could infect a mosquito. He served as physician to the Seamen's Hospital Society, the Medical Advisor to the Colonial Office and later was the founder of the London School of Tropical Medicine and the Hong Kong College of Medicine.

Figure 24. Historic marker, Savannah, Georgia, emphasizing that this cemetery was a burial site for yellow fever victims.
(image courtesy of David Seibert/Georgia Info)

There were, of course, scores of other protagonists; no such large undertaking as the control of yellow fever could be completed without the cooperation and hard work of many. One example is Stanford Emerson Chaille, Head of the Havana Yellow Fever Commission of 1879, a group established to study the disease after an epidemic of yellow fever struck New Orleans in 1878. Chaille was known as the "Father of Hygiene and Health Education" in America because he spoke out for the establishment of community sewerage and drainage systems, street paving, pure water supplies, and mosquito control. He later was instrumental in the establishment of the National Board of Health, forerunner of the United States Department of Health, Education and Welfare, now the United States Department of Health and Human Services.

Among those ridiculed for suggesting that mosquitoes were somehow involved in the transmission of yellow fever was Carlos Juan Finlay, an eminent Cuban physician. Born in what is now Camagüey, Cuba, Finlay trained at Jefferson Medical College in Philadelphia, Pennsylvania, graduating in 1855. He completed his studies in Paris and Havana and eventually settled in Havana, opening a medical practice there. In 1881 he hypothesized that somehow mosquitoes were carriers of yellow fever. That was not exactly correct: mosquitoes are carriers of the virus (the virus vector) that causes yellow fever, but they do not carry or transmit diseases. Finlay, who had read some of Beauperthuy's publications, theorized that mosquitoes feeding on yellow fever patients might subsequently feed on healthy people and somehow pass the disease to them.

His hypothesis was a great deal more useful than the rather odd ideas that had been circulating previously. If mosquitoes carried the disease agent, it might be possible to prevent the disease by avoiding the mosquitoes that carry the cause of the disease. The next year Finlay reported that he had identified *Aedes aegypti* mosquitoes (then called *Stegomyia fasciata*) as the culprits in this transmission cycle. He further extended his theory to recommend controlling mosquito populations to control the disease.

In 1881 Finlay traveled to Washington, D.C. to an International Sanitary Conference, where he volunteered his expertise and service to the American Government. He asked his friend, Dr. George Miller Sternberg, the Surgeon General of the Army, to be sent to the epidemic area to take part in the control campaign around Santiago. On his return to Havana later that year, Finlay brought his views of the cause and means of transmission of yellow fever to the attention of the United States Army medical officers, the United States Government and the medical press in the United States and wrote a plan to control yellow fever. The plan achieved remarkably good results, but the cause of this disease still was not known and the exact details of its natural history not yet revealed.

Although apparently unrelated, other findings around that time had considerable influence on studies of infectious diseases and on the field of arbovirology. For example, in 1889 physician Theobold Smith (Figure 25) and veterinarian Fred L. Kilbourne, both working for the Bureau of Animal Industries of the United States Department of Agriculture (U.S.D.A.) studying Texas cattle fever (e.g. Texas fever, Texas red water fever), discovered that a protozoan, *Babesia bigemina,* causes that disease and, further, that the agent is transmitted by *Boophilus annulatus* ticks. This was the first time a tick had been associated with transmission of an infectious disease. Smith did not care for working in a bureaucratic environment and, in 1915, left to work at the Rockefeller Institute for Medical Research as Director of the Department of Animal Pathology, where he remained until he retired in 1929.

Other discoveries followed quickly. In 1892, the English physician Ronald Ross began studies of malaria. Though he originally doubted the malaria parasite's existence, he became an enthusiastic convert to the belief that these parasites were in the blood when Manson demonstrated this to him during a period of home leave in 1894. Knowledge of malaria as a disease was not new. The symptoms of malaria had been described in ancient Chinese medical writings. In 2700 B.C.E., several signs and symptoms of what would later be named

Figure 25. Theobold Smith (1859 - 1934)
(image courtesy of Myron Schultz, U.S. Centers for Disease Control)

malaria were described in the *Nei Ching* (the "Canon of Medicine"), edited by Emperor Huang Ti. Malaria became widely recognized in Greece by the 4th century B.C.E., and was responsible for the decline of many of the city-state populations. Even Hippocrates noted the principal symptoms. By the age of Pericles, extensive references to malaria outbreaks appeared in the literature and consequent depopulation of rural areas was recorded. The Susruta, a Sanskrit medical treatise, described symptoms of malarial fever and attributed those symptoms to the bites of certain insects. A number of Roman writers attributed malarial diseases to the swamps near which people acquired this disease. (Latin: *mala aria* means "bad air").

In China, during the 2nd century B.C.E., the Qinghao plant (*Artemisia annua*) was described in the medical treatise, *52 Remedies,* found in a tomb. In 340 C.E., Ge Hong of the East Yin Dynasty first described the antipyretic properties of Qinghao. Although it was long used to treat malaria and other parasitic infections, Chinese scientists did not isolate the active ingredient of Qinghao, known as artemisinin, until 1971.

Ross became so fascinated by malaria that he decided to test the hypotheses of Charles Louis Alphonse Laveran and Patrick Manson. Laveran had observed what he (correctly) thought was an organism in blood and tissues from patients with malarial parasites. This revelation came to him when he worked at a military hospital in Constantine (Algeria), in the early morning hours of November 6, 1880. Examining the blood of a patient who had been febrile for 15 days, he saw "on the edges of a pigmented spherical body, filiform elements which move with great vivacity, displacing the neighboring red blood cells." By chance, but also thanks to his tenacity and patience, he had seen the exflagellation of a male gametocyte, a phase in the life cycle of malaria parasites that usually occurs in the abdomen of anopheline mosquitoes. The motility of these elements immediately convinced Laveran that he had discovered the agent causing malaria and that it was a protozoan parasite. After observing these motile elements again, some adhering to the spherical bodies and others free, Laveran sent two notes to the Academy of Medicine, in November and December 1880 on this "New Parasite Found in the Blood of Several Patients Suffering from Marsh Fever."

When he returned to India in 1895, Ross took up the quest to prove the hypothesis of Laveran and Manson that mosquitoes were somehow connected to the propagation of malaria and regularly corresponded with Manson on his findings. However, his progress was hampered by the Indian Medical Service which ordered him from Madras to a malaria-free environment in Rajputana. Ross threatened to resign but, following representations on his behalf by Manson, the Indian Government put him on special duty for a year to investigate malaria and kala azar (visceral leishmaniasis), now known to be caused by the parasite *Leishmania donovani.*

On August 20 1897, in Secunderabad, Ross made his landmark discovery. While dissecting the abdomen tissue of an anopheline mosquito fed four days previously on the blood of a malarious patient, he found the malaria parasite and went on to prove the role of anopheline mosquitoes in the transmission of malaria parasites to humans. Thus Ross confirmed the hypothesis of Laveran and Manson and of those Italian investigators who showed conclusively that mosquitoes of a particular species transmit the malarial parasite.

Ross, who considered himself more of a poet than a scientist, wrote to his wife on the day of that discovery –

"This day relenting God
Hath placed within my hand
A wonderous thing; and God
Be praised. At His command,
Seeking His secret deeds
With tears and toiling breath
I find thy cunning seeds,
O million murdering Death.
I know this little thing
A myriad men will save.
O Death, where is thy sting?
Thy victory, O grave"

(Fortunately for us, he was a good scientist!)

The knowledge accumulated by studying these various diseases provided the Army with critical information when it took up the investigation of yellow fever. A growing, expansionist America, sympathetic to the wishes of many of the Cuban people, had demanded that Spain peacefully resolve the desire for independence, but these demands were rejected. Under the guise of protecting American interests, the United States sent the warship U.S.S. Maine to Havana harbor, for what has come to be called "gunboat diplomacy". The ship was destroyed by an explosion, possibly caused by a defective boiler, and the Assistant Secretary of the United States Navy, Theodore Roosevelt, used that incident, supported by sensationalist newspaper editorials, to order an attack on Spanish ships and garrisons in Cuba and in the Philippines. The brief war ended in 1898 and the Treaty of Paris was signed four months later, with the United States given ownership of the former Spanish colonies of Cuba, the Philippines, Puerto Rico and Guam. The provisions of this treaty had far-reaching consequences. For one, Puerto Rico, which had expected to become an independent nation, was annexed by the United States, to be used as a coaling station for ships using the not-yet-built Panama Canal. When the Spanish-American War began, yellow fever already was a problem in Cuba.

In 1899, Henry Rose Carter, a graduate of the University of Virginia and of the University of Maryland Medical School, observed that there was a fairly regular interval, never fewer than 12 days, never more than 15 days, between the first "infecting case" of yellow fever from outside an area and the appearance of the first "secondary cases" among residents of the area. He called this "the period of extrinsic incubation of yellow fever infection" and noted that once an infection appeared in a house, yellow fever in non-immune newcomers could occur after as few as three days of exposure. Finlay had not known about this period of extrinsic incubation, which explains why he had failed to transmit yellow fever virus experimentally to volunteers. He had not waited long enough for the virus to be amplified and therefore attain a high enough titer so as to be sufficiently infectious.

The year before Carter presented his observations in scientific journals, mosquitoes had been shown to transmit the organism causing malaria, so he wondered whether yellow fever was also transmitted by mosquitoes or other insects. The learned Carter pored over Mayan writings and speculated on the origin of yellow fever in the Americas. He concluded that the disease might have been endemic in the former Mayan empire, particularly along the east coast of the Yucatan Peninsula and adjacent areas south to Guatemala, where the center of that empire had been located. However, he strongly disagreed with those who hypothesized that yellow fever originated in the Americas, instead suggesting that it had come from Africa. Recent molecular evidence supports Carter's conjectures and indicates that yellow fever virus arose in Africa within the past 1,500 years. Historical evidence supports the emergence (not the origin) of yellow fever in the Americas only after the beginning of the slave trade, 300 to 400 years ago.

Because of the horrific symptoms and suffering caused by this disease and because of its high case-fatality rate, the United States Army established a Yellow Fever Commission in Cuba. Major Walter Reed, who had visited Cuba in 1899 to look into the diseases occurring among troops at United States Army encampments, was put in charge. During the Spanish-American War (April-July 1898), thousands of United States military personnel had been affected by yellow fever. The Army wanted to determine if any of these cases could have been prevented or if the mortality rates associated with yellow fever could be reduced.

In addition to Reed, the Yellow Fever Commission included Aristides Agramonte (born in Cuba), James Carroll (born in England), and Jesse Lazear (born in the United States). The Commission tested the hypothesis that mosquitoes were involved in the transmission of the causative agent, determination of the causative agent, recorded clinical findings and hazarded experimental infections of humans. The major conclusion was that "The mosquito serves as the intermediate host for the parasite of yellow fever, and it is highly probable that the disease is only propagated through the bite of this insect."

In one fell swoop, they discovered the cause of yellow fever, were the first to recognize a human virus, detected what later was shown as the first recognized flavivirus, were the first to detect an arbovirus (although they certainly did not know that) and determine its transmission cycle. They called it a "parasite", which was correct, because viruses are parasites, though not in the traditional sense of their time.

Born in 1851 in Virginia, Walter Reed entered the University of Virginia at age 16 and obtained his medical degree there just before his 18th birthday, the youngest graduate of that medical school to this day. He obtained a second M.D. degree at Bellevue Hospital Medical College, in New York City, interned at a number of hospitals in the New York metropolitan area and, in 1873, assumed the position of assistant sanitary officer for the Brooklyn Board of Health. The large and diverse population of New York City with its many immigrants and dense housing, provided opportunities for Reed to study and treat a variety of illnesses and stimulated his interest in public health and epidemiology. Because his youth seemed to be an impediment to having a private practice of medicine, Reed joined the Army Medical Corps, spending many years in difficult assignments in the American West, East, and South, and remaining a member of the Corps until his untimely death from peritonitis in 1902. While on assignment in Baltimore, Reed studied advanced pathology and bacteriology at Johns Hopkins University and later joined the faculty of the Army Medical School in Washington, D.C. He became curator of the Army Medical Museum and joined the faculty of the Columbian University (now the George Washington University) in Washington, D.C. Reed had had some experience in Cuba in 1899 studying typhoid fever, malaria, and yellow fever and returned there the following year as head of the Army board commissioned by Surgeon General George Miller Sternberg to examine tropical diseases, including yellow fever. This was a propitious convergence of need and personnel.

In June 1900, Reed, Carroll, Agramonte, and Lazear became the fourth successive board of United States medical officers assigned to solve the mysteries surrounding yellow fever. They were assisted by Finlay, who provided them with information and mosquitoes, with which they would make their remarkable discoveries in experiments based on Finlay's hypotheses, including the influence of temperature on the spread of yellow fever through its effects on the habits of the mosquito.

Also in 1900, Herbert E. Durham and Walter Myers, of the Liverpool School of Tropical Medicine, stopped for a few days in Havana on their way to their assigned task of studying yellow fever in Brazil. One of Dr. Durham's reports states:

> "It is incontestable that Dr. Charles [sic "Carlos"] Finlay, of Havana, was the first to undertake direct experiments to substantiate his ideas of the part played by the mosquito in the transmission of yellow fever. His method was to feed the mosquitoes upon yellow fever patients (not later than the sixth day [after disease onset]), and then after an interval of from 48 hours to four or five days to allow them to feed upon sus-

> ceptible persons; the idea was to produce a slight attack of the fever in order to produce immunity."

While in Havana, Durham and Myers visited both Finlay and the Yellow Fever Commission in mid-July 1900 and made the connection between the two-week extrinsic incubation period of yellow fever identified by Carter and Finlay's hypothesis that mosquitoes were the vector. They presumed that "Some means of transmission by the aid of an intermediate host – a town-loving host for this town-loving disease – is to some extent more plausible than might be anticipated." Both Durham and Myers contracted yellow fever while in Para (probably Belem), Brazil; Myers died (1901), Durham survived.

Finlay's empirical studies of yellow fever led to considerations of experimental design but it was Henry Rose Carter whose accumulated data eventually were used to design and conduct the studies. Carter's persistent and meticulous clinical studies while in what was to become the United States Public Health Service led him to an accomplished career in the epidemiology, clinical aspects, and control of yellow fever.

At essentially the same time that Durham and Myers were visiting Havana, Reed first proposed human experimentation, saying:

> "There is plenty of material in Havana, with every probability of its rapid increase—our last case here died on Monday—we will therefore expect to transfer our field of work to Military Hospital No. 1—Lazear, Carroll and Agramonte are all deeply interested in the problem, Personally, I feel that only can experimentation on human beings serve to clear the field for further effective work—with one or two points cleared up, we could then work to so much better advantage."

The Commission members decided to experiment on humans, including themselves (Figure 26). Carroll might have been the principal designer of these experimental infections, which were based on Carter's data. According to Carroll:

> "The final determination to investigate the mosquito theory was arrived at during an informal meeting of the Board (Dr.

Figure 26. "Conquerors of yellow fever", 1939 painting by Dean Cornwell (1883 - 1960); oil on canvas, commissioned by Wyeth-Ayerst (now part of Pfizer, Inc.) [Note: Painted with artistic license, this represents the first experimental inoculation of a human with yellow fever virus; not all these people were in attendance when the experiment was conducted, however.]
(image courtesy of the National Library of Medicine)

> Agramonte being absent) at Columbia Barracks on the evening before Dr. Reed's departure for the United States early in August 1900. The proposal to submit ourselves to inoculation was made by myself, twice, before it was brought up by Dr. Reed, for the first time, at the meeting above mentioned, where it was finally decided upon by actual vote."

Immediately after that meeting, Reed departed Cuba for Washington, D.C. Again according to Carroll, "On the evening of the 3rd of August, Reed, Lazear and I agreed to be bitten. On the following morning Reed sailed for the United States, without a word of explanation so far as I knew." It is believed that Reed had been summoned to Washington to complete the report of the Typhoid Fever Commission, which in fact he did during this visit, but no military orders documenting this have been found.

It is pointed out here that William Henry Welch, Reed's mentor at Johns Hopkins Hospital in 1891 where they had worked on the pathology of typhoid fever and on the identification of the hog cholera bacillus, had written to Reed, pointing out the findings of Loeffler and Frosch, who had transmitted foot-and-mouth disease to guinea pigs (*Cavia porcellus,* Figure 27) and cattle using porcelain-filtered serum samples from cattle with the disease. Loeffler and Frosch had examined two possible hypotheses: Whatever passed through the filter either was a soluble toxin or a particle so small it could pass through filters that would retain bacteria. The Reed group decided to test their hypothesis on yellow fever. They injected otherwise healthy "volunteers" with 3 ml of serum from a yellow fever patient; two developed

Figure 27. The sculpture "Guinea pigs" by F. Cremer, Berlin, at Reims Island, near Greifswald, Germany, where early studies by Friedrich Loeffler and Paul Frosch helped us understand foot and mouth disease and the viruses that cause it.
(photo by Charles Calisher)

yellow fever. Yellow fever virus became the first recognized arthropod-borne virus ("arbovirus") infecting humans.

Reed was in the United States when Carroll and then Lazear developed yellow fever from self-experimentation. He said he was remorseful to be gone while his colleagues were ill:

> "I have been so ashamed of myself for being here in a safe country, while my associates have been coming down with Yellow Jack. The General has suggested that I do not return, but somehow I feel that, as the Senior member of a [Board]—investigating yellow fever, my place is in Cuba, as long as the work goes on—I shall, of course, take every precaution that I can against contracting the disease, and I certainly shall not, with the facts that we now have, allow a "loaded" mosquito to bite me! That would be fool-hardy in the extreme."

The controversy over Reed's absence continued for years. After recovering from yellow fever, Carroll, in a letter to his wife, wrote:

> "I had occasion to call at the office of the Commanding Officer today and General Baldwin, Colonel of the 7th Cavalry (Custer's old regiment) amused me. After congratulating me upon my recovery he said suddenly, 'By the way when is Maj. Reed coming back? I think I shall have to accuse him of running away.' I thought to myself, you have no idea how nearly you have come to the truth."

Lazear died of yellow fever during those studies (Figure 28).

It was at this time of ferment in microbiology and with a background of research on various pathogens and the diseases they cause that in 1901 Reed and his colleagues reported their findings that yellow fever virus was transmitted by mosquitoes, although the definition of a virus was barely known. What Reed and his associates did was nothing short of remarkable for that time or for any time. Because Nott had suggested that mosquitoes might somehow be involved in yellow fever transmission, that Beauperthuy had suggested much the same thing long before that, and that Finlay had provided both a hypothesis and at least some evidence for mosquito transmission of whatever was causing yellow fever, the Commission embarked on experimental studies to determine whether any of these ideas were correct, which, they proposed, would lead them to means of prevention of the disease. Giuseppi Sanarelli, a prominent Italian bacteriologist, had proposed in 1896 that *Bacillus icteroides,* which he had detected in a number of yellow fever patients, was the cause of that disease (Figure 29) but Carroll and Reed disproved that, showing that that bacterium was a secondary invader in those people. That hurdle out of the way, the four members of the Commission embarked on further studies, additional bacteriologic studies and studies designed to test Finlay's hypothesis.

First, they received from Finlay ova of mosquitoes with which he had done his studies. From these they established a colony of mos-

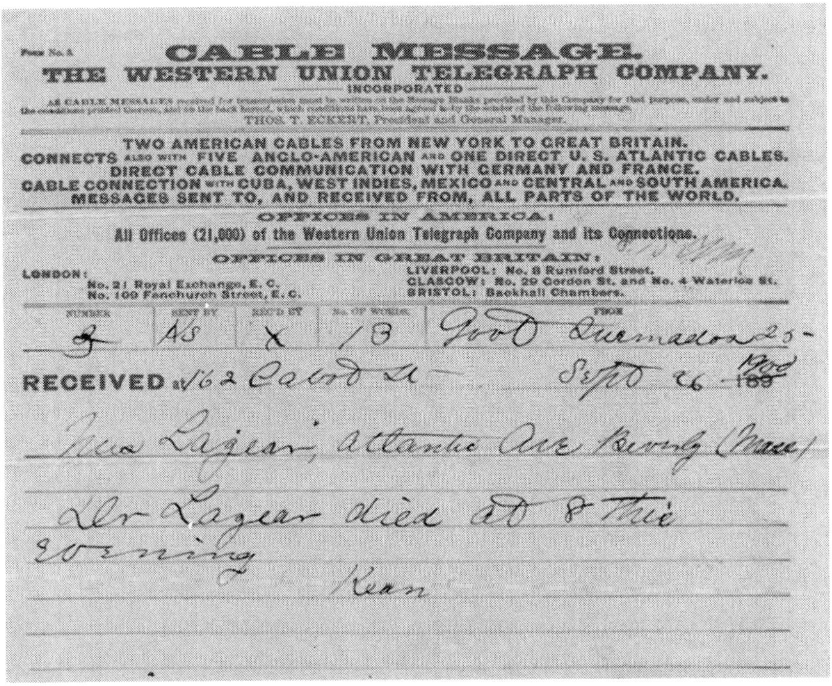

CABLE MESSAGE.
THE WESTERN UNION TELEGRAPH COMPANY.
INCORPORATED
THOS. T. ECKERT, President and General Manager.

TWO AMERICAN CABLES FROM NEW YORK TO GREAT BRITAIN.
CONNECTS ALSO WITH FIVE ANGLO-AMERICAN AND ONE DIRECT U. S. ATLANTIC CABLES.
DIRECT CABLE COMMUNICATION WITH GERMANY AND FRANCE.
CABLE CONNECTION WITH CUBA, WEST INDIES, MEXICO AND CENTRAL AND SOUTH AMERICA.
MESSAGES SENT TO, AND RECEIVED FROM, ALL PARTS OF THE WORLD.

OFFICES IN AMERICA:
All Offices (21,000) of the Western Union Telegraph Company and its Connections.

OFFICES IN GREAT BRITAIN:
LONDON: No. 21 Royal Exchange, E. C. No. 109 Fenchurch Street, E. C.
LIVERPOOL: No. 8 Rumford Street. GLASGOW: No. 29 Gordon St. and No. 4 Waterloo St. BRISTOL: Backhall Chambers.

RECEIVED at 162

Mrs Lazear, Atlantic Ave Beverly (Mass)
Dr Lazear died at 8 this evening
Kean

Figure 28. Cable from Major Jefferson Kean, Havana, to Mabel Lazear, the recent widow of Jesse Lazear, who had been involved in experimental studies of yellow fever in humans (1900). The message, dated September 26, 1900, reads: "Mrs. Lazear, Atlantic Avenue, Beverly (Mass.) Dr. Lazear died at 8 this evening. Kean"
(image courtesy of the National Library of Medicine)

quitoes with which they could conduct further experiments. Next, they fed mosquitoes on yellow fever patients and then fed those same mosquitoes on healthy individuals, three of the latter becoming ill with yellow fever. Ensuing studies showed that (1) *Aedes aegypti* mosquitoes were the vectors of yellow fever (more correctly, the vectors of the virus that causes yellow fever), (2) about 12 days elapsed between the time the mosquito fed on an infected blood meal and the time when it could transmit the virus – the "period of extrinsic incubation" recognized by Carter the previous year, (3) yellow fever could be produced in otherwise healthy people by inoculating them with blood from yellow fever patients who were in their first or second day of illness (for obvious reasons, a forbidden procedure today), and (4) yellow fever was not transmitted via fomites, inanimate objects such as clothes or bedding. However, knowing how the disease is transmitted is not the same as knowing what causes the disease.

William Crawford Gorgas was born in Toulminville (near Mobile), Alabama in 1854, the attending obstetrician having been Josiah Nott. The son of Confederate General Josiah Gorgas, later president of the University of Alabama, William Crawford Gorgas was trained as a physician at Bellvue Hospital Center, New York City. Having survived a bout of yellow fever while stationed in Texas, he was named Chief Sanitary Officer in Havana, charged with reducing the incidences and prevalences of mosquito-borne diseases in Florida, Cuba and Panama. It was not without political and economic difficulties that Colonel Gorgas accomplished his great work. He arrived in the Canal Zone in June of 1904 as Chief Medical Officer. Years earlier, while living in Havana, he read of discoveries linking mosquitoes with malaria. Considering the novel possibility that mosquitoes also could be involved in the transmission of yellow fever, he had successfully eradicated them and the disease from the area in 1901. Confident that he could halt these infections in Panama, he realized that he needed the political will and the financial resources to eliminate mosquitoes from nearly 500 square miles of swamp and jungle. In the fall of 1904, Gorgas returned to Washington with a $1 million plan to fumigate the

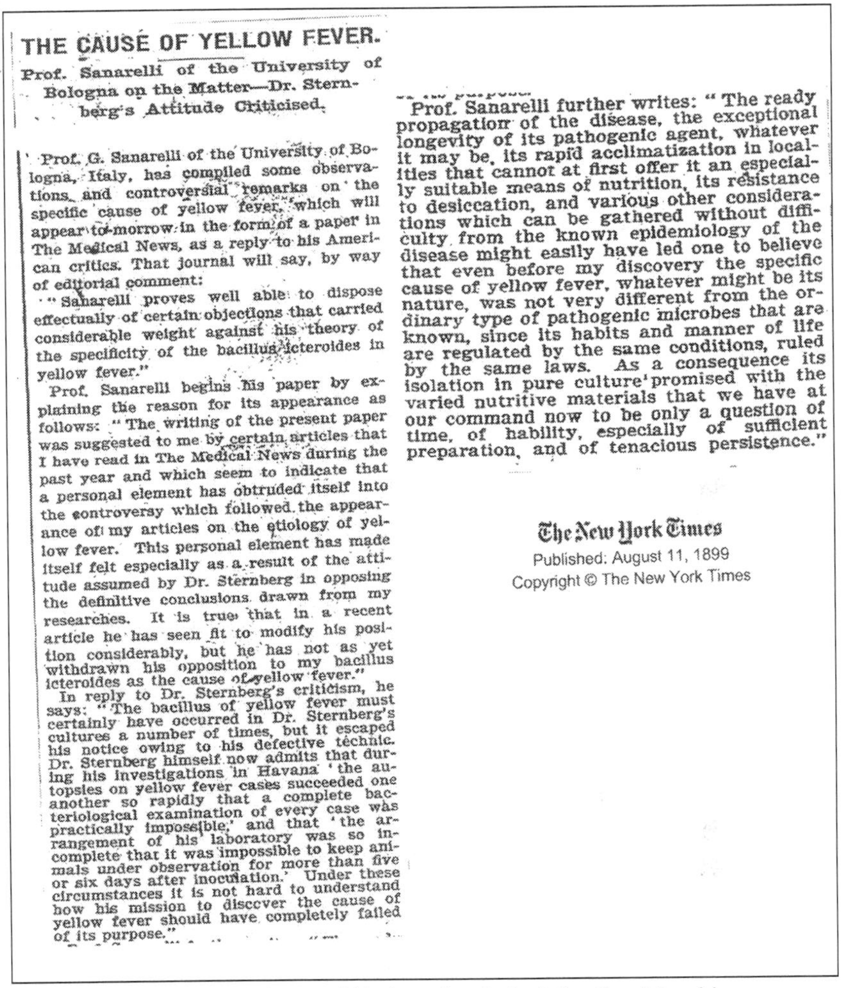

THE CAUSE OF YELLOW FEVER.

Prof. Sanarelli of the University of Bologna on the Matter—Dr. Sternberg's Attitude Criticised.

Prof. G. Sanarelli of the University of Bologna, Italy, has compiled some observations and controversial remarks on the specific cause of yellow fever, which will appear to-morrow in the form of a paper in The Medical News, as a reply to his American critics. That journal will say, by way of editorial comment:

"Sanarelli proves well able to dispose effectually of certain objections that carried considerable weight against his theory of the specificity of the bacillus icteroides in yellow fever."

Prof. Sanarelli begins his paper by explaining the reason for its appearance as follows: "The writing of the present paper was suggested to me by certain articles that I have read in The Medical News during the past year and which seem to indicate that a personal element has obtruded itself into the controversy which followed the appearance of my articles on the etiology of yellow fever. This personal element has made itself felt especially as a result of the attitude assumed by Dr. Sternberg in opposing the definitive conclusions drawn from my researches. It is true that in a recent article he has seen fit to modify his position considerably, but he has not as yet withdrawn his opposition to my bacillus icteroides as the cause of yellow fever."

In reply to Dr. Sternberg's criticism, he says: "The bacillus of yellow fever must certainly have occurred in Dr. Sternberg's cultures a number of times, but it escaped his notice owing to his defective technic. Dr. Sternberg himself now admits that during his investigations in Havana 'the autopsies on yellow fever cases succeeded one another so rapidly that a complete bacteriological examination of every case was practically impossible,' and that 'the arrangement of his laboratory was so incomplete that it was impossible to keep animals under observation for more than five or six days after inoculation.' Under these circumstances it is not hard to understand how his mission to discover the cause of yellow fever should have completely failed of its purpose."

Prof. Sanarelli further writes: "The ready propagation of the disease, the exceptional longevity of its pathogenic agent, whatever it may be, its rapid acclimatization in localities that cannot at first offer it an especially suitable means of nutrition, its resistance to desiccation, and various other considerations which can be gathered without difficulty from the known epidemiology of the disease might easily have led one to believe that even before my discovery the specific cause of yellow fever, whatever might be its nature, was not very different from the ordinary type of pathogenic microbes that are known, since its habits and manner of life are regulated by the same conditions, ruled by the same laws. As a consequence its isolation in pure culture promised with the varied nutritive materials that we have at our command now to be only a question of time, of hability, especially of sufficient preparation, and of tenacious persistence."

The New York Times
Published: August 11, 1899

Figure 29. Sanarelli's defense of his hypothesis that *Bacillus icteroides* causes yellow fever
(image courtesy of The New York Times)

Isthmus of Panama and eradicate the disease. But officials derided the high costs and his mosquito hypothesis, instead adhering to the still prevailing "miasma theory" which postulated that diseases are carried by bad air or toxins in tropical soil.

The following spring, the first significant yellow fever scare hit the Canal Zone. Quarantining patients in hospital did little to slow the rate of disease acquisition and the panic reached a fever pitch as additional workers fell ill. Chief Engineer John Wallace was powerless to calm his workers and a quarter of the workforce deserted the project. If the numbers of ill and deserting laborers continued to rise, the project would face significant production delays or worse. In Washington, Alexander Lambert, President Roosevelt's personal physician, appealed to the president. He told him, "You are facing one of the greatest decisions of your career. If you fall back on the old methods you will fail, just as the French failed. If you back Gorgas you will get your canal." Roosevelt granted the funding and Gorgas established one of the most extensive sanitary campaigns in history.

The control of yellow fever allowed the construction of the Panama Canal. Along with malaria, yellow fever had accounted for hospitalizations of 85 percent of the workers and more than 27,000 deaths, not including any of the more than 100,000 who died building the Panama railroad. It has been estimated that before Gorgas' policies and procedures were implemented 10 percent of the workforce on the Panama Canal project died each year due to these diseases. Between February and September 1901 Gorgas ordered the destruction of mosquito breeding areas, provision of mosquito nets as protection for people while they slept, prevention of mosquitoes from feeding on yellow fever patients, and teaching mosquito avoidance techniques to everyone. Thereafter, yellow fever was eradicated in Cuba and did not reappear in Panama until 1974. As an additional benefit, the incidence of malaria there was greatly reduced because of the general anti-mosquito campaign.

Emile Marchoux (Figure 30) was born in France, studied medicine in Paris and in 1887 wrote his thesis on the history of typhoid fever in marine troops. He then embarked on a career as an army doctor in Dahomey (now the Republic of Benin) and Indochina (now Vietnam, Laos, and Cambodia). First taking a course at the Pasteur Institute, then administrating a laboratory in Saint-Louis, Senegal, he participated in a mission to study yellow fever in Brazil with Paul-Louis Simond (Figure 31).

At this time Oswaldo Gonçalves Cruz (Figure 32), an accomplished Brazilian physician, bacteriologist, epidemiologist, and public health officer, initiated a successful campaign against yellow fever in Rio de Janeiro, Brazil. Cruz went on to found the Oswaldo Cruz Institute in Rio de Janeiro.

As yellow fever increased in its West African colonies, the French government sent a scientific mission to Rio de Janeiro to find new ways to prevent the disease. Under the authority of the Institut Pasteur, Simond,

Figure 30. Emile Marchoux (1862 - 1943)
(image courtesy of the Pasteur Institute)

Figure 31. Paul-Louis Simond (1858 - 1947)
(image courtesy of the Pasteur Institute)

Figure 32. Oswaldo Gonçalves Cruz (1872 - 1917)
(image courtesy of the Oswaldo Cruz Foundation, Casa de Oswaldo Cruz)

who had recently discovered the role of fleas in the transmission of plague bacilli (*Yersinia pestis*), was designated to carry out this mission with the assistance of Marchoux and Alexandre Salimbeni. From November 1901 to May 1905, the three men studied the epidemiological and clinical aspects of the disease in Rio de Janeiro. Working with female *Aedes aegypti* mosquitoes, they made some useful discoveries and conducted experimental infection studies with human volunteers, eventually developing a vaccine using heated or filtered serum from infected individuals, and establishing sanitary protocols to prevent the spread of the disease, all of which contributed to the success of Cruz' campaign against yellow fever.

One of the major contributions of this group was providing evidence that the causative agent of yellow fever could be transmitted from an infected female mosquito to its eggs and larvae. By the completion of the mission, French authorities had the information necessary to control yellow fever more efficiently in their African colonies as well as in the West Indies and French Guyana.

Leaving military service, Marchoux took the position of head of the tropical microbiology service at the Pasteur Institute, leading fundamental studies on leprosy and malaria. He also co-founded and later became President of the Société de Pathologie Exotique, President of the International Leprosy Association, and founder of the Institut Central de la Lèpre at Bamako, Mali. Like other French researchers during colonial times, Marchoux made significant contributions to our knowledge of many infectious diseases.

Around that same time, in 1903, "The Society for Tropical Medicine of Philadelphia" was established, with Thomas H. Fenton as its first President. Merging many disparate interests, the intent of the society was to address tropical disease threats in the subtropical United States. These health problems included malaria and hookworm in various states and yellow fever, typhoid fever, and dengue in the new United States possessions of Puerto Rico, Cuba, and the Philippines. The following Honorary Members were elected on December 7, 1903: William H. Forwood (Surgeon General, US Army), P.M. Rixey (Surgeon General, US Navy), M.J.Rosenau, Charles W. Stiles, William C. Gorgas, James Carroll, D.E. Salmon, Aristides Agramonte, John Guiteras, Patrick Manson, George H. Nuttall, Alphonse Laveran, Robert Koch, George Lamb, A. Calmette, William Murrell, C.F. Martin, William H. Welch, George M. Sternberg, Ralph Stockton, Charles D.F. Philips, and Frederick Montizambert. Those prominent scientists undoubtedly constituted an excellent group to begin such a venture. The first public meeting of the new society was held at the University of Pennsylvania on January 9, 1904, and featured an address by Yellow Fever Commission veteran James Carroll, Surgeon, US Army, on "The Etiology of Yellow Fever." Not long after that, the founders expanded their vision and changed their name to "The American Society of Tropical Medicine." In 1951, the American Society of Tropical Medicine merged with the National Malaria Society to give rise to our modern American Society of Tropical Medicine and Hygiene, whose first President was Martin D. Young, an internationally recognized expert on malaria and later Director of the Gorgas Memorial Laboratory in Panama. The American Society of Tropical Medicine and Hygiene is a large and vibrant organization at whose annual meetings gather specialists in a wide variety of clinical and laboratory research problems concerning general health and tropical medicine and hygiene in particular. Its journal, the American Journal of Tropical Medicine and Hygiene had an impact factor of 2.446 in 2011.

In addition to serving as Reed's mentor, William Henry Welch helped found the Johns Hopkins School of Public Health. In 1913, the Rockefeller Foundation sponsored a conference on the need for public health education in the United States. Foundation officials believed that a new profession of public health was needed, one allied to medicine but also distinct, with its own identity and educational institutions. Deliberations between public health leaders and foundation officials resulted in the Welch-Rose Report of 1915, which laid out the need for adequately trained public health workers and envisioned an "institute of hygiene" for the United States. The Report reflected the different preferences of the plan's two architects: Welch, who favored scientific research and Wickliffe Rose, who wanted to emphasize public health practices.

In June 1916, the executive committee of the Rockefeller Foundation approved a plan to organize an institute of public health at the Johns Hopkins University in Baltimore, Maryland. The institute was named the School of Hygiene and Public Health, indicating a compromise between those who wanted the practical public health training based on the British model and those who favored basic scientific research based on the German model. Welch, the first Dean of the Johns Hopkins School of Medicine also became the founding Dean of the first school of public health in the United States.

In sum, the Yellow Fever Commission confirmed Beauperthuy's speculations. Finlay's hypotheses and more detailed studies were also confirmed, albeit nearly 20 years after his publications, scientific presentations, and accurate assessments; he became the chief health officer of Cuba from 1902 to 1909. Although Reed received and still receives much of the credit for sorting out the cause of yellow fever and identifying the principle vector of the virus causing it, he credited Finlay with these findings and cited Finlay's work in his own publications, though his original report failed to mention Finlay's hypotheses or research. General Leonard Wood, a physician and the United States military governor of Cuba in 1900 said, "The confirmation of Dr. Finlay's doctrine is the greatest step forward made in medical science since Jenner's discovery of vaccination [for smallpox]." Nonetheless, it was not until 1954, 39 years after Finlay's death, that the International Congress of Medical History granted Finlay the proper credit.

Thus, the progression of discoveries that led to the development of arbovirology was as follows:

- Ivanovsky and Beijerinck described the infectious nature and identification of a virus.
- Manson, then Smith and Kilbourne, determined that arthropods could serve as vectors of infectious agents.
- Laveran and Ross found that malaria was caused by a parasite of mosquitoes.

- Loeffler and Frosch discovered the viral etiology of foot-and-mouth disease.
- Arnold Theiler discovered a viral etiology of African horse sickness.
- Beauperthuy, Nott, Carter, and Finlay proposed significant hypotheses that were based on fundamental findings by Pasteur and Koch, then proven by Reed, Carroll, Agramonte, and Lazear and carried forward by Gorgas.

Key findings by these and other scientists eventually led Max Theiler, the son of Arnold Theiler, to conceive of a vaccine against this dreadful disease, as described in the next chapter.

Yellow fever virus today is endemic in tropical areas of Africa and Latin America with a combined population of more than 900 million people, therefore vaccination of individuals in those areas is imperative. The World Health Organization (W.H.O.) estimates (January 2011) that even with a safe and effective vaccine available, yellow fever causes 200,000 illnesses and 30,000 deaths each year in unvaccinated populations. About 90 percent of the infections occur in Africa. There are two reasons. First, in rural settings yellow fever virus is maintained in a natural mosquito-monkey-mosquito cycle, making it impossible to totally eradicate. Second, a lack of both political will and public education continues. Yellow fever in dead and dying monkeys in tropical rain forests still serves as a harbinger of human yellow fever. A single person need only expose himself in a yellow fever virus habitat to become infected by mosquitoes involved in the monkey-to-monkey cycle. When that person, already sick or not yet symptomatic, returns to a village, town or city, and is fed upon by *Aedes aegypti* or other mosquitoes capable of transmitting the virus, an urban cycle can be established among people who are not immune to the virus.

The number of yellow fever cases has increased in the past two decades, which W.H.O. attributes to declining population immunity to infection as well as to deforestation, urbanization, population movements, and climate change; the situation appears unlikely to improve. It might be added that isolated cases, outbreaks, and epidemics continue to occur because of irresponsible and incompetent governments, the aforesaid mentioned lack of political will, and wars, but they do not occur for lack of information or vaccine, which is always obtainable through commercial sources or through the offices of the W.H.O.

Figure 33. Thomas Patrick Charles Monath (1940 -)
(image courtesy of Thomas Monath)

As the reader might imagine, there is a huge literature covering all this, in scientific journals and reviews by the protagonists, in the popular press, and now on the web. Thomas Monath (Figure 33), the modern expert on this disease, published a marvelous review and a University of Virginia web site contains an abundant amount of information regarding the history of yellow fever research. The reader is directed to those and other sources for further specific details.

The fight against yellow fever in the Americas ushered in an era in which we began to throw off superstitions and folklore about infectious diseases. This has helped propel us into today's research environment, with its reliance on careful and documented observations (and repeatability) by skilled researchers, peer review of manuscripts, and technological advances plus a dollop of serendipity.

CHAPTER 3

A door is opened: a breakthrough in yellow fever control

Only four years after Karl Landsteiner and Constantin Levaditi reported the identification of a virus, subsequently called "poliovirus", as a cause of poliomyelitis, John D. Rockefeller, Sr., along with John D. Rockefeller, Jr. and Frederick Taylor Gates, established the Rockefeller Foundation, in 1913. Their avowed intent was to create a philanthropic organization to "promote the well-being of mankind throughout the world" by addressing the root causes of serious problems. With multiple global efforts, this well-funded foundation declared its goal to improve opportunities for the many poor and for others. At the time of its establishment, Rockefeller, Sr. said, "The best philanthropy is constantly in search of the finalities—a search for a cause, an attempt to cure evils at their source." The foundation produced remarkable breakthroughs, including the development of a yellow fever vaccine; professionalization of public health; the so-called "Green Revolution" in Latin American, Asian, and Indian agriculture; and the current concept of public-private partnerships to develop promising new vaccines.

The Foundation created an International Health Commission in 1913, directed by Wickliffe Rose, who recognized that people in Asia and elsewhere worried that the Panama Canal, which was to open the following year, would somehow promote the movement of yellow fever from the Americas to other parts of the world. He passed these impressions to General William C. Gorgas, who understood the potential medical and political problems but reiterated his belief that complete eradication of yellow fever was possible and could be accomplished within a reasonable time and at reasonable cost. This overly optimistic outlook reflected an understandable ignorance of the complexity of the ecology of yellow fever. The next year, having had a communication from Gorgas, then Surgeon General of the United State Army, that he was willing and ready to join the Rockefeller Foundation to help in these efforts, the International Health Commission resolved to eradicate yellow fever wherever it occurred and appointed Gorgas to head these efforts. At the time it was thought that the life cycle of yellow fever involved only *Aedes aegypti* mosquitoes, that there were certain geographic foci of yellow fever infections, and that these were few in number. Public health workers believed that if these foci were eliminated yellow fever would be eradicated.

In 1914, the Rockefeller Foundation became heavily involved in widespread efforts to control yellow fever, efforts that required a considerable amount of money and a large number of people. The initial purposes were to determine the world-wide extent of the problem, to elucidate the epidemiology of the disease, and to devise methods for controlling a deadly scourge. Early on, however, it became abundantly clear that this would not be a simple task; both the problem and solution were more complex than first thought.

Certain members of this newly established Rockefeller Foundation Yellow Fever Commission (General Gorgas, Dr. Henry Rose Carter, Dr. Juan Guiteras (Figure 15), Major T.C. Lyster, Major E.R. Whitmore, and Mr. W.D. Wrightson) visited known yellow fever sites in Ecuador, Colombia, Peru, and Venezuela, as well as the port cities of Brazil, from Rio de Janeiro to Pará. They concluded that the only one of these sites where yellow fever was prevalent was Guayaquil, Ecuador, and recommended elimination of the infection from that city. They further recommended monitoring the east coast of Brazil and the southern Caribbean for infection and surveillance for yellow fever in Mexico and West Africa. A special working group was sent to Central America and South America to study not only yellow fever but Oroyo fever (now known to be caused by *Bartonella bacilliformis,* a bacterium), poliomyelitis, and trachoma (caused by the bacterium *Chlamydia trachomatis*).

The group, which included the renowned bacteriologist Dr. Hideyo Noguchi, arrived in Guayaquil in 1918, intending to accumulate detailed information about yellow fever. Noguchi had moved from Japan to the United States in 1900, obtaining a position at the Rockefeller Institute for Medical Research in 1904. In 1913 he had demonstrated the presence of the bacterium *Treponema pallidum* in the brain of a patient with clinically diagnosed syphilis, suggesting that the patient's illness was caused by this spirochete (a bacterium). This classic discovery eventually led to the use of penicillin to control the disease. Other studies led Noguchi to believe that a leptospira could produce yellow fever-like symptoms in experimentally infected guinea pigs. This was reminiscent of Sanarelli's report concluding that *Bacillus icteroides* was the cause of yellow fever. Reed's group and many others later showed this conclusion to be incorrect by demonstrating that a virus causes yellow fever. Noguchi and co-investigators persisted, isolating the same leptospira from yellow fever patients in Mexico, Peru, and Brazil and naming it *Leptospira icteroides.* In 1928 Noguchi went to Africa to test his hypothesis. While working in Accra, Ghana, he acquired yellow fever; his famous last words were said to have been "I don't understand." Nonetheless, his contribution, erroneous and sad as it was, should not be minimized. He helped to eliminate at least one possible cause of the disease.

The diary of Oskar Klotz, a Canadian pathologist who traveled to Lagos at the invitation of Frederick F. Russell, at the time the director of the International Health Board of the Rockefeller Foundation, is worth reading (see *Suggested Readings*). Although written in the style of the times and understandably naïve regarding aspects of yellow fever and other diseases, his diary seems honest and full of fascinating details pathologic, diagnostic, epidemiologic, personal, and otherwise. In summary, Klotz said:

> "By means of monkey inoculation we were able to prove the yellow fever nature of an epidemic occurring among the natives, and which, because of the mild nature of the disease, would have been difficult if not impossible to prove by clinical methods."

A career in public health, particularly in the early years of that field, was not without risk. Noguchi (died in 1928) was not the only investigator who died of yellow fever. Howard B. Cross (died in 1921), Adrian Stokes (died in 1927) (Figure 34), William A. Young (died in 1927), Paul A. Lewis (died in 1929) and Theodore B. Hayne (died in 1930) all succumbed to the disease in the line of duty. As a boy of 16, Hayne had spent his summer vacation with Henry R. Carter of the United States Public Health Service, assisting in anti-malaria work. There Hayne became interested in mosquitoes and the possibility of their transmitting disease agents.

Stokes, a visiting scientist at the Rockefeller Foundation laboratory in Lagos succeeded in passing the virus from one leptospira-free monkey to another leptospira-free monkey, thus effectively disproving Noguchi's leptospira hypothesis. Stokes died of yellow fever before he could complete his research. It was his death, and the death of William Young who had performed the autopsy on Stokes, that prompted Max Theiler (who also had become infected with yellow fever virus) to redouble his efforts to find less unwieldy experimental hosts than monkeys. For the majority of his research, Theiler used the yellow fever virus strain isolated by Stokes.

This all involved a progression of thoughts and changing administrative goals. The name "International Health Commission" was changed in 1916 to "International Health Board" for the purpose of expanding the work of the Rockefeller Sanitary Commission for the

Figure 34. Adrian Stokes (1887 - 1927) (image courtesy of the Rockefeller Archive Center)

Eradication of Hookworm Disease. In addition to efforts to understand and control yellow fever, the Board also supported studies of malaria, tuberculosis, public health education, virus studies, and related research. In 1927, the Board was disbanded, its work continued by the new International Health Division of the Foundation. In 1951, the International Health Division was merged with the medical sciences program and public health activity was de-emphasized.

Under the leadership of Dr. Michael E. Connor, in 1918 the International Health Board, with the cooperation and assistance of the Director General of Health of Ecuador, set out to eradicate yellow fever from Guayaquil by reducing or eliminating breeding areas of *Aedes aegypti* and by killing adult mosquitoes.

By June 1919, no new cases of yellow fever were reported in Guayaquil and none has been recorded there to this day. The belief that yellow fever was caused by a virus transmitted only by *Aedes aegypti* mosquitoes and only to humans was not completely correct. Mosquitoes of other species and vertebrates other than humans are also susceptible. However, measures designed to eradicate *Aedes aegypti* eliminated other mosquitoes as well.

It was a huge disappointment to all involved to recognize outbreaks of yellow fever occurring in Guatemala (1918) and in Peru, Brazil, and other countries of South America, in Honduras, El Salvador and Nicaragua in Central America, in Mexico (1919), and in Colombia (1923). Control measures similar to those employed in Guayaquil were applied in affected countries, and Brazilian physician, epidemiologist, bacteriologist and public health officer, Oswaldo Cruz, became deeply involved in attempts to control yellow fever in Brazil.

Founder of the institute that bears his name, Oswaldo Gonçalves Cruz was born in São Paulo. Completing medical school there in 1892 at age 20, he studied at the Pasteur Institute in Paris, where he worked for three years. When he returned to Brazil, Cruz brought a dramatically changed outlook on medicine in general and infectious diseases in particular to his work, He immediately began implementing these new ideas and introducing them to Brazilian medicine and soon became well known for stemming a plague epidemic in coastal Santos, south of Rio de Janeiro.

In 1902 Cruz became the director general of public health of Brazil. That country's progress to secure international respect had been hindered by the frequent epidemics that ravaged the population, discouraging immigration, upsetting normal patterns of trade, and debilitating workers and managers alike. With the backing of the President of Brazil, Cruz initiated a campaign to modernize and improve sanitary standards in the capital city. He also worked to eradicate the *Aedes aegypti* mosquitoes responsible for the transmission of yellow fever virus and, at the same time, successfully lobbied the Brazilian congress to pass a law requiring compulsory smallpox vaccination. As a result of these measures, epidemic diseases became much less common in Brazil. This accomplishment was not without political dissent and violence, however, as people were convinced this was an effort by the government to control the population. The laws passed nonetheless, and a potential smallpox epidemic was squelched by the new national program, convincing the population of the need for such programs.

After becoming director of the newly formed Institute of Experimental Pathology in Rio de Janeiro, Cruz conducted field studies in the upper Amazon region and launched programs that led to the control of malaria in Brazil. His successful efforts to eradicate yellow fever in Rio de Janeiro and a few other cities before the availability of a vaccine were a tribute to Cruz and to Brazilian science. However, similar success in other parts of Brazil was not achieved because of the widespread distribution of the virus over an exceedingly large area of that country.

Epidemic yellow fever was under effective attack by public health workers wherever the disease occurred. The last epidemic of yellow fever in North America occurred in New Orleans in 1905. By the end of 1924 yellow fever, had been eradicated from Mexico, Central America, and Ecuador, with efforts underway to control it in other areas.

World War I interrupted plans to investigate what was described as yellow fever in West Africa, but in 1920 the Yellow Fever Commission, headed by General Gorgas, traveled there from Rockefeller Foundation headquarters in New York. The group was assisted by experts from many countries, including Cuba, Ireland and Great Britain. While in England and on his way to this meeting, Gorgas suffered a stroke and died before he could apply his expertise to yellow fever in Africa.

Charged with determining whether the reported disease in Africa actually was yellow fever and, if so, whether it could be controlled by the methods used in the Americas, the members of the commission visited Dahomey (now Republic of Benin), the Gold Coast (now Ghana), Senegal, Sierra Leone, and the Belgian Congo (now Democratic Republic of the Congo). They observed no yellow fever cases but anecdotal evidence suggested that this disease was present. The Commission recommended that a better equipped delegation continue and extend this work to include laboratory studies of fevers occurring within this very large region. That suggestion laid the groundwork for all subsequent yellow fever studies and, indeed, for the establishment of arbovirology.

Objectives of the new delegation in West Africa aimed to identify the geographic areas where yellow fever occurred, study the epidemiology of yellow fever in those areas, isolate the agent that causes yellow fever, and determine the mechanism of transmission of the virus. Within a relatively short time, the team performed clinical, pathological, and bacteriological characterizations, which failed to isolate *Leptospira icteroides* from any of the first 67 yellow fever patients intensely studied. That finally put an end to this distraction. By this time, researchers in Brazil, Cuba, Mexico, and the United States had also refuted Noguchi's hypothesis.

A major problem in conducting further research studies was the need for a standard and inexpensive host for experimental and diagnostic studies of yellow fever virus infections. French researchers isolated a strain of yellow fever virus from a man named Francois Mayali in 1927. They called this the French virus or French viscerotropic (tending to affect the internal organs of the body) virus. This isolate was passaged serially 128 times through the brains of adult mice and provided the French neurotropic vaccine virus, which was attenuated for viscerotropism in primates and did not replicate in mosquitoes but which retained a neurotropic phenotype. It was further passaged in mouse brain until passage 260. This was used as a yellow fever vaccine in French-speaking areas of Africa, from the late 1930s until 1980, when use of that vaccine was discontinued because of the high incidence of neurological disease it caused in children (3 in 1000 children given the vaccine had neurological complications, probably due to impurities in the vaccine).

In investigating reported cases of yellow fever in Ghana in 1927, A.F. Mahaffy, one of the Rockefeller Foundation Commission members stationed in Ghana, collected blood from two patients with mild illnesses, one of whom was a 28-year-old African male named Asibi (Figure 35). These blood samples were taken to the Rockefeller Foundation laboratory in Lagos, Nigeria and inoculated by Mahaffy and Johannes H. Bauer into a rhesus monkey (*Macaca mulatta,* an Asian species), a marmoset (*Callithrix leucocephala,* from the New World), and two guinea pigs (also from the New World). On the fourth day after inoculation, a monkey was found to be febrile and on the fifth day moribund. This was the first time yellow fever virus had been transmitted to an animal other than a human, a finding that provided a model for laboratory and field research. Known as the "Asibi strain", for the person from whom it came, this virus has served as a prototype virus for yellow fever virus studies since then. These scientists

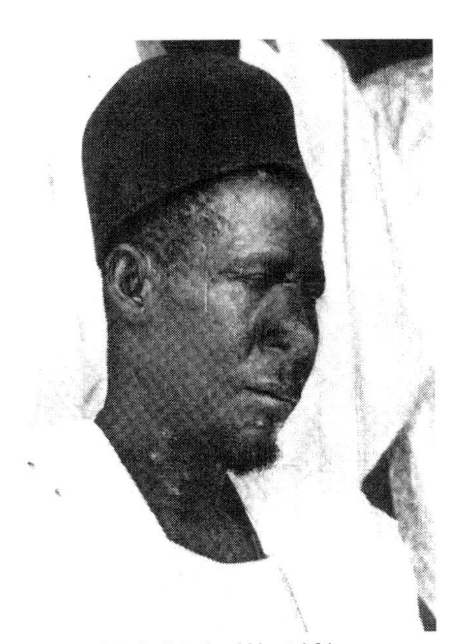

Figure 35. Asibi, the West African (Ghana) survivor of yellow fever (1927) and whose blood was the source of the classical "Asibi" strain of that virus with which so much work has been done. (image courtesy of McGraw-Hill Companies)

in Nigeria and others confirmed that the causative agent of yellow fever was a virus, that infection could be transmitted from monkey to monkey and from human to monkey (and, unfortunately, from monkey to human in the case of Stokes), and that the virus could be transmitted between monkeys by *Aedes aegypti* mosquitoes. They also learned that infected mosquitoes remained infected for the remainder of their lives, and that being fed upon by a single infected mosquito was sufficient to transmit the virus and cause yellow fever. Those findings were clearly advances, but further observations regarding yellow fever virus and its life cycle were to reveal even more complexities.

In the Americas, where most early work on yellow fever had been done, only *Aedes aegypti* mosquitoes had been shown to serve as vectors of yellow fever virus; studies of other commonly occurring mosquitoes there suggested that they were not competent to transmit this virus. When *Aedes aegypti* was eliminated yellow fever disappeared, which suggested that it was the only vector of the virus. The situation in West Africa proved more complex. Johannes H. Bauer and N. Paul Hudson determined the incubation period of yellow fever virus in mosquitoes and then Cornelius B. Philip (Figure 36) of the Yellow Fever Commission and others reported that mosquitoes of many species in West Africa could transmit yellow fever virus.

It is interesting and historically significant to recognize links among people, institutes and disease agents. For example, Philip arrived in

Lagos as a member of the Yellow Fever Commission in 1928 and spent 19 months there, after which he returned to the United States, accepting a position at the Rocky Mountain Laboratory of the State of Montana (now part of the United States National Institute of Allergy and Infectious Diseases) in Hamilton. Philip's work helped to establish this laboratory as it undertook entomologic and other studies of Rocky Mountain spotted fever and, later, under the direction of Willy Burgdorfer, discovered the causative agent of Lyme disease, *Borrelia burgdorferi,* a spirochetal bacterium.

Figure 36. Cornelius Becker Philip (1900 - 1987)
(image courtesy of Rocky Mountain Laboratories, National Institute of Allergy and Infectious Diseases, National Institutes of Health)

By the end of the assignment of the Yellow Fever Commission, it was clear that the natural cycle of yellow fever virus was not as simple as had been thought. Because there was not yet agreement as to the cause of yellow fever (some still clung to the idea that it was *Leptospira icteroides*), Frederick F. Russell, the new Director of the International Health Board, decided that a laboratory was needed that could study the yellow fever viruses of both the Americas and Africa. With the assistance of Simon Flexner, the first Director of the Rockefeller Institute for Medical Research, Russell found space for his yellow fever laboratory in New York City.

Thomas M. Rivers (Figure 37) published a paper in 1927 describing the differentiation of bacteria and viruses, establishing virology as a field of study distinct from bacteriology, and establishing virology as a separate clinical necessity. The next year, Wilbur A. Sawyer (Figure

Figure 37. Thomas Milton Rivers (1888 - 1962)
(image courtesy the Rockefeller Archive Center)

Figure 38. Wilbur Augustus Sawyer (1879 - 1951)
(image courtesy of the Rockefeller Archive Center)

38), Frank Horsfall, Max Theiler, Richard Shope, and others joined Rivers in founding the Rockefeller Foundation Virus Laboratory.

Activities of the laboratory, begun in earnest in 1928 with Sawyer as director, supplemented those of on-going laboratories in West Africa and Brazil. Safety was of utmost importance, but experience and proper equipment soon somewhat reduced such concerns and allowed researchers to conduct an increasing volume of work. Still, laboratory deaths due to yellow fever virus infection occurred from time to time. Paul Lewis, a Rockefeller Foundation worker in Bahia, Brazil, died of yellow fever virus infection after determining the crude survival of that virus at various temperatures and in various media.

Yellow fever viruses were obtained from Africa (the French strain from Andrew W. Sellards and Jean Laigret, the Asibi strain from Henry Beeuwkes of the Rockefeller Laboratory in Lagos) and elsewhere (the French neurotropic strain from Max Theiler, the F.W. strain from Henrique de B. Aragão in Brazil, among others). Cross-protection (neutralization) tests were performed; each virus was tested against antibody to itself and to the other viruses. Results of such tests provide information as to whether two or more viruses are or are not related to each other and, if they are, how closely related they are. The results of these tests showed clearly that these all were strains of the same virus – yellow fever virus but with some differences. The Foundation laboratory tested serum samples from patients in each region who had recovered from the disease; results supported the conclusion that these patients had all suffered from the same disease, yellow fever. Those neutralization tests required multiple rhesus monkeys as indicator hosts, and the search began for less expensive, more readily available, and easier to handle laboratory hosts.

At the Department of Tropical Medicine of the Harvard Medical School, Max Theiler and his colleagues demonstrated that the laboratory albino mouse could be used to propagate yellow fever virus, obviating the need for monkeys. By 1930, with this work published, Theiler joined the Rockefeller Foundation to continue his work with yellow fever virus. Theiler worked to standardize the virulence and pathogenicity of the French strain of the virus and, concomitantly, found that the incubation period (time from inoculation to signs of illness) likewise decreased and that work could proceed apace. Nonetheless, 32 infections, including five deaths, were reported in workers in the New York, Brazil and African laboratories. Sawyer rightly considered it high priority to devise a vaccine to protect those working with the virus.

With Wray Lloyd (Figure 39), a Canadian, and others, Sawyer showed that *Aedes aegypti* mosquitoes could transmit yellow fever virus to laboratory mice and to monkeys. They adapted yellow fever virus to replicate and persist in various tissue cultures and showed that the adapted virus was at least partially attenuated. These colleagues developed an intraperitoneal protection test in mice, showed that monkeys given this virus preparation became immune to challenge with fully virulent yellow fever virus, and observed that otherwise susceptible monkeys administered serum from immune mon-

Figure 39. Wray Lloyd (1902 - 1936) (image courtesy of the Rockefeller Archive Center)

keys could withstand challenge with virulent strains of yellow fever virus. Using a less virulent strain developed by Theiler, they mixed a suspension of 10% yellow fever virus-infected mouse brain (easy and inexpensive to produce and to measure the potency of the virus preparation) with fresh, sterile human immune serum. When administered to monkeys that had been given serum from monkeys that had recovered from yellow fever virus infection, they found that the monkeys which had received the immune monkey serum were resistant to challenge with Theiler's yellow fever virus. Ten people were vaccinated successfully with this adapted strain and no laboratory-acquired cases of yellow fever occurred in those laboratories afterward. This was the first vaccine against yellow fever. Such an experiment could not be done today, and for good reason. The mouse brain tissue itself could cause an allergic encephalomyelitis and serum from an immune monkey could contain unrecognized but pathogenic viruses or other agents of disease. Another drawback was that a liter of human immune serum was necessary per dose of virus, so that was not going to be a useful vaccine for a general population. Although Sawyer's vaccine was protective, a better, cleaner, and less reactogenic vaccine still was needed. Nonetheless, these had been pioneering efforts to develop not simply a vaccine but useful techniques for studying viruses and for conducting studies which provided information about yellow fever virus and the disease it causes, a huge series of forward leaps.

Theiler, Hugh Smith (Figure 40), and their colleagues working in the Yellow Fever Laboratory in New York had been manipulating the Asibi strain in vitro, that is, in tissues cultured on the surfaces of

Figure 40. Hugh Hollingsworth Smith (1902 - 1995)
(image courtesy of the Rockefeller Archive Center)

glass vessels in the laboratory. This particular virus strain was amplified and maintained for more than three years without passing it through an intact vertebrate host. Passaging a virus involves infecting a series of hosts. For each passage the virus is incubated (at about the body temperature of a human) and then the next host is infected with the virus.

Mutations occur regularly in all genetically based life forms, including viruses. When a genetic mutation occurs in a virus, the virus is then either more or less virulent or displays other changes. Using cells from embryonic mice fed with medium consisting of 10% serum from a normal monkey and a solution of various salts, Theiler and Smith passed the virus 18 times and then passed the virus into a similar medium but one containing cells from minced whole chicken embryos as a replacement for the mouse cells. After 58 more subcultures of the virus in this system, they grew the virus in cells from chicken embryos from which the brain and spinal cord had been removed. An additional 160 subcultures, provided them with a virus strain named "17D" (4th experiment of a 17th series of cultures). Theiler passed this virus more than 200 times in medium containing chick embryo brain cells and, at intervals, inoculated monkeys intracerebrally to determine whether the resultant virus was neurotropic, i.e., capable of or even preferentially infecting nerve cells; it was not. A stable mutation had occurred between the 89th and 114th subcultures in medium containing no (or minimal) neural tissue, and no reversion to neurotropism had occurred. For his remarkable efforts and successes in developing this highly safe (few adverse side effects) and effective vaccine, Theiler received a Nobel Prize in Physiology or Medicine in 1951, the only Nobel Prize ever given for development of a vaccine. By now, more than 400 million doses of YF 17D vaccine have been distributed worldwide.

In the summer of 1964, as a recent Ph.D., I went, uninvited and unannounced, to Yale University, hoping to speak with people there working with arboviruses. I had read two fascinating papers in Science written by CDC investigators who had described the discovery of a Venezuelan equine encephalitis virus, an arbovirus, in mosquitoes and vertebrates in the Everglades National Park, Florida, and of antibody to that virus in Native Americans living in that area. I was interested in finding out more about arboviruses, about which I knew virtually nothing. None of the people I had hoped to meet were there at the time, but Max Theiler was.

Theiler was a Nobel Laureate but I had no idea of that at the time. He invited me into his office, and we chatted for a few hours about these fascinating viruses. Theiler encouraged me to pursue my dreams and provided tips as to how I might do that. During the course of our conversation (I did not say much) I noticed that the small and only window in his office was being propped open with a statuette. When I examined it closely, I found that it was the Albert Lasker Award, which Theiler had been given for "major contributions to medical science". He explained that his office was not air conditioned and that propping open the window was the only way he could survive the sweltering heat; "The lack of air conditioning is no big deal", he said about the unusual use of that award. We not only discussed viruses, we discussed science in general, baseball, the merits of various Yale personnel, and a large number of other topics.

He related that before he had been awarded the Nobel Prize, he was known to the people who got on the train with him each morning as "the strange little guy who lives down the street from

Alvin Dark" (at the time the shortstop of the New York Giants baseball team), but that after he received the Nobel Prize things had changed. He then became known as "the strange little guy with the Nobel Prize who lives down the street from Alvin Dark." Later, we went to New York City and had dinner and drinks and more delightful conversations.

I thought then that if Max Theiler represented arbovirologists in general, that was the field I wanted to pursue. He didn't, but that turned out to be a small matter.

In the early days of yellow fever work, researchers did not recognize that the virus had a sylvatic or "jungle" cycle, with transmission between nonhuman primates and mosquitoes in the forest. Instead, researchers believed that person-to-person transmission of the agent by *Aedes aegypti* mosquitoes was the most complicated characteristic of the cycle. It was, therefore, a surprise when sylvatic yellow fever, often called "jungle" yellow fever, was recognized. That complicated the picture considerably and did not auger well for plans to completely eradicate the disease. Beginning with studies by Roberto Franco and his associates who were attempting to differentiate malaria, relapsing fever and yellow fever at Muzo, Colombia, in 1907 and 1908, and followed by more specific studies of yellow fever by Jorge Boshell Manrique in the 1930s and others later, yellow fever virus was shown to cycle between monkeys and to be transmitted by mosquitoes other than *Aedes aegypti.* Rain forest mosquitoes of the genus *Haemagogus* were also found to transmit yellow fever virus. Sir Patrick Manson, who had shown that arthropods could serve as vectors of an infectious agent (a parasite), on the basis of H. Wolferstan Thomas's work at Manaus, Brazil in 1905, raised the question of the importance of forest animals, especially monkeys, in yellow fever. He suggested that if mosquitoes could carry the virus from humans to other vertebrates, then they also could carry it in the reverse direction.

Figure 41. Anton Breinl (1880 - 1944) (image courtesy of the Rockefeller Archive Center)

Thomas had not traveled alone on that adventure into the Amazonian forest; Anton Breinl (Figure 41) accompanied him. Breinl, an Austrian physician with an itch for seeing the tropics and the new diseases he knew or suspected existed there, traveled to Liverpool in 1904, and secured a fellowship studying under Ronald Ross at the Liverpool School of Tropical Medicine, which had been founded only five years previously. The school actively sent people to investigate tropical diseases throughout the world, particularly in South America and Africa. Not all the expeditions succeeded and some had sad endings. For example, John Dutton, who in 1901 had discovered *Trypanosoma gambiense,* the cause of West African sleeping sickness, died of tick-borne relapsing fever, a bacterial disease, the next year.

Breinl and Thomas arrived in Manaus to study yellow fever, which was decimating workers in the rubber-harvesting industry; both soon acquired the disease. Complicated by bacterial septicemia, Breinl's illness proved severe. The numerous abscesses that appeared were opened under "brandy anaesthesia". He and Thomas recovered but Breinl suffered partial facial paralysis. While he was being evacuated to Liverpool his ship was wrecked near the mouth of the Amazon (near Para, Brazil). All his records and instruments were lost and he was left with only his pajamas and toothbrush.

In 1914, Andrew Balfour called the Trinidadian woodlands a "silent forest". Influenced by the evidence that red howler monkeys

(*Alouatta seniculus*) had been involved in epidemics of yellow fever in Trinidad, he suggested to the British Colonial Office that the possibility of monkeys acting as reservoirs of yellow fever virus would justify a careful study of the monkeys of West Africa. The onset of World War I prevented this plan from proceeding, and many years passed before any adequate studies addressed this question.

Scientific work, particularly in the foundational days of a particular study, is much like working in a familiar room with the light off. You know generally where you are and what you are looking for, but you simply cannot see all the components and do not know exactly where to begin looking for them. So it was with laboratory investigations of yellow fever virus. Yes, monkeys were susceptible and suffered the same terrible signs as did humans. However, monkeys are difficult to obtain, difficult to maintain, and difficult to manage. They have their own viruses (one of which, B virus, a.k.a. macacine herpesvirus 1 or herpesvirus simiae, is a significant human pathogen although, fortunately, uncommon). It is difficult to assemble enough monkeys at one time to provide statistical significance of the results, and they are expensive, not to mention the ethical and procedural complications of working with higher primates.

Therefore, a search was begun to find a more suitable laboratory animal for subsequent studies. Until the virus was available for laboratory study, little definitive work in this area was possible. Meanwhile, control and eradication of yellow fever in urban areas, based on knowledge of the human-*Aedes aegypti*-human cycle, was quite successful. The 1932 rural epidemic of yellow fever in Espirito Santo, Brazil, in the absence of *Aedes aegypti* mosquitoes, destroyed any complacency regarding the eradication of yellow fever and opened an exciting new chapter in this story. The surface had been scratched but a great deal more work remained.

CHAPTER 4

Development of laboratory procedures for work with yellow fever virus

The Rockefeller Foundation of the United States and the Pasteur Institute of France each sought to determine the details of yellow fever transmission. After controlling the virus, members of each organization assumed they would eventually eradicate it. We now know that this was (and perhaps is) an impossible goal. However, the work done by scientific personnel employed and encouraged by those organizations provided increasing amounts of information about the disease. In an attempt to find less expensive and more convenient laboratory hosts than monkeys, Max Theiler in 1930 adapted the use of adult albino laboratory mice for infection with yellow fever virus by inoculating them intracranially. The mice became sick, exhibiting paralysis of the limbs and other signs of encephalitis. Who would have expected that mice would be of such great value in such an endeavor? Finding a relatively inexpensive laboratory model for yellow fever allowed research to proceed more quickly. Charles Armstrong (Figure 42), for example, used albino laboratory mice for a variety of studies of viruses.

Figure 42. Charles Armstrong (1886 - 1967)
(image courtesy of Frederick A. Murphy)

Armstrong obtained an M.D. degree from Johns Hopkins Medical School in 1915 and interned at Yale New Haven Hospital. Upon completion of his internship he was commissioned in the United States Public Health Service (1916) and from the fall of 1918 to the winter of 1919 investigated local outbreaks of pandemic influenza. He became an Epidemiological Aide to the Ohio State Department of Health. In 1921 he began work at what was then called the United States Hygienic Laboratory, remaining there through its various administrative and name changes as it became the National Institute of Health, Laboratory of Infectious Diseases. He worked there until his formal retirement in 1950 and stayed on at NIH until 1963 as an unpaid volunteer.

Beginning his career with an insightful study of the acquisition of botulism resulting from eating canned olives, Armstrong investigated outbreaks of influenza and typhus in rural communities in the United States, responses to allergens, and problems with commercial pasteurization and tetanus. He showed his epidemiologic skills as he pin-pointed the use of unsanitary pads used after vaccinations as the source of tetanus in a few vaccinees, a complication that could have diminished the acceptability of vaccination. Armstrong went on to study dengue, herpesvirus encephalitis, psittacosis (showing that it was caused by a filterable agent), Q fever, and toxoplasmosis. With Robert Huebner he investigated rickettsialpox (*Rickettsia akari*) and coxsackie viruses. In 1933 Armstrong was involved in classic studies of an epidemic of what was shown to be St. Louis encephalitis. He coined the term "lymphocytic choriomeningitis" for a disease caused by a virus of the same name, now known as the prototype virus of the family *Arenaviridae* (the arenaviruses), which are rodent-borne. His experimental infection studies provided essential information and insights regarding clinico-pathology, immunity, epidemiology, and the development of serum protection neutralization tests for these and other viruses, including the poliomyelitis viruses.

Neutralization tests are critical for studying viruses. They are used to determine the antiviral potency of a serum by inoculating susceptible animals or cell cultures with a mixture of the serum and the virus. If the animals or cells do not sicken or die, then the serum had neutralized the virus. Measurement of antibody potency is a measurement of the capacity of that antibody to protect the host from which the serum was derived. Thus, neutralization tests and other tests can be done to determine whether a person or other host had been infected with a virus; if they have antibody, then they had been infected or vaccinated with the virus at some time in the past. If a serum is collected in the acute-phase of illness and another in the convalescent-phase, an increase in antibody titer can be used to determine whether the infection was related to that illness. Permutations of the neutralization test (testing dilutions of the serum against a constant amount of virus, testing dilutions of the virus against a constant amount of serum) can be devised to determine the titer of a serum, a reflection of its concentration or potency of the serum or the capacity of the serum to protect the host. This is extremely important for disease diagnosis, surveillance of human and wildlife populations, and determination of the presence of a virus in a particular location. The development of this test became a giant leap forward in terms of epidemiology, virus identification, vaccine creation, and many laboratory studies of viruses.

Armstrong's 1939 studies of the experimental transmission of a poliomyelitis virus to cotton rats (*Sigmodon hispidus*) and from them to laboratory mice was the revolutionary tool subsequently applied by others to cultivate arboviruses and produce uniform reagents suitable for virus isolations and properly controlled experiments. Armstrong

Figure 43. Edwin H. Lennette (1908 - 2000)
(image courtesy of Steven Specter, University of South Florida College of Medicine)

acquired numerous illnesses over the years from repeated exposure in the laboratory to disease organisms, including malaria (1927), dengue (1928), psittacosis (1930), encephalitis (1933), choriomeningitis (unknown date), Q fever (1940), and pulmonary tularemia (1942). He also suffered from prostatitis, bladder ulcers, abscessed tooth, appendicitis, amyloidosis of the kidney and ureter, bowel obstruction, diabetes mellitus, Bence-Jones protein, osteoporosis, uremia, cardiac difficulties, and uremic pericarditis. These illnesses resulted from the poor biosafety practices of the time, yet he continued to work and to produce to the end of his life.

By 1944, Edwin Herman Lennette (Figure 43) and Hilary Koprowski had reported that suckling mice could be used as hosts for determining the presence of neutralizing antibodies to eastern equine encephalitis, western equine encephalitis and Venezuelan equine encephalitis viruses. By that time they had developed reliable diagnostic tools, including laboratory mice, useful for tracking yellow fever and other arboviral diseases. That viruses differ in regard to their affinities for neural tissue (neurotropism) or for the internal organs (viscerotropism) provides information useful in determining the chain of events that lead to the development of a particular disease. The findings of Lennette and Koprowski with yellow fever virus and many other viruses paved the way for important studies of viral neurotropism and viscerotropism, as well as investigations of the different incubation periods of a disease which occur when the host is infected by different routes of infection. Lennette and Koprowski's work also allowed determination of differences among virus strains by outlining studies using different hosts and different ages of the same hosts, routes, and doses. Some strains (virus isolates) will be pathogenic for very young but not adult laboratory mice (or monkeys or rabbits or guinea pigs or other hosts) by the intraperitoneal route but not the subcutaneous route, or cause cytopathic effects and kill cultured cells from monkey kidneys but not cultured cells from fetal rabbit lung, etc. Strain variation nowadays can be traced to mutations in the viral genome, the knowledge of which then might allow molecular biologists to produce viruses that are suitable vaccine candidates.

Among other advances, they have accomplished virus transmission studies using vector mosquitoes, determined mosquito blood meal engorgement patterns, made precise measurements of the intrinsic and extrinsic virus incubation periods in various hosts, and developed rapid and inexpensive methods for preparing superior reagents for other laboratory studies, including the development of diagnostic methods, and methods to distribute reagents for use by other laboratories. The ability to distribute uniform reagents provided a means to conduct quality control tests in laboratories worldwide, a process generally accepted because of the close personal relations among arbovirologists.

The observations of Christopher H. Andrewes and Dorothy M. Horstman, by Max Theiler and by many others that most arboviruses have a lipid envelope led to the development of means to classify hitherto unclassified viruses. Previously, viruses had been classified on the basis of size, pathologic changes and symptoms in the infected host. With the recognition that diethyl ether or sodium deoxycholate or other biological detergents lyse cells and solubilize viral and cellular components, it was found that they could be used to categorize a virus (sensitive or not sensitive to treatment), and that viruses now could be classified by means other than physical, pathological, or clinical. Later, however, researchers found that certain arboviruses, orbiviruses (family *Reoviridae*), do not have lipid envelopes. Still, for many years newly discovered viruses from humans, mosquitoes, and other sources were tested for their sensitivity to lipid solvents.

In concert with that simple but elegant first venture into determining a physical character of an arbovirus, methods were devised for determining viral titers (the lowest concentration/highest dilution that infects cells) by applying one of the statistical methods of estimating end-points, one devised by C. Spearman and applied by G. Kärber, another devised by L.J. Reed and Hugo A. Muench, of the Department of Biostatistics and Johns Hopkins University School of Hygiene and Public Health and the International Health Division of the Rockefeller Foundation. In the end-point dilution assay as done today, identical cell cultures are inoculated with different concentrations of a virus stock. When the highest dilution of virus that kills these cultures is known, it is then possible to calculate the 50 percent end-point, using a simple calculation.

Soon thereafter one-step growth curves, plots of the replication dynamics of a virus when all cells are infected against elapsed time, were devised. With increasing rapidity and novelty, methods using various fluorescent dyes to visualize virions and nucleic acid clusters during viral replication and other techniques were devised and applied. These allowed virologists to more fully and accurately characterize the replication cycles of viruses, to develop and test anti-viral compounds, and to corroborate and extend physical observations made by electron microscopy.

Many researchers contributed key elements in discovering effective laboratory procedures for work with yellow fever virus. These new procedures spurred the detection of the causes of diseases other than yellow fever, as each discovery laid the groundwork for another. In addition, scores of previously unrecognized viruses were found, with most of them not associated at the time with human or wildlife diseases.

The turn of the century brought remarkable advances to the study and understanding of infectious diseases. The first arbovirus discovered was yellow fever virus in 1900. In that same year J. M'Fadyean,

T. Edgington, and Arnold Theiler discovered the cause of African horse sickness and, in 1902, J. Spruell described bluetongue, a disease of sheep and cattle. Theiler prepared a vaccine against bluetongue to add to the South African armamentarium he already had developed: vaccines against rinderpest and smallpox (which are not caused by arboviruses; both viruses have been eradicated). Today we know of 25 distinct bluetongue group viruses, each transmitted by culicoids. Although viruses have been carefully and extensively studied and a great deal is known of their epidemiologies, they remain incompletely characterized. Ecologic changes, human-made or natural, may already be responsible for expansion of populations of the culicoid vectors of these viruses and we may see further spread of these viruses from their current geographic limits.

In 1907 Percey M. Ashburn and Charles F. Craig reported the discovery of dengue viruses in the Philippines. Also known as "breakbone fever" and "dandy fever", dengue can be caused by any of four viruses. Uncomplicated dengue disease is characterized by fever with rash, headache, and muscle aches. Under certain circumstances, it can cause a hemorrhagic disorder leading to shock and death in humans.

While working for the Austrian War Office, R. Doerr, K. Franz and S. Taussig (1908) described sandfly fever (papataci [It. pappataci = silent sufferer] fever, phlebotomus fever) as a newly recognized disease. They had been sent to Dalmatia and Herzegovina to investigate a 3-day fever occurring in troops there. The disease occurred only from May to October and usually in newcomers to the area. Although the disease had a relatively mild course, convalescence lasted from 3 to 14 days. These physicians considered sandflies as the possible source of the infectious agent and later proved this, also transmitting the disease by inoculating volunteers with blood from a diseased patient. After the Sicilian campaign of World War II, an analysis was made of the possible extent of sandfly fever cases, nearly all of which might have been erroneously diagnosed as malaria or conservatively labeled "fever of unknown origin".

In September 1943, Major (later Lieutenant Colonel) Albert B. Sabin (Figure 44) used this analysis as the subject of a special report. The "report was published in part by Major Sabin, Lt. Col. Cornelius B. Philip, MC, and Dr. John R. Paul. The conclusion reached by Major Sabin was that sandfly fever was probably responsible for as many, if not more, cases of fever as [was] malaria." Note that this was the same Albert Sabin who devised a live-attenuated poliovirus vaccine to protect the world population from that awful disease, the same Cornelius Philip who, while working for the West African Yellow Fever Commission studied entomological aspects of that disease, and the same John Paul who worked on poliomyelitis and many other diseases before becoming Chair of Epidemiology and Preventive Medicine at Yale University. By the late 1940s, studies of diseases caused by various disease agents (viruses, bacteria, parasites, and fungi) were being pursued at an increasing rate, funding was becoming available for such endeavors, and expenses for laboratory and field studies were not what they are today.

Figure 44. Albert Bruce Sabin (1906 - 1993)
(image courtesy of the Rockefeller Archive Center)

One of the landmarks of arbovirology was the discovery and remarkable description of Nairobi sheep disease by Eustace (a.k.a. R.E.) Montgomery (Figure 45). As a veterinary pathologist in Britain's East African Protectorate, now Kenya, Montgomery had responded to a 1910 report from the district veterinary officer regarding mortality among sheep grazing in a commons in Nairobi, which Montgomery named "Nairobi sheep disease", and described it as having a hemorrhagic component. As was common at the time, sheep were traded from Masai, Suk, and Turkana tribal areas and from along the northern frontier (bordering Ethiopia) to areas inhabited by members of the Kikuyu people. This disease was reported frequently but sporadically in many years, and is so even today. In 1917 Montgomery summarized for publication his extraordinary innovative studies, done in isolation, with few reliable tools and methods available, and essentially by himself. He showed that in certain areas the disease was not recognized at all and in other areas the mortality rate was quite high. The Kikuyu people called the disease "Kuharo", meaning simply "diarrhea", and Montgomery related that they had told him up to half their sheep died of it but that they treat it as a usual occurrence, not as an epidemic problem. The tribesmen looked on this disease as they did East Coast fever, a disease of cattle now known to be caused by the protozoan parasite *Theileria parva* and transmitted by *Rhipicephalus appendiculatus* ticks. Because newborn sheep died of East Coast fever but young sheep brought into their area died of Nairobi sheep disease, Montgomery mapped the geographic distributions of each disease. He concluded that in areas where *Rhipicephalus appendiculatus* ticks were uncommon these diseases were uncommon too. Furthermore, the illness in sheep from Nairobi was due to local infection. In fact, he showed that two-thirds of sheep died of Nairobi sheep disease within

Figure 45. Robert Eustace Montgomery (1880 - 1932)
(image from the archives of the Royal Society of Tropical Medicine and Hygiene and the Royal College of Veterinary Surgeons; used with permission)

a month of arrival in one area, 179 of another 200 sheep within 16 days, and 74 of another 100 within a month in the same general area.

After a detailed description of the clinical signs and course of infection with Nairobi sheep disease, Montgomery described post-mortem appearance, determined the susceptibility of animals of various species, determined which sheep body fluids and exudates were infectious and described his experimental techniques. He went on to determine lethal doses, perform bacteriological evaluations, and describe filterability of the virus, stability of the virus, and mode of transmission. The latter included feeding sheep grass from the area where the disease occurred, pasturing muzzled (non-feeding) sheep on that same area, and feeding ticks on sheep in many combinations (ticks from infected sheep, laboratory-bred ticks from female ticks that had fed on infected sheep, and ticks of various stages among them). He also determined sheep immunity, prepared immune sera, and wrote extensively on the gross pathology of the disease in sheep. His studies of the susceptibility of livestock and other vertebrates showed that sheep and goats, but not cattle, buffalo, horses, mules, donkeys, pigs, dogs, rabbits, guinea pigs, rats or mice, provided evidence of infection.

This extraordinary series of observations and studies, done under considerably less than optimum technical and personal conditions, and with inadequate funding, revealed the presence of a newly recognized virus, the prototype virus of the family *Bunyaviridae,* genus *Nairovirus,* which was not classified as such until many decades later. (Chapter 10 discusses the concept, practicality, and development of viral taxonomy in more depth).

Montgomery was also the first to recognize and characterize African swine fever virus (1921), a tick-borne virus unlike other arboviruses in that its genome comprises double stranded DNA, rather than RNA. This further illustrates Montgomery's astuteness and the significance of his contributions. African swine fever virus is vectored by *Ornithodoros* species soft ticks and is, thus far, the only recognized member of the family *Asfarviridae* and the only member of the single genus in that family, *Asfivirus*.

Virus discoveries were made with increased rapidity after that. In 1930, Karl F. Meyer, C. Haring and B. Howitt of the Hooper Foundation isolated a virus from an encephalitic horse in the San Joaquin Valley of California, and described the disease and its pathology. The humorous details of this adventure have been described by Albert Sabin.

> "What is not widely recognized is that Meyer and his associates found a dying horse and wanted its brain for study. The farmer-owner of the horse would not allow him to kill the horse and take its brain, so Meyer stayed until after dark, and after the farmer went to bed he crept to the house and asked the farmer's wife to allow him to take the samples, offering her a small amount of money if she allowed him to do so; she agreed." The rest, as they say, is history.

The virus was named western equine encephalomyelitis virus and was distinguished by Carl Ten Broeck (Figure 46) and Malcolm H. Merrill from eastern equine encephalomyelitis virus, isolated from brain tissue in 1933 by Leslie T. Webster (Figure 47) and F. Howell Wright at the Rockefeller Institute, and then by members of the Harvard Medical School and Boston Children's Hospital staff. Vladimir Kubes and Francisco A. Rios then isolated Venezuelan equine encephalomyelitis virus from a donkey on the Guajira peninsula of

Figure 46. Carl Ten Broeck (1885 - 1966)
(image courtesy of the Rockefeller Archive Center)

Venezuela in 1938. These three viruses are principal causes of equine encephalitis in the Americas.

Figure 47. Leslie Tillotson Webster (1894 - 1943)
(image courtesy of Leslie T. Webster III)

R. Daubney, John R. Hudson and P.C. Garnham described an enzootic hepatitis of sheep, cattle and humans in East Africa; they called it Rift Valley fever and isolated the virus in 1931. Ralph S. Muckenfuss, Charles Armstrong, Howard A. McCordock, Leslie Webster, and George L. Fite isolated St. Louis encephalitis virus during an outbreak of encephalitis in that city in 1933. For many years after its discovery, Rift Valley fever virus was considered "unclassified"; that is, it had not been shown to be related to other recognized viruses; thanks to Robert E. Shope, it is now recognized as a phlebovirus (family *Bunyaviridae*, genus *Phlebovirus*). St. Louis encephalitis virus was shown to be antigenically related to yellow fever, and some other viruses (family *Flaviviridae*, genus *Flavivirus*).

An explanation of antigenic relationships between viruses is necessary for an understanding of all this. Viruses are composed of a nucleic acid core, which contains the viral genes. It is these genes which code for the viral proteins that provide the characteristics of the virus, including its protein coat. These proteins are similar in related viruses (that is one way we know they are related) and antibody to a particular virus may react with the proteins (antigens) of the related virus. For example, antibody to St. Louis encephalitis flavivirus reacts with antigens of Japanese encephalitis flavivirus, and vice versa; all flaviviruses stimulate the host to produce antibody to antigens of other flaviviruses. The same cross-reactivities occur between alphaviruses, closely related bunyaviruses (viruses of the family *Bunyaviridae*) and between viruses of other groups. This characteristic provides us with a tool to determine relatedness among viruses, a tool useful for diagnosis and for studies of virus evolution. However, the intensity of antigen-antibody interactions differs between viruses within a group of viruses. That is, antibody to one virus in a group may react at high titer to another virus in that group and at low titer to yet another virus in the group. The intensity of the reaction indicates the similarity (or difference) between the viruses. St. Louis encephalitis virus, for instance, is closely related to Japanese encephalitis virus but distantly related to yellow fever virus, although all are flaviviruses. These antigenic characteristics are reflections of the genetic similarities and similarities of the viruses. Antibody to flaviviruses do not react with antigens of alphaviruses, bunyaviruses or to viruses of other groups, and vice versa. A newly isolated virus can be tested with antibody produced against viruses of many groups ("group-specific") and, when one of those antibodies reacts with the newly isolated virus it can be said that the newly isolated virus is a member of the group to which that antibody was prepared. Any of many different tests (neutralization, immunofluorescence, hemagglutination-inhibition, complement fixation, enzyme-linked immunosorbent assays, etc.) can be used to detect such a reaction but the potency of the antibody should be high to be useful. Once a virus is placed in a group by such tests, type-specific antibody tests can then be applied so that the identity of the virus can be determined as one previously recognized or as a newly recognized virus. Studies of the virus are then done to determine the exact sequence of the genome, which provides information about geographic and evolutionary origins of the virus.

A 1924 outbreak of encephalitis in humans in Japan affected 6,125 patients. The disease was differentiated from von Economo's encephalitis by its seasonality and by its signs and symptoms. It was called "Japanese B encephalitis", but is now known simply as Japanese encephalitis. Similar outbreaks occurred in late summer to fall 1871 to 1873 and were described. It was not until 1933 that M. Hayashi,

S. Kasahara, R. Kawamura, and T. Taniguchi isolated the virus from a patient and from monkeys and not until 1938 that T. Mitamura proved that the virus was transmitted by mosquitoes by isolating it from *Culex tritaeniorhynchus*. Most infections are not apparent but about 1 in 200 infections results in severe disease, characterized by rapid onset of high fever, headache, stiff neck, disorientation, coma, seizures, spastic paralysis and death. The case-fatality rate can be as high as 60% among those with disease symptoms; 30% of those who survive suffer from lasting damage to the central nervous system. In areas where the virus is common, encephalitis occurs mainly in young children because older children and adults have already been infected or vaccinated and therefore are immune. Japanese virologists maintain their excellent tradition of studying this virus and the disease it causes and others have added to the wealth of knowledge about it.

Now that poliomyelitis has almost been eradicated from Asia, Japanese encephalitis is a leading cause of viral encephalitis on that continent, with 30,000 to 50,000 clinical cases reported annually according to the W.H.O. It occurs from the islands of the Western Pacific in the east to the Pakistani border in the west, and from Korea in the north to Papua New Guinea and northeastern Australia in the south. Distribution of the virus and of the disease is significantly linked to irrigated rice production combined with pig rearing.

Japanese encephalitis virus infects humans and other vertebrates, especially pigs and birds. The virus is transmitted principally by zoophilic mosquitoes of the *Culex tritaeniorhynchus* and *Culex vishnui* complexes, which breed preferentially in flooded rice fields, and is transmitted among ardeid birds, herons and egrets. Pigs are amplifying hosts; the virus reproduces in pigs and infects mosquitoes that take blood meals from them, but does not cause disease in the pigs. The virus tends to spill over into human populations when populations of infected mosquitoes build up; consequently, the rate at which humans are fed upon increases. Over the past two decades intensification and expansion of irrigated rice production systems in South and Southeast Asia have increased the disease burden caused by Japa-

Figure 48. (l.-r.) Thomas Harry Gardner Aitken (1913 - 2007), Robert Bradfield Tesh (1936 -) and Barry J. Beaty (1944 -)
(image courtesy of Barry J. Beaty)

nese encephalitis. Where irrigation expands into semi-arid areas, the flooding of fields at the start of each cropping cycle leads to an explosive build-up of the mosquito population. This may cause the circulation of Japanese encephalitis virus to spill over from its zoonotic hosts, the birds and pigs, to infect humans. Because of the critical role of pigs in the cycle of this virus, its presence is negligible in countries with a high proportion of Muslims.

An effective killed virus vaccine is available for Japanese encephalitis, but it is expensive and requires one primary vaccination followed by two boosters. This is an adequate prophylaxis for travelers but has limited public health value in areas where health services have limited resources. An inexpensive live-attenuated virus vaccine is used in China but is not available elsewhere. Chemical vector control is not an effective solution, as the irrigated rice fields which serve as breeding sites are extensive. Using polymerase chain reaction assays, Amy J. Schuh, Li Li, Robert B. Tesh (Figure 48), Bruce L. Innis and Alan D.T. Barrett (Figure 49) have shown that Japanese encephalitis virus con-

Figure 49. Alan David Thomas Barrett (1957 -)
(image courtesy of Alan Barrett)

sists of five genotypes (GI–V) that are separated geographically and chronologically. This is an important epidemiological observation because determination of the genotype can allow determination of the geographic source of the virus.

Mention of "polymerase chain reaction assays" (PCR) here and elsewhere refers to a remarkable and sophisticated technique now in routine use in virology and other fields, such as identifying microorganisms, diagnosing genetic diseases, studying human evolution, and criminology. To conduct a PCR assay, multiple copies of a gene region are made by separating the two strands of DNA (deoxyribonucleic acid) containing the gene segment, marking its location with short DNA primers, using the enzyme DNA polymerase to make a copy, and then continuously replicating the copies. This DNA polymerase is also called Taq polymerase, named for the thermophilic bacterium from which it was isolated, *Thermus aquaticus*, first discovered in one of the geysers at Yellowstone National Park.

PCR was invented by Kary Mullis in 1983. At the time, Mullis was working for one of the first biotechnology companies, Cetus Corporation in Emeryville, California. Mullis was responsible for producing short chains of DNA for other scientists. One night, driving his motorcycle along the Pacific Coast Highway and thinking of methods he might use to analyze mutations in DNA, he realized that he had conceived a method to amplify any DNA region. For this remarkable development, Mullis was awarded a Nobel Prize in Chemistry in 1993.

DNA comprises two strands of genetic material in a double-stranded configuration. Ribonucleic acid (RNA), which serves as the sole genetic material of most arboviruses and many other viruses, comprises a single strand. In order to conduct a PCR assay with RNA, one first must reverse transcribe (RT-PCR) the RNA strand into its DNA complement (complementary DNA, or cDNA) using the enzyme reverse transcriptase. The resulting cDNA is then amplified using PCR.

Using PCR assays, it is possible to reproduce minute quantities of DNA or RNA and, by continuous amplification, produce large quantities of selected regions of the nucleic acid for analysis; assays can be completed in but a few hours. In brief, two "primers", short single-stranded DNA or cDNA sequences are synthesized to correspond to the beginning and ending of the cDNA stretch to be copied, the polymerase then moves along the segment of DNA or cDNA, reading its code and assembling a copy from free nucleotides. An automated cycler, a device which rapidly heats and cools the test tubes containing the reaction mixture is used to denature (separate), anneal (join) and extend the product, each step taking place at a different temperature. As the cycles are repeated, more and more copies are generated and the number of copies of the template is increased exponentially. Having a relatively large amount of DNA or cDNA with which to work has made testing faster, cheaper and more accurate.

The 1930s were an eventful and exciting period for the soon-to-blossom field of arbovirology. First there was the isolation of western equine encephalitis virus (1930), then the isolation Rift Valley fever virus (1931), then St. Louis encephalitis and eastern equine encephalitis viruses, and the isolation of Japanese encephalitis virus (1933), and finally the discovery of Venezuelan equine encephalitis and its etiologic agent (1938). The epidemics of St. Louis encephalitis, which occurred during one of the driest summers on record, affected not only the metropolitan area of St. Louis but also St. Joseph, Missouri; Kansas City, Missouri; Kansas City, Kansas; and Louisville, Kentucky. In all, a startling 1,350 cases including 266 deaths were recorded in 1933.

At first, it was not understood how the virus spread. In 1933, an outstanding United States Public Health Service sanitarian, Leslie Leon Lumsden, wrote a report to the Surgeon General, laying out his hypothesis suggesting that *Culex pipiens* mosquitoes were the principal vectors of the virus. He had based that premise on his observations that people in unscreened homes acquired the disease but people in sanitaria with screened windows and doors did not. The St. Louis Metropolitan Health Council rejected the idea that spread was via mosquitoes and at least tentatively accepted the likelihood of human-to-human transmission. Lumsden further suggested that if a decent sewer system were to be installed, mosquito breeding grounds would be decreased and therefore so would the prevalence of the virus. The Surgeon General apparently either did not read that report or read and ignored it because it remained unpublished until 1958.

St. Louis encephalitis was for many years a major concern of public health workers. William Reeves at the University of California at Berkeley estimated that at least 10,000 clinical infections and 1,000 deaths from St. Louis encephalitis occurred between 1933 and 1980. The virus was found from west to east, north to south within the United States and into Canada. It was detected in *Culex tarsalis* mosquitoes in irrigated areas of western North America, in *Culex pipiens-quinquefasciatus* mosquitoes in eastern North America, and in *Culex nigripalpus* mosquitoes in Florida. Researchers also found it in wild vertebrates, mostly house sparrows (*Passer domesticus*) but also terrestrial mammals and, of course, humans. The geographic distribution of this virus extends to Argentina but most human disease caused by St. Louis encephalitis virus occurs in North America, possibly due to the genetic and antigenic differences that have been documented between strains occurring throughout its range and to the presence of vector mosquito populations of sufficient size to maintain the virus.

Reeves, whose group at the University of California, Berkeley, did by far the most intense studies of this virus, and of western equine encephalitis virus, also estimated that when the number of female *Culex tarsalis* dropped to 10 to 20 per trap-night, St. Louis encephalitis disappeared as a human disease. When that index fell below 10 the virus was not found. They thus concluded that there was a critical threshold level of the vector essential for maintenance of the virus cycle (mosquito-bird-mosquito). At higher vector population levels sufficient numbers of vectors diverged from their usual hosts to feed on other warm-blooded vertebrates and the ensuing "spill-over" resulted in infections of humans, a tangential host. This likely was also the situation in other parts of North America.

Human infections with St. Louis encephalitis virus occurred regularly, most of them resulting only in antibody production, rather than illness. Over time, the human population in a particular area developed immunity to infection with the virus, with the few clinical illnesses occurring in children. In temperate areas of the United States, St. Louis encephalitis neuroinvasive disease cases occur primarily in the late summer or early fall. In the southern states, where the climate is milder, cases can occur year round. The majority of cases have occurred in eastern and central states, where episodic urban-centered outbreaks have recurred since the 1930s. In the rural west, transmission has followed a more endemic pattern. The largest epidemic of neuroinvasive St. Louis encephalitis ever recognized occurred in the United States in 1975, with nearly 2,000 cases reported, primarily from the central states in the Ohio-Mississippi River Basin. Because of the serious nature of this disease, epidemiologic, virologic, diagnostic and other studies of this virus and the illness it causes command high priority. Although fluctuations in the number of cases occurring have been considerable (a mean of 102 cases per year from 1964 to 2009 but a range in number of annual cases of from 2 to 1,967), only a few cases have been detected from 2004 to the present, possibly due to competition between this virus and the invasive West Nile virus, competition between the invasive *Aedes albopictus* and *Culex* species that have traditionally transmitted St. Louis encephalitis virus, or other factors.

A cascade of virologic discoveries and associated activities occurred in the period from the 1930s to the end of World War II. Many of these are summarized in Table 1. It is essentially inexorable

Figure 50. Mary E. Stevick Taylor, Richard M. Taylor (1887 - 1981) and William McDowell Hammon (1904 - 1989), who is presenting the first Richard Moreland Taylor Award to Richard Taylor.
(image courtesy of American Society of Tropical Medicine and Hygiene)

that science moves forward, usually little by little but sometimes with a gigantic leap forward as a result of a flash of brilliance, persistence or fortuity.

After the end of World War II, Albert Sabin traveled to Japan to search for Japanese encephalitis virus in mosquitoes, but it was William McD. Hammon (Figure 50) and William Tigertt (later, Editor of the American Journal of Tropical Medicine and Hygiene) and others, including Louis LaMotte (Figure 51), who found that virus in *Culex tritaeniorhynchus* mosquitoes. Additional arbovirological work done by Edward Buescher, William Scherer (Figure 52), James Hardy and others was intended to stimulate laboratory, field and epidemiologic research studies by Japanese workers and it soon did, more like the opening of a floodgate than an isolated series of studies. Not only were arboviruses being discovered and studied, but other viruses were being shown to be human and livestock pathogens. Akira Oya

Figure 51. Louis Cossitte LaMotte (1928 -) at the mouth of a cave on a mountain in Luzon, Republic of the Philippines, 1956, collecting birds and bats. It was during this unsuccessful effort to find evidence for the presence of Japanese encephalitis virus in birds migrating from Japan to the Philippines that William McD. Hammon recognized dengue hemorrhagic fever and made the first isolations of dengue virus 3 and dengue virus 4 from patient samples. (image courtesy of Louis LaMotte)

(Figure 53) and his colleagues isolated Sagiyama alphavirus as well as Akabane and Aino orthobunyaviruses, the latter two of which are important causes of congenital abnormalities of the central nervous systems in fetal cattle in Asia and Australia. These viruses do not cause overt disease in the dam; the effect is on the fetus, which makes their epidemiology difficult to define because the consequences of infection are seen belatedly.

Oya, who had worked for the Rockefeller Foundation Virus Laboratories in New York City, had spent at least some of that time with Hernando Groot at the Carlos Finlay Institute in Bogota, Colombia – long enough to be involved in the isolation and identification of Guaroa orthobunyavirus and to obtain additional training in virology. He eventually became director of the National Institutes of Health of Japan and then Director General of the Southeast Asian Medical

Table 1. Findings key to arbovirologic research, 1930 to 1948.

Year	Relevant discovery	Discoverer(s)
1930	development of the mouse as an experimental host of viruses	Theiler, Furth, and Armstrong
1930	discovery of western equine encephalitis	Meyer, Haring, and Howitt
1931	discovery of the first influenza virus	Shope
1933	discovery of human influenza viruses	Smith, Andrewes, and Laidlaw
1933	discovery of the first papillomavirus	Shope, Rouse and Beard
1933	recognition of the jungle cycle of yellow fever	Soper, Penna, Shannon, Whitman, Boshell-Manrique
1934	discovery of eastern equine encephalitis virus	Merrill and Ten Broeck
1934	discovery of Japanese encephalitis virus	Hayashi, Kasahara, Kawamura, and Taniguchi
1935	publication of the classic book *Rats, Lice and History*	Zinsser
1936	discovery of lymphocytic choriomeningitis virus	Armstrong, Rivers, and Traub
1937	elucidation of persistent central nervous system infection by a virus	Theiler
1937	establishment of necessary criteria for proof of causation of a virus disease	Rivers
1937	discovery of tick-borne encephalitis (Russian Spring-Summer encephalitis) virus	Zilber, Chumakov, Seitlenok, and Levkovich
1938	discovery of Venezuelan equine encephalitis virus	Kubes and Rios
1940	discovery of West Nile virus	Smithburn, Hughes, Burke, and Paul
1941	recognition of the relationship between congenital defects in newborns and rubella ("German measles") in their mothers	Gregg
1942	development of an immunofluorescence test to detect antigens or antibodies	Coons and Kaplan
1944	identification of DNA as a material of inheritance	Avery, McLeod, and McCarty
1945	discovery of Crimean hemorrhagic fever virus	Chumakov
1948	discovery and application of hemagglutination and hemagglutination-inhibition for serologic surveys and diagnosis and the discovery of the influenzavirus neuraminidase ("receptor-destroying enzyme")	Hirst

Information Center/International Medical Foundation of Japan. Akira Igarashi, Ichiro Kurane, Tomoyuki Tsuda, and scores of other excellent virologists, molecular biologists, and epidemiologists continue to grow Japanese arbovirology.

Figure 52. William Franklin Scherer (1925 - 1982)
(image from U.S. Army Medical Department, Office of Medical History)

Times had been difficult for Russian workers at least as far back as 1937. Nonetheless, by means of what must have been heroic efforts, L.A. Zilber, M.P. Chumakov, N.A. Seitlenok, and E.N. Levkovich described a disease of humans in Siberia which they called Russian Spring-Summer encephalitis (a tick-borne viral encephalitis). They described the clinical course and the pathology, outlined its epidemiology, and isolated the etiologic agent from ticks, finding that the virus is distantly related to Japanese encephalitis, St. Louis encephalitis, yellow fever, and other viruses, soon after known as the "Group B arboviruses" (i.e., the flaviviruses).

Anton Breinl, the same physician who had begun to study yellow fever in Brazil, only to become ill and flee there shortly after arriving was an early investigator of what was then known as "Australian X disease", later called Murray Valley encephalitis. Beginning in 1917, small clusters of encephalitis were investigated, first by Breinl in Queensland, then by John Burton Cleland in New South Wales. The virus was experimentally transmitted to monkeys, which caused a poliomyelitis-like disease but the virus was not retained for later comparison with other isolates. The 45 severe cases of illness reported in 1951 were essentially identical to the earlier cases, 34 infected in northern Victoria, 10 in western New South Wales, and one in South

Figure 53. Brač, Croatia, former Yugoslavia, 1978
l. to r.: Dmitri K. Lvov, Erika Arslanagić, S. Salja, Akinyele Fabiyi, Paul Bres, Jelka Vesenjak-Hirjan, Charles Calisher, Harry Hoogstraal, and Akira Oya, some of the attendees at a meeting "Arboviruses in the Mediterranean Countries". Others at that meeting included: Horst Aspöck, David H.L. Bishop, Markus Brummer-Korvenkontio, Mikhail P. Chumakov, Medhat A. Darwish, Armando R. Felipe, Jon Gentsch, Ana Gligić, C.E. Gordon Smith, Terry Maguire, James Meegan, Patricia A. Nuttall, James S. Porterfield, Volga Punda, Hugh W. Reid, Francois Rodhain, R.Walter Schlesinger, Pierre Sureau, Mitsuo Takahashi, H.A.E. van Tongeren, Danica Tovornik, Paola Verani, Vlasta Vince, Marina M.K. Vorošilova, and Raul Walder, as well as representatives from arbovirus laboratories in Africa, Asia, Europe, and Oceania.
(image courtesy of Jelka Vesenjak-Hirjan)

Australia. Eric L. French (Figure 54) in Victoria and John A.R. Miles (Figure 55) in Adelaide, South Australia eventually isolated Murray Valley encephalitis virus during that outbreak (Figure 56) and identified it as a new member of the viruses causing arthropod-borne encephalitides, closely related to, but distinct from, Japanese encephalitis virus. Miles went on to become Professor of Microbiology and Head of the MRC Virology Unit at the University of Otago, New Zealand, where he collaborated with Terry Maguire and Frank J. Austin.

Figure 54. (l. to r.) Leslie Frazer, Eric L. French and S. Gray Anderson standing in front of the Walter and Elisa Hall Institute of Medical Research mobile laboratory used in the field investigations of the first outbreak of Murray Valley encephalitis, 1951.
(image courtesy of John S. Mackenzie)

Investigators were isolating an increasing number of arboviruses, many of which were associated with diseases. Kenneth Smithburn, Thomas P. Hughes, A. Burke, and John Paul isolated another Group B arbovirus (flavivirus) from the blood of a febrile human in the West Nile District of Uganda in 1937: West Nile virus. Smithburn and co-workers also discovered Ntaya, Semliki Forest, Bunyamwera and other viruses during their successful efforts to find sylvan yellow fever virus in Africa.

Max Theiler, who played such an integral role in studies of yellow fever and other diseases, joined the Department of Tropical Medicine at the Harvard Medical School. In 1930 he joined the staff of the International Health Division of the Rockefeller Foundation to further his studies of yellow fever. At a time of advances in virology, he became Director of Laboratories of the Rockefeller Foundation's Division of

Figure 55. John Arthur Reginald Miles (1913 - 2004)
(image courtesy of John S. Mackenzie)

Medicine and Public Health in New York City in 1931. His early work at Harvard had dealt with amoebic dysentery and rat bite fever but he retained his interest in yellow fever, demonstrating that the virus could be transmitted to mice. Theiler and his colleagues worked on vaccines against the disease and in 1935 developed a safe, standardized vaccine, 17D, that could be mass produced.

Theiler's other work at the Institute concerned causes and immunology of disorders

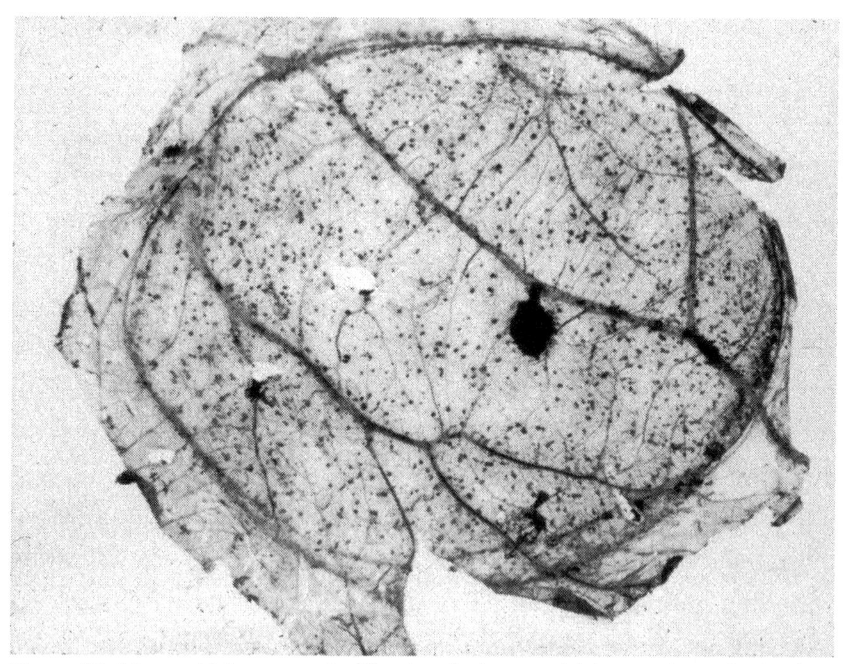

Figure 56. Murray Valley encephalitis virus lesion on chicken embryonic chorio-allantoic membrane; Eric L. French, 1951; the first isolation of this virus.
(image courtesy of John S. Mackenzie)

including Weil's disease (leptospirosis), dengue fever and Japanese encephalitis. Poliomyelitis had been of interest to Theiler and, among other discoveries, he recognized a similar disorder in laboratory mice, a condition now called Theiler's encephalomyelitis, which is caused by Theiler's murine encephalomyelitis virus (family *Picornaviridae*, genus *Cardiovirus*).

Because laboratory diagnosis of viral infections was becoming an important new tool for clinicians, the recognition that mice could be used for virus isolation and other studies of viruses stimulated the discovery of other means for isolating and manipulating viruses. Rebecca Lancefield, Edwin Lennette and others essentially founded the field of viral diagnostics beginning in about 1928. When added to the availability of laboratory mice as a diagnostic and research tool, the work of Armstrong, Theiler and others, the use of embryonating chicken eggs as virus hosts, work done by Alice M. Woodruff, Ernest W. Goodpasture, Macfarlane Burnet and Herald R. Cox in 1931, led to even more sophisticated techniques for virus diagnostics.

It became obvious that the same criteria for proof of cause of a bacterial disease could not be used to prove the cause of a viral disease. Thomas Rivers offered a series of criteria for proof of viral disease causation, a modification of the 1840 Henle-Koch postulates (Robert Koch had been a student of Jakob Henle). In an extremely detailed and historically relevant paper published in 1976, entitled *Causation and Disease: The Henle-Koch Postulates Revisited*, Alfred Evans, of the Department of Epidemiology and Public Health, Yale University School of Medicine summarized the more modern views of viral causation. That landmark summary formed the foundation for today's views on viral causation of disease.

George Hirst had added to the resources for viral disease diagnosis, almost by accident, with his discovery of hemagglutination, the aggregating (clumping) of red blood cells by an influenza virus. In 1941, one of Hirst's technicians at the New York Public Health Institute, was manipulating the embryo of a chicken infected with an influenza A virus and accidentally lacerated a blood vessel of the chicken. Red blood cells (erythrocytes) of the chicken escaped and agglutinated viruses in the infected amniotic fluid. Hirst recognized the peculiarity of this incident, subsequently showed that the agglutination was transient, and considered that the kinetics of disagglutination and the interreaction of virus and erythrocytes reminded him of enzyme-substrate reactions. He then demonstrated that enzymes mediated the elution reaction and that the enzyme neuraminidase was an intrinsic part of the virus itself. We now know, of course, that the influenzaviruses comprise eight viral RNA segments, making influenzaviral segment reassortment common and confounding our efforts to reduce the impact of the disease it causes by reducing the efficacy of vaccines we apply and requiring newly constituted vaccines each year. In any case, if hemagglutination by a virus could occur, perhaps inhibition of that viral reaction by antibody against the virus could also occur. Such was the case and before long a hemagglutination-inhibition test for antibody was incorporated into routine serologic diagnostic and surveillance efforts.

In 1942, the United States federal government founded the Office of National Defense Malaria Control Activities and the Office of Malaria Control in War Areas in Montgomery, Alabama, creating the foundation for what would become the Communicable Disease Center, established in Atlanta, Georgia, in 1946. Offices were located on the sixth floor of the Volunteer Building on Peachtree Street and laboratory work was to be done in what was the barrack housing of a former Army hospital in nearby Chamblee.

However, according to unpublished notes of Morris Schaeffer (Figure 57), the M.D.-Ph.D. Director of CDC's Virus and Rickettsia Section from 1949 to 1959, the CDC judged that facility as unsafe for virus work, and so established a temporary laboratory on the outskirts of Montgomery, Alabama. Some years earlier, the Alabama State Health Department, with the assistance of the Rockefeller Foundation, established the site to study rabies, at the time a public health problem in the southeastern United States. When Harald Johnson (Figure 58) and Charles N. Leach of the International Health Divi-

Figure 57. Chen Pien Li and Morris Schaeffer conducting poliomyelitis virus research in Montgomery, Alabama during a 1953 study.
(image courtesy of U.S. Centers for Disease Control and Prevention)

sion of the Rockefeller Foundation completed their work, helping to reduce the incidence of that disease, the laboratory was abandoned. In 1947 the State of Alabama deeded the land, two small wooden buildings and an animal facility, to the United States Public Health Service.

Virology as a field was still in its infancy, the technology was primitive, and few trained virologists were available. Seward E. Miller, a clinical pathologist with the United States Public Health Service and Director of CDC's Laboratory Branch, recruited the accomplished Beatrice F. Howitt to work at the new facility. Howitt, a Californian, had worked with Karl F. Meyer at the Hooper Foundation in California to obtain the first isolate of western equine encephalitis virus from the brain of a horse and, eight years later, isolated that virus from the brain of a human. Howitt organized an excellent diagnostic laboratory but could find no time for research. Meanwhile, a newly appointed veterinarian, Robert E. Kissling, began interesting inves-

Figure 58. Thomas Harry Gardner Aitken, Harald Norlin Johnson, Harold Trapido, Robert H. Kokernot, Calista Causey, Ottis Causey, Belem, Brazil (image courtesy of Thomas H.G. Aitken)

tigations on rabies and encephalitis. In collaboration with Kissling, Ernest S. Tierkel and a young Harry Rubin, also CDC veterinarians, began studies of then-available rabies virus vaccines. That was when Morris Schaeffer arrived in Montgomery.

As a child, Schaeffer had suffered from poliomyelitis and remained interested in this disease for the remainder of his life. Trained first as a Ph.D. and then as a physician, he had served as Assistant Professor in the Department of Pediatrics and Microbiology at Western Reserve University (now Case Western Reserve University) and Physician in Chief, Contagious Diseases Pavilion, City Hospital, Cleveland. Schaeffer had inquired about positions at CDC and Miller invited him to present a lecture to the staff in Atlanta. Herald Cox, who was chief virologist at Lederle Laboratories, and Willam Friedewald, who was Chair of the Department of Microbiology at Emory University both attended. Schaeffer's lecture was warmly received and he later toured the Montgomery facilities, which housed about 25 people at the time. The CDC offered him the position of Director of that facility and Schaeffer reported for duty in May 1949.

Figure 59. (standing l. to r.): the ever devilish William C. Reeves, W. Daniel Sudia, James W. Leduc, Roy W. Chamberlain, and Louis C. LaMotte; (seated l. to r.) William Reeves, Jr., James G. Olson
(image courtesy of Louis LaMotte)

Schaeffer oversaw considerable improvements at the Montgomery facility – new buildings, improved sewerage facilities, improved animal facilities and even the addition of some air conditioning. Over time additional staff members came to work there, including Roy W. Chamberlain (Figure 59) and W. Daniel Sudia (Figure 59) in entomology and Donald D. Stamm as an assistant to Kissling. It was not long before this foursome began to generate publications of their findings on the entomology, epidemiology and diseases caused by arboviruses; the CDC then developed an outstanding reputation in those fields.

The high and increasing volume of diagnostic work left little time for research, which led to a high rate of turnover among scientific staff. Thomas P. Hughes, a yellow fever diagnostician working in Brazil for the International Health Division of the Rockefeller Foundation, also joined the staff as chief of the diagnostic unit. In relatively short order, he was replaced by Michael Siegel, who was replaced by Seymour S. Kalter, who was replaced by Andrew R. Fodor – all sound scientists.

In 1950 Kissling and Chamberlain went to New York University to further their training in the emerging field of virologic techniques.

When Rubin followed for the same reason, he so impressed the instructors that they suggested he might consider moving to Nobel Laureate Wendell Stanley's laboratory at the University of California at Berkeley. Stanley had been at the Rockefeller Institute before moving to Berkeley, where he involved himself in sophisticated studies of virus crystals. Rubin moved to Berkeley where he made outstanding contributions in basic virology, particularly the concept of "helper" viruses; helper viruses facilitate the development of a defective virus by supplying or restoring the activity of the viral gene or enabling the defective virus to form a protein coat.

Max Delbrück offered Renato Dulbecco (Nobel Laureate) a position at the California Institute of Technology and Dulbecco offered Rubin a post-doctoral position to work with Rous sarcoma virus, which had been difficult to titrate. When Rubin asked a graduate student, Howard Temin, to try to measure the amount of Rous sarcoma virus, the world of virology changed. Remaining in Dulbecco's laboratory as a post-doctoral fellow, in 1959 Temin performed the experiments that led to the formulation of the provirus hypothesis for Rous sarcoma virus and later led to the discovery of RNA-dependent DNA polymerase in retroviruses and a Nobel Prize for Temin. It does not matter where brilliant, innovative and collaborative people work.

Also in 1950, the Montgomery facility of CDC inaugurated a course in diagnostic virology, the first such course to be taught anywhere. The course was offered to state laboratory personnel but attracted applicants from academia, industry, and foreign health organizations – so many that the number of attendees had to be limited, with preference given to state laboratory personnel. The staff of the Montgomery facility gave the course but prominent scientists served as guest lecturers. The effect was that in 10 years the number of states that provided at least some diagnostic services increased from five to 20.

An increasing number of visiting scientists paid brief or long-term visits to the Montgomery laboratories. One was Robert Goldwasser from the Israeli Institute for Biological Research in Ness-Ziona. During the year he worked with Kissling, they succeeded in applying the immunofluorescence technique to detect Negri bodies in rabies virus-infected tissues (1958). Immunofluorescence is any of various methods that use antibodies chemically linked to a fluorescent dye to identify, quantify and localize antigens in a tissue sample. This became the standard method for the laboratory diagnosis of rabies and for rabies virus research.

Chen Pien Li (Figure 57) also visited. According to Schaeffer, Li was a refugee from mainland China, a former faculty member of Peking Union Medical College, a youthful companion of Mao Tse Tung and Chou Enlai and at one time a General in Chang Kai-Shek's Nationalist Army, where he was responsible for producing smallpox vaccine. He had been in the United States from 1927 to 1928, when he worked with Thomas M. Rivers, the American virologist and Director of the Rockefeller Institute Hospital in New York City. Li returned to the USA in 1949 and worked with Karl Habel at NIH, adapting human poliovirus 3 to mice, which required multiple passages. Somehow, Schaeffer was able to invite Li to Montgomery, where he helped adapt human poliovirus 1 to mice, so that mice, instead of monkeys, could be used for experimental studies.

In addition, and even more significantly, they were able to manipulate human poliovirus 1 through cell cultures and mice, obtaining by chance and hard work a series of human poliovirus 1 variants (mutants) that were of considerably lower virulence than the original Mahoney strain. These were named the Li-Schaeffer (LS) strains, of which the LSc strain had lost its virulence for monkeys and mice but replicated in monkey kidney cells in culture. That strain infected humans and monkeys by the gastrointestinal route but did not produce clinical signs or symptoms. However, it stimulated an adequate antibody response, therefore appearing to be a perfect vaccine candidate. Just as they were about to begin a field trial with this variant, an accident occurred in a commercial vaccine laboratory.

Between April 22 and May 27, 1955, some 40,000 of the children who had been administered supposedly inactivated poliomyelitis vaccine produced by Cutter Laboratories developed an abortive type of poliomyelitis, one not involving the central nervous system; inactivation of the virus had been incomplete. Fifty-six developed paralytic poliomyelitis, and of these, five died. In addition, the abortive infections led to an epidemic of poliomyelitis in their families and communities, and 113 other people became paralyzed, five of whom died. The Surgeon General of the United States temporarily suspended all inoculations with commercially-produced vaccines intended for use against human poliomyelitis viruses. Human trials planned by the Montgomery laboratories were suspended, never to be re-started. However, Albert Sabin obtained the LSc strain and showed that subpassages of it were safe and effective in large-scale trials in Mexico and Russia, where Chumakov was principal collaborator (Figure 60). An oral vaccine containing LSc progeny (Sabin's LSc/2ab strain) was licensed in 1961. Because of the "Cutter incident" and the subsequent order by the Surgeon General to stop all work with this virus until more information was available, CDC was prevented from becoming recognized for its most important contribution in the control of poliomyelitis.

Even while making progress in building a virus competence in Montgomery, Schaeffer felt that too little was being done in rickettsiology and decided that the reason for this was a lack of expertise in that field. He therefore recruited Charles C. Shepard from a CDC toxicology laboratory to join the group in Montgomery. Shepard was eager to make the move, given the tissue culture and animal facilities already in place there. The success of Shepard's work with *Mycobacterium leprae* was so great (growth of the tubercle bacillus in HeLa cells and then the growth of the leprosy bacterium in armadillos (*Dasypus novemcinctus*) and in the footpads of mice) that he never got around to his hoped-for work on rickettsiae. Later, Shepard and Joseph E. McDade, working at CDC in Atlanta, discovered the organism that causes Legionnaire's disease, *Legionella pneumophila*.

The 1957 influenza pandemic brought further responsibilities, so others were hired to take on the growing number of tasks for which the Montgomery laboratories were now answerable. Keith Jensen, from

Figure 60. (left to right) 1960: Marina K. Voroshilova (1922 - 1986), Irina K. Lavrova (1932 -), Mikhail Petrovich Chumakov (1909 - 1993) and Albert Bruce Sabin (1906 - 1993): note monkey being inoculated with experimental poliomyelitis virus vaccine
(image courtesy of Vanda Pogodina, Chumakov Institute of Polio and Viral Encephalitides, Moscow, Russia)

Thomas Francis' laboratory at the University of Michigan was put in charge of the laboratory work and Roslyn Q. Robinson, recruited from a nearby air base, served as his assistant. When Jensen left, Robinson took his place. Robinson eventually rose to Chief of the W.H.O. Influenza Reference Center at CDC, Chief of the Virology Section, and Director, Laboratory Program at CDC, overseeing all virus work, including arbovirus work, at CDC Atlanta, CDC Fort Collins (Figure 61), and CDC San Juan, Puerto Rico. Although Schaeffer could see the progress that had been made in developing the Montgomery labora-

Figure 61. U.S. Centers for Disease Control and Prevention, Division of Vector-Borne Infectious Diseases building on Colorado State University Foothills Campus, Fort Collins, Colorado.
(photo by Charles Calisher)

tories, he was convinced that the only way to prove that it was truly accepted as a world-class facility would be when preeminent scientists such as Joseph E. Smadel and Edwin H. Lennette took notice of its accomplishments.

Smadel, a member of the virological team that first recognized the outbreak of St. Louis encephalitis in 1933, worked for and with Thomas Rivers at the Rockefeller Institute, making significant contributions to our understanding of viral encephalitis, myxomatosis, smallpox, vaccinia, and psittacosis. He became Director of the Department of Virus and Rickettsial Diseases at the Walter Reed Army Institute of Research, where he headed programs on hemorrhagic fevers, arboviral diseases, and much more, then became Associate Director of the NIH, and finally Chief of the Laboratory of Virology and Rickettsiology at the Division of Biologics Standards at NIH. Smadel was, no doubt, by recognition of his peers, one of the great virologists of our time and a leader of arbovirological studies.

A physician-virologist, Edwin Lennette earned his Ph.D. degree in virology at the University of Chicago, one of the first people to earn a doctorate in virology, then completed an M.D. degree at Rush Medical College, University of Chicago, in 1936. Following an internship, he spent brief periods at the Department of Pathology of the Washington University School of Medicine in St. Louis and then at the Rockefeller Foundation laboratories in New York City. During World War II, he was assigned by the International Health Division in Brazil, to study yellow fever and encephalitis viruses. In 1944 he was transferred to the International Health Division's laboratories in Berkeley, California, to work on hepatitis and encephalitis. When that laboratory subsequently was transferred to the California Department of Public Health in 1947, Lennette became its Director, but not until he had spent a year as Chief of the Medical-Veterinary division of the United States Army facility at Fort Detrick.

For the next 31 years Lennette molded the California Department of Public Health laboratories into a world-renowned training laboratory as well as the leading laboratory for diagnosis of viral and rickettsial diseases. It conducted studies of Q fever and arboviral encephalitis, infections of humans with polioviruses and other infections and on the role of viruses in causing human carcinomas. Many of the people trained in those laboratories went on to become leading scientists and administrators of laboratories and health agencies worldwide. Lennette also served as a consultant to many government agencies and participated in many advisory committees.

Beginning in 1934, Lennette published more than 400 scientific papers, including *Studies on influenza virus: the complement-fixing antigen of influenza A and swine influenza viruses* in 1941 and others with Frank L. Horsfall; *Effect of in vitro cultivation on the pathogenicity of West Nile virus* and others with Hilary Koprowski (both at the time of the Rockefeller Foundation's Yellow Fever Research Service, Rio de Janiero); *Intra-erythrocytic location of Colorado tick fever virus;* and papers on as breathtakingly wide a variety of other viruses and conditions as imaginable for one person.

Figure 62. Richard William Emmons (1931 -)
(image courtesy of Richard Emmons)

Richard William Emmons (Figure 62) was the principal leader in the ground-breaking work on the natural cycle of Colorado tick fever virus and the disease it causes. He and his colleagues proved that this virus is only transiently detected in serum alone but can be isolated for extended periods from whole blood, this persistence being the result of infection of erythrocytes. They also suggested that erythrocyte precursor cells are infected in the bone marrow and subsequently released into the circulatory system, persisting for prolonged periods despite the presence of serum antibody. Continuing these studies, they developed diagnostic assays and conducted epidemiologic studies of the virus and disease. *In toto,* their findings helped establish the recognition that arbovirus infections are not analogous one to another, which added to our understanding of arboviruses as a widely and multiply varied class of viruses, rather than a group of similar viruses.

Reflecting his wide interests and many collegial relationships, Lennette's co-authors included a remarkable array of outstanding scientists, including Frank R. Abinanti, Trygve O. Berge (a former editor of the arbovirus catalogue), James Chin, Emmons, Anne A. Gershon, William McD. Hammon, Gertrude Henle, Werner Henle, Robert J. Huebner, Harald N. Johnson, Robert H. Kokernot (Figure 58), Kelly T. McKee, Jr., Joseph L. Melnick, Lyndon S. Oshiro, Fred Rapp, William C. Reeves, John L. Riggs, Gladys E. Sather, Nathalie J. Schmidt, Rex Spendlove, Reuel A. Stallones, as well as hundreds of others. With Schmidt and Emmons, Lennette is deservedly famous for the editions of *Diagnostic Procedures for Viral, Rickettsial and Chlamydial Infections.*

Lennette seemed to have encyclopedic recall and practical insights, in addition to his remarkably wide experiences. To the end, he strongly supported the importance of seeking experiences in addition to knowledge, as opposed to relying exclusively in technical procedures. Lennette was tough, diplomatic and always polite, socially adventurous, generous of his time, and patient with young people ("It is not their fault that they are young", he told me), and had a marvelous sense of humor that supported him through a life of great joys and sorrows.

Both Smadel and Lennette sent people to the Montgomery laboratories to learn from its workers what they were doing with various viruses and how they were doing it, so Schaeffer could at last relax in this regard because the laboratory he had built was accepted by virologists who were respected by other virologists. The laboratories were moved to Atlanta between June and September 1960, the hottest months in the South. Moving from Montgomery was difficult, however. The staff was reluctant to move, and Schaeffer decided not to move with the laboratory, leaving CDC in 1959, the same year Telford Work (Figure 63) became the director of virology at CDC. The logistics of moving viruses and rickettsiae included using plastic bags filled with wet sawdust, which the staff put into freezers for the move. Animals were moved too, and special escort cars went along for the ride in case of a traffic accident; no one wanted rabies virus-infected dogs loose in the countryside. The buildings in Atlanta were officially dedicated September 8, 1960 and the Montgomery laboratories merged nicely into what was called the Virology Section.

Morris Shaeffer became Assistant Commissioner of Health and Director of the Bureau of Laboratories in New York City and remained an accomplished scientist-administrator until his retirement. As one final and significant contribution, Schaeffer campaigned for quality control in laboratories. The eventual result was the much-needed Clinical Laboratory Improvement Amendments (CLIA), which the United States Congress passed in 1988. This Act established quality standards for all laboratory testing to ensure the accuracy, reliability,

Figure 63. Telford Hindley Work (1921 - 1995) with his friend Pushpa in India. (This photo tells one more about Work than words can adequately express.) (image courtesy of Martine Work)

and timeliness of patient test results, regardless of where the test was performed.

With a budget of about $1 million, 59 percent of CDC's personnel in 1946 were engaged in mosquito abatement and habitat control, with the ultimate objective of eradicating malaria in the United States. Among its 369 employees were only seven medical officers; most jobs at CDC at the time were for entomologists and engineers but in CDC's first years more than 6.5 million homes were sprayed to kill mosquitoes.

The founding director of CDC, Joseph W. Mountin, spoke out in support of various public health issues and pushed for CDC to extend its responsibilities to many communicable diseases. In 1947, CDC made a token payment of $10 to Emory University for 15 acres (61,000 m^2) of land, where its headquarters stands today; employees of CDC collected the $10 to pay for the purchase. The sponsor of the gift was

Robert Woodruff, Chairman of the Board of the Coca-Cola Company, who had a long-time interest in malaria.

Mountin continued to lead the CDC when it became the National Center for Disease Control (1967), later renamed multiple times: the Center for Disease Control (1970), the Centers for Disease Control (1980) and the Centers for Disease Control and Prevention (since 1992). By this time, institutions, funding, enthusiasm, and the right scientists were in place, so that further progress was inevitable. One innovative and unique program within CDC is the Epidemic Intelligence Service (EIS), developed by Alexander D. Langmuir beginning in 1949. This two-year post-graduate (doctoral degree in medicine, veterinary science, dentistry or Ph.D.) training program of service and on-the-job learning is for health professionals interested in the practice of applied epidemiology. EIS officers are ready to go anywhere they are invited to investigate reports of an epidemic or an unusual cluster of cases. Since 1951, more than 3,000 EIS officers have responded to requests for epidemiologic assistance within the United States and throughout the world. EIS officers, sometimes called "disease detectives", work on the front line of public health, conducting epidemiologic investigations, research, and public health surveillance both nationally and internationally. This and associated programs at CDC resulted in the eradication of smallpox and the near eradication of guinea worm (*Dracunculus medinensis*) infection (dracunculiasis). As with efforts to eradicate poliomyelitis, national and international partners of CDC and the United States have played leading roles in such efforts.

Using monkeys and horses, even guinea pigs, laboratory rats, rabbits, mice or other vertebrates for laboratory studies of virus and for amplifying viruses for vaccine and reagent production is expensive and labor-intensive, requiring large spaces and specially trained technicians, and dangerous because of the likelihood of exposure of technical and professional staff members to aerosols from infected animals. Beginning in 1912, investigators attempted to cultivate cells from various sources inside glass bottles. Cleanliness of the glass, use of spe-

Figure 64. Thomas Huckle Weller
(1915 - 2008)
(image courtesy of Peter Weller)

cial media, pH of the medium, and temperature were among the many important conditions that had to be recognized and controlled.

Slowly but surely, using numerous clever and innovative techniques, procedures toward this end were developed. The intent of all this was not only to grow cells but to use them to try to isolate viruses, study them, and provide inactivated ("killed") virus or live-attenuated virus to be used as vaccines.

In 1936, Albert Sabin and Peter Olitsky at the Rockefeller Institute had demonstrated that poliovirus could be grown in human embryonic brain tissue, but they feared that this method might risk central nervous system damage in those who received the vaccine. The advantage of embryonic tissue, however, was that it grew quickly. A breakthrough came in 1948 when a research group headed by John Franklin Enders at the Children's Hospital in Boston cultivated a poliovirus in non-neural human tissue in the laboratory. By demonstrating that a poliovirus could be amplified in non-neural tissue, they refuted the persistent and incorrect dogma that the virus was strictly neurotropic. This greatly facilitated poliovirus vaccine research and provided a milieu for production of vaccines against these viruses. In 1954 Enders and his colleagues, Thomas Huckle Weller (Figure 64) and Frederick Chapman Robbins, received a Nobel Prize in Medicine or Physiology for their efforts.

In the 1950s, the Rockefeller Foundation began a key worldwide program of arboviral investigations. With headquarters in New York City and laboratories in Africa and South America, collaborative efforts by French, Brazilian, Colombian, British, and other investigators ensured the mapping of the geographic distribution of yellow fever. Incidental isolations of hundreds of other viruses from humans, other primates and other vertebrates, from mosquitoes, ticks and other arthropods, and from a variety of other sources complemented the studies of yellow fever. Something had to be done to identify the plethora of viruses arriving almost daily and to test the serum samples that were being collected. The development of a neutralization test using mice, rather than monkeys, allowed the involved scientists to conduct essentially worldwide surveys to establish the distribution of yellow fever. Led by Sawyer, these extensive efforts to map epidemics led to the concepts we use today to delineate epidemic areas, not only of yellow fever, of course, but of essentially all virus diseases.

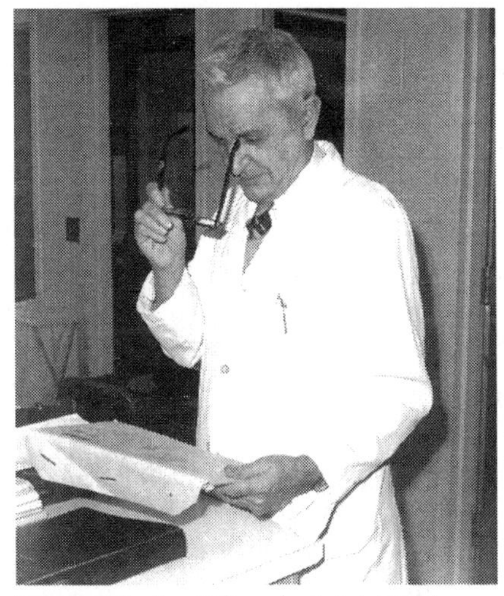

Figure 65. Jordi Casals-Ariet (1911 - 2004)
(image courtesy of Ellen and Christina Casals)

An outbreak of encephalitis in humans and horses in Massachusetts in 1938 drew the attention of Webster and his "trainee", Jordi Casals (Figure 65), of the Rockefeller Foundation laboratories. In order to determine whether these viruses were related, similar in some way, they compared the etiologic agent of that outbreak, eastern equine encephalitis virus, with other viruses known at the time to cause encephalitis, including western equine encephalitis virus, Russian Spring-Summer encephalitis virus, louping ill virus, rabies virus, and poliomyelitis viruses. Casals, a meticulous and methodical worker ("First try to prove yourself wrong.", he said), applied to these viruses the complement-fixation technique taught to him by Jules Freund, the inventor of the well-known adjuvant that still carries his name.

Freund had been studying tuberculosis, the details of which had been taught to him by Léon Charles Albert Calmette, a co-developer of the BCG (Bacillus Calmette-Guérin) vaccine and himself a student of Louis Pasteur. (In terms of "degrees of separation", Casals was two degrees removed from Pasteur. These relations between mentor and mentee continue to be common in science but are particularly common among arbovirologists.) Casals and Webster found that, whereas antibody to rabies, poliomyelitis, and other viruses that cause encephalitis (encephalitogenic) did not react with antibody to certain other viruses, an antigenic relationship between Russian Spring-Summer encephalitis and louping ill viruses could be demonstrated. Casals also detected antigenic cross-reactivity between these two viruses and St. Louis encephalitis, Japanese encephalitis, and Murray Valley encephalitis viruses but noted that antigenic proximity between them varied; that is, whereas all were related, some were more distantly and some more closely related one to another. This was the first hint that virus antigenic complexes existed.

Because Theiler thought it might be applicable to arboviruses, he suggested to Casals and Lenore Brown that they modify Hirst's hemagglutination technique (used for influenzaviruses) and determine whether it was useful for studies of arboviruses. Using antigens produced by acetone or ether extraction (to rid them of non-specific lipids and other interfering substances), they found that many arboviruses hemagglutinated. It was soon noted that whether an antigen did or did not hemagglutinate depended on the pH of the buffer used to suspend the erythrocytes to be hemagglutinated. Then James Porterfield (Figure 66) at Oxford, who spent considerable time and efforts in virus discovery, particularly in Africa, showed that erythrocytes from male geese were more reliable (more uniform and repeatable results) than were erythrocytes from female geese or from chickens or other sources used in such tests. Using this information, Albert Sabin produced hemagglutinins of yellow fever virus and dengue viruses. He showed by hemagglutination-inhibition that these viruses were related to each other (antibody to one virus reacted with antigen of the other virus, and vice versa) and, with Edward Buescher, demonstrated that the hemagglutination-inhibition test could be applied in the same way to other arboviruses. It is now recognized that hemagglutination-inhibiting, neutralizing and complement-fixing antibodies are made by the host against different components of a virus, such recognition adding to their usefulness.

Figure 66. James Stuart Porterfield (1924 - 2010)
(image courtesy of William James, Oxford University)

Soon after Theiler suggested using hemagglutination-inhibition as a serologic test for evidence of infection by arboviruses (J. Casals, personal communication, 1972) it was fine-tuned and applied to diagnosis of arbovirus infections of vertebrates. At the time, hemagglutination-inhibition was the *sine qua non* of serologic testing because it provided a method for simple, relatively inexpensive, and fairly rapid assessment of antigenic similarities as well as differences between arboviruses.

The advantage of the hemagglutination-inhibition test actually was its lack of complete specificity. Arboviral hemagglutinins, now known to be a property of the viral glycoprotein, which is mostly, but not completely, shared by all viruses of a particular group, are inhibited to some degree by antibody to any of the viruses of the group. Therefore, while it was not possible to determine from a positive hemagglutination-inhibition test of serum from a vertebrate that the detected antibody had been elicited by a particular virus, it could at the very least be used as evidence that the vertebrate had been infected at some time in the past with a virus of that group. For example, if one uses hemagglutinin prepared from Murray Valley encephalitis flavivirus (which occurs in Australasia) to test serum samples from a community of people in North America, and finds some of the sera positive, (i.e., having hemagglutination-inhibiting antibody to Murray Valley encephalitis virus), that merely indicates that the positive sera were from people who had been infected with one of the flaviviruses, not with a particular flavivirus. It is certain that people in that community were not infected with Murray Valley encephalitis virus, unless (1) those people have histories of travel, and probably illness, while they were in Australasia or (2) Murray Valley encephalitis virus is now in North America, each an unlikely but not impossible scenario (c.f. West Nile virus is in North America). Often, such results are good enough to conclude a preliminary inference regarding the prevalence of antibody to flaviviruses in that community and further studies are then done.

Thus armed with hemagglutination-inhibition tests, Casals and his colleagues tested thousands of people for antibody to yellow fever virus and to scores of other arboviruses. Results of those surveys determined the presence or absence of viruses in one area or another and provided evidence that justified or did not justify further work. Moreover, applying the hemagglutination-inhibition test to paired acute-phase and convalescent-phase serum samples from a patient provided a serodiagnostic assay. If the hemagglutination-inhibition titer of the serum rose (or fell) at least four-fold the patient was considered to have been infected with the virus used to test the samples or to a virus related to it.

The performance and interpretation of the hemagglutination-inhibition test, being more subjective in regard to the results (hemagglutinated, did not hemagglutinate), is an art as much as it is a science, but because it has so many advantages, it was applied worldwide by arbovirologists, particularly after the paper by Delfine Harriet Clarke (Figure 67) and Casals laid out all the details for anyone to reproduce and apply. In addition, the complement-fixation test became a very useful tool for virus comparisons, a test with which Casals was so familiar because of his earlier work with Freund, Peter K. Olitsky, Albert Sabin, Ralph O. Anslow and others at the Rockefeller Foundation. Casals, Shope, Lennette, and many others favored this test, not over other tests but as an adjunct to them. The CDC was so enthusiastic about the complement-fixation test and its promise for use in state and local health departments that it produced a monograph, written by the serologist Helen L. Casey, which explained in detail not only how to do the test but how to adapt it to microtiter use. Because the CDC version of the complement-fixation test was accepted by most laboratories, results of tests done by different laboratories were comparable, so that interpretations of the results could be compared.

Figure 67. Delphine Harriet Clarke (1912 - 1985)
(image courtesy of the Rockefeller Archive Center)

The basis of the complement-fixation test is the use of complement (a normal component of serum from guinea pigs) to lyse sheep erythrocytes (red blood cells) that had been sensitized to such action by antibody to these cells. Thus, when complement was bound to a virus (virus antigen)-antibody complex, it was not free to bind to and lyse the sensitized sheep erythrocytes. Lysis of the sensitized sheep erythrocytes was taken as evidence that the complement had been free to do so because it had not been bound to a virus (virus antigen)-antibody complex. In contrast, when the sensitized sheep erythrocytes were not lysed it was because the complement had been bound by a virus (virus antigen)-antibody complex. Complement-fixation was, and remains a very useful method for detecting antibody, although it is rarely used these days because of its various complexities. The complement-fixation technique is useful for differentiating antibodies to closely related viruses but not for serologic surveys because complement-fixing antibodies do not persist for long or decline precipitously after infection. That it is no longer a test of choice is influenced more by its relative complexity, requirement for understanding, lack of available commercial kits and uniform reagents, and lack of sensitivity. It is, however, quite specific and for many years was used almost exclusively by Casals and others to at least preliminarily identify viruses by their antigenic signatures. It is also considered "old fashioned", but it is unclear as to why a useful test is considered such.

We now know that the viral antigen participating in the complement-fixation test for arboviruses is the nucleocapsid protein, the protein associated with the viral shell (capsid). In the 1950s, however, this test and the hemagglutination-inhibition test (which is now known to detect antibody to the viral glycoprotein), might have been crude, but they were the most sophisticated tests available. Although not specific, they were relatively rapid and inexpensive and proved to be invaluable for use in disease diagnosis assays, serologic surveys, and preliminary virus identifications. Neutralization tests were icing on the identification cake. The hazards of using non-inactivated viruses were well known but considered an acceptable risk or at least a recognized risk for laboratory workers.

More recently, enzyme-linked immunosorbent assays (ELISAs) have replaced hemagglutination-inhibition, complement-fixation, and immunofluorescence tests because ELISAs are more sensitive, may be configured to be more specific, and are relatively simple to accomplish. Before the development of the ELISA, the only option for conducting an immunoassay was radioimmunoassay, a technique using radioactively labeled antigens or antibodies, as first described in 1960. Because radioactivity poses a potential health threat, a safer alternative was sought. Fundamentally, ELISAs require an antigen, an antibody, and an antibody linked to an enzyme which will change the color of an appropriate substrate. This change in color is the signal of a positive reaction (i.e., evidence of the presence of an antigen-antibody reaction. Numerous configurations of the basic ELISA can be devised – to test for presence of a certain antigen or a certain antibody or to test for antibody in immunoglobulin M , immunoglobulin G or other immunoglobulins from patient sera, spinal fluid, saliva or tears – so that this test now is the principal test of choice for diagnostic or survey purposes. As with hemagglutination-inhibition, complement-fixation, and immunofluorescence tests, ELISAs can be confirmed by neutralization tests, the consummate serologic assay.

The higher the titers of viruses, antigens, and antibodies, the more useful they are for detecting distant antigenic relationships between viruses (higher titered reagents can be diluted more and thus are less expensive, need replacing less often, and contain fewer non-specifically interfering substances when diluted). Therefore the report by Joseph Melnick and Nada Ledinko that coxsackieviruses (enteroviruses, not arboviruses) replicate to high titer in newborn mice led Casals, Olitsky, and Ralph O. Anslow to replace adult mice with newborn mice for studies of arboviruses. In addition to the age-susceptibility of the mice, an important aspect of this host selection was the use of the particular strain of inbred mice. The stock, still in use, was the outcome of selective inbreeding by Webster at the Rockefeller Foundation. He began with albino mice from Rockefeller Foundation mice, which had been derived from a large colony in Switzerland, received from there in 1926. Although already highly inbred, the line was eventually reduced to a single pair and progeny outbred to form a new stock. These mice fortuitously served as exquisitely susceptible hosts not only for arboviruses but for many other viruses as well.

By 1951 Casals and coworkers adapted human poliomyelitis virus type 2 to replicate in newborn mice and developed a complement-fixation test to detect it. Similar applications of newborn mice to studies of arboviruses resulted in shorter incubation periods, higher titers, and more satisfactory polyclonal antibodies. Polyclonal antibodies are those that recognize multiple epitopes (binding sites) either on a single virus protein, multiple viral structural proteins on the same virion, or multiple viral proteins encoded by the same viral genome as expressed in infected cells. To produce these, it is usual to immunize laboratory animals with a series of related viruses but it is also possible and useful to immunize them with unrelated viruses, so that the antibody produced can be used to test for antigens of many viruses. In this way, a relatively few antibody products can be used to test for hundreds of different viruses, making virus identification more rapid, somewhat less expensive, and easier.

Newborn mice and serologic tests became invaluable tools for studies of the many insect and vertebrate viruses being sent to the New York laboratories by investigators at Rockefeller Foundation outposts throughout the world. Casals, Loring Whitman, Robert Shope, and their co-workers were in the unique position of having available not only a large number of viruses but superb reagents (which they had meticulously prepared) with which to compare them. They thus began the classical investigations so integral to our knowledge of the interrelationships among arboviruses and other viruses.

Casals and others attempted to categorize these scores of viruses and many hundreds of isolates and from the results Casals formulated three dicta, which he explained to me, paraphrased as follows: "(1) No virus can belong to two antigenic groups. (2) If two viruses cross-react antigenically, they are related. (3) If viruses of different groups cross-react, they do not belong to different groups." These simple premises have never been disproven but they have been modified. Their significance can best be understood in the context of phenotypic expression of genotypes and in terms of phylogeny. However, for many years after, all that was possible was classification (grouping by relatedness), not taxonomy (molecular characterization and biological properties), of arboviruses.

With the Pasteur Institute system, the Rockefeller Foundation laboratories, and the CDC now all involved, the time had come for the establishment of some remarkable collaboration within and among those institutions, as well as with various governmental, state and local laboratories and non-governmental organizations worldwide. The exchange of scientists between laboratories, sharing of methods and knowledge, and personal interactions were adopted by arbovirologists as a means of information exchange. By this time, these arbovirologists, shared a great deal in common professionally and that facilitated personal interactions. They enjoyed each other's company and had great fun exchanging ideas. More recently it seems, investigators become so involved in the details of their own work that they often are, if not oblivious to their colleagues, less or only belatedly aware of what others are doing. This is particularly ironic in an age when an increasing number of communication methods are touted as the next great step forward. Note that finding that a virus sequence identifies it as belonging to this or that family of viruses is important but is only a first step towards understanding its epidemiology.

In 1959, to further these exchanges, the Rockefeller Foundation organized and sponsored a meeting and provided funds to establish an informal organization that would provide an environment for such interchanges. From this meeting, held at the Gould House in Ardsley-on Hudson, New York, emerged the American Committee on Arthropod-borne Viruses, ACAV (http://www.astmh.org/subgroup/acav.asp). The group agreed at the time it would not constitute a formal organization, one with by-laws, but would provide a forum for exchange of information among people interested in arbovirus research. Directly or indirectly the word "arbovirus" and the expanding compendium known as the "International Catalogue of Arboviruses Including Certain Other Viruses of Vertebrates" emerged from this forum. This first appeared as a "working catalogue", a series of large cards on which was printed detailed information; it was distributed to collaborators around the world. ACAV was successful beyond anyone's imagination and expectations. Below is reprinted (with necessary modifications) the frank musings of William Reeves on the establishment of the ACAV. As he was intimately involved in all this, as well as articulate, it seems best to hear it from him. It is rather extensive but important to be documented here. This was taken from Reeves' oral history, available on the University of California – Berkeley web site. It is more appropriate for the reader to get this from the horse's mouth, Reeves, than from the compiler of this history:

> "Establishing Research and Communication Networks
>
> "An International Congress of Tropical Medicine and Malariology was held in Lisbon in 1958. This organization began to have meetings in different parts of the world every three or four years after World War II. It would bring together people interested in tropical diseases. For some reason they kept the identification, Tropical Medicine and Malariology, I guess because malaria was and still is such an important disease.
>
> "That meeting in Lisbon probably was the largest international congress of people with these interests that had been held after the war. They had smaller conferences before that, but this was a huge meeting, with probably over a thousand people there. It seemed like almost everybody in the world who was interested in arboviruses showed up at that congress. The Rockefeller Foundation paid a number of people's way. Almost all of the people in their international program were sent to the meeting. The Rockefeller Foundation paid my way to go to the meeting. Why they picked me, I don't know. The people from Russia came--Smorodintsev and Chumakov. People showed up from various parts of Africa, India, South America--wherever arbovirus work was going on and had been for many years. So having that population there resulted in a number of symposia that were focused on arthropod-borne diseases. The Rockefeller Foundation and W.H.O. [World Health Organization] representatives got together and said, "Let's have a special session at this time to see what the people in this field want to talk about as their problems and what sort of things they might share in the way of interests.
>
> "So they called this informal meeting, and it was interesting because it was co-sponsored by the W.H.O. and Rockefeller Foundation. I went to it with the greatest of interest. However, I made a horrible discovery when I got there. I was pretty naive about some things. They came up to me and they said, 'We'--and that was the W.H.O. and Rockefeller people—'have

decided that you will preside at this meeting.' Now, 1958--how old was I? I guess I was forty-two years old at that time. I had not gone there with anticipation that I was going to be asked to preside at anything. They said, 'We've decided Telford Work,' who at that time was with the Rockefeller Foundation, 'will be the rapporteur for this meeting, and you will preside.'

"They didn't have an agenda organized, and there was no specific objective to be accomplished. The idea was just to get a group of people together who shared an interest and see what they wanted to talk about and what they thought their needs were. In retrospect, I'm sure that the real objective was to get a recommendation that the W.H.O. should have an organized program in this area, which they didn't have. They had nothing at that time in arbovirology. The Rockefeller Foundation did not want the responsibility for this. They felt that it should be some other agency. I think they felt that if they were to organize something, it would interfere with their objectives, which were quite different from W.H.O.'s. They wanted to gather information, get information exchanged between different geographical areas and operations in different areas, [they wanted to deal with] different workers, get a network of information available to the W.H.O., make sure there was centralized action when it was necessary. For instance, there had to be a centralized way in which virus identifications could be done. It just couldn't be done in everybody's laboratory.

"The Rockefeller Foundation lab in New York at that time was doing all it could, but it didn't have a network which was feeding it all the viruses of the world. They were getting what their laboratories were collecting. I would send them any new viruses I had because I wanted help on their identification, but basically there wasn't even an informal or organized network to do a lot of these things.

"We exchanged information at this meeting for the first time. I'll give you an example. The Russians kept talking about a certain type of mite that was a primary vector of viruses in Russia. It turned out there was a language barrier. They were talking about some sort of mite, but in fact they really were talking about ticks, and we couldn't cross that language barrier. We were talking about the same thing but just using a different vocabulary. A lot of vocabulary differences came up in these meetings that had to be resolved. We had the authorities of the world together as far as they and we were concerned, and the authorities of the world as far as I was concerned were sitting there talking about the same thing but arguing about it.

"There was discussion about [forming a consensus regarding arbovirus identifications]. Also, there was agreement that there had to be an exchange of people and information so that we would be talking about the same things and know what was going on. We had a tremendous argument at that meeting about the latest diagnostic methodology, which was the hemagglutination-inhibition test for arboviruses.

"Albert Sabin had recently developed it. It was something that was modified from work that had been done earlier with influenza [virus]. He had people in his laboratory like Bob Chanock, who became one of the world's authorities on influenza later at NIH. He had had Ed Buescher in his laboratory, who later became the head of Walter Reed Army Institute of Research in Washington, D.C. Anyway, he had a group who developed this hemagglutination test, which was a significant addition to the neutralization and complement fixation tests.

"The difficulty at this meeting was that a shouting match began between Ed Buescher, Albert Sabin, and Jordi Casals from the Rockefeller Foundation about the hemagglutination test--whether it was as good as or better than complement fixation and neutralization tests and small details on techniques. I was trying to preside, and these three people were all standing and yelling at each other at the same time. The Russians and some of the other international people were getting very confused by all this because they thought the Americans would all agree and take a unified front. I finally just slammed my hand on the table and I said, 'Albert, shut up and sit down for a minute.' Albert Sabin doesn't usually respond, but he shut up and he sat down. I turned and I said, 'Now, Ed, Albert has sat down and shut up. How about you?' He did. Then, without saying anything more, Jordi Casals sat down and just sort of smiled.

"The result of this meeting was that a consensus evolved very rapidly that we shared interests and recognized what the major problems were. These agreements were put together in a report which I don't even have a copy of anymore. It's possible that Tel Work at UCLA may have a copy; he was the rapporteur. The report went to the W.H.O. It stated that central or reference laboratories ought to be established that would cover the needs of the field laboratories all over the world to identify the virus strains. Locations for these laboratories were not specified at that time, but it also came out that there normally would have to be a central laboratory for the world, and it probably would be the Rockefeller Foundation laboratory in New York, which was later moved to Yale. It was obvious; they had the largest collection of viruses as a result of the early work on yellow fever and associated viruses in Africa and in South America. They had field laboratories established all over the world that were feeding new material to them. No other country and no other single facility had anything like that. The W.H.O. is not a research organization in the sense of establishing a laboratory [at headquarters] in Geneva to do this.

"About the same time, it was recognized that there were these other laboratories that could serve regional areas, such as the CDC laboratory, which is now at Fort Collins. The Moscow laboratory of Chumakov was one, and laboratories were to be established in Latin America and in Canberra, Australia. These laboratories were established rather rapidly, because the W.H.O. then said that these would be their officially-designated reference resource laboratories. They provided token funding, and I do mean token. They didn't supply a working budget, but they supplied a small budget that would allow shipment of materials back and forth, sending out of reports, summaries, and things like that; but they didn't supply staff. This had to be done by federal governments or by foundations like the Rockefeller Foundation. W.H.O. facilitated visits between workers in different laboratories, because the W.H.O. had the ability to get visas and to get government approval for people to move across lines that sometimes governments couldn't or wouldn't necessarily endorse.

"Also at that time, the recommendation was made that the Pan-American Health Organization [P.A.H.O.] should become involved. Most people don't realize the Pan-American Health Organization is not a part of W.H.O. It was formed before W.H.O. [was formed] by Fred Soper and company, and they feel they are autonomous; they're responsible to the governments in the western hemisphere, and they're not responsible to W.H.O. W.H.O. likes to pretend that they're part of it, but basically PAHO insists on its autonomy, and their agreements with governments are quite separate from the W.H.O. agreements. They generally work together; however, sometimes they work in opposition. I really don't want to get into details, although I ran into it several times. These two international agencies had to be willing and able to help open doors to get materials and personnel back and forth.

"[The Pan-American Health Organization was not itself doing the work.] It did establish some laboratories in the western hemisphere that included arboviruses in their activity. They had a zoonoses center in Argentina, and they established a laboratory in Venezuela that did some arbovirus work. Sometimes they put arbovirus research into agricultural laboratories that were working on hoof and mouth disease or other virus diseases of animals so they could utilize some of the same people and equipment.

"We also agreed in Lisbon that, in addition to visits between the field and central laboratories for training or for exchange of information and techniques, there would probably be a need for training programs for people who were going to be coming into the field, and that there was going to be a need to develop laboratories in various parts of the world where there were none at that time. We agreed that the study of migratory birds would be important, because it was increasingly recognized that birds and other animals moving from one area to another could be moving these viruses around. So a whole series of rather specific studies were recommended; it was a very ambitious project proposal.

"Things moved very rapidly, because in November of 1958, after the Lisbon meeting, the first W.H.O. Scientific Group on Virus Diseases met in Geneva. They had such an organization because of their basic interest in influenza, polio, smallpox, and a lot of other virus diseases. They rapidly ratified the recommendations of the Lisbon meeting. They had other advisory groups that dealt with immunological surveys and so on, and they also agreed to the arbovirus proposal.

"The virus commission meetings [of the Armed Forces Epidemiological Board] were always held in Washington, D.C., because we met at Walter Reed Army Institute of Research. In 1959, at a commission meeting, there was a large group of us there who were concerned with arboviruses and who also were consultants to W.H.O., the NIH, or the army, and we realized that W.H.O. alone was not going to take care of all the problems. So one night we got together to see if we couldn't get something organized in the way of a working group in the United States that would concern itself with such problems. Now, the difficulty was that some of us worked for universities, others worked for the Rockefeller Foundation or the army. We represented a variety of different organizations. We didn't have an interchange between us that was organized in any sense, and we decided that with a little bit of support from some agency like the Rockefeller Foundation we could organize some meetings and get us together again on a completely voluntary, unpaid basis. We had enough interests in common that maybe we could start implementing some of the recommendations made to W.H.O. That really was the beginning of what later became the American Committee on Arthropod-borne Viruses.

"The Gould House Meeting, 1959

"The outcome was that the Rockefeller Foundation was very eager to have the recommendations implemented, so they called a meeting very shortly after that in 1959 at what was called the Gould House Meeting; The Gould House is a meeting place in Ardsley-on-Hudson that the Rockefeller has available to them. They organized a group of nineteen of us scientists and administrators to meet there to discuss how we might implement some of the recommendations that had been made, not in an organized fashion in the sense that we were going to be put together as a research unit to do this, that, and the other thing, but to consider the possible approaches to the problems.

"They were all American workers, but some of these people represented the international projects of the Rockefeller Foundation. So what that group agreed would be most helpful was an exchange of current information on what was going on in research in this field. We had to have some way of finding out what this guy is doing and that guy is doing, so we would complement each other and learn from each other. We agreed that, given an opportunity, we would make all our information available to everybody else in a completely voluntary fashion. There didn't seem to be any [hesitance to this plan]. It was a very interesting group of people. The people who were in that original group represented a wide variety of organizations. It was almost unbelievable. Sure, they argued about a few things; it wouldn't be any fun if you didn't. But we had people from the Rockefeller Foundation, the United States Army, United States Navy, United States Public Health Service, three universities, and one state health department. We came to agreement on all the things that we could do.

"The Second Meeting of the Gould House Group, in Chicago, 1960

"That seemed like a good beginning, but it just wasn't going to go on without something else, so we got them to call another meeting, in April 1960, in Chicago at an international meeting. It was a follow-up meeting to pursue the Gould House recommendations. At that meeting they recommended there ought to be a formal organization meeting to be held in Atlanta, Georgia, within a relatively short period of time. The Rockefeller Foundation funded the meeting in Atlanta in April 1961. It had a very interesting outcome, because we decided there should be an organization to be named the American Committee on Arthropod-borne Viruses (ACAV) with the charge to implement research in this area. We even agreed that if Rockefeller Foundation provided some funding, this organization would be able to get information disseminated and have a small budget, not to hire people but to pay for miscellaneous expenses.

"Now, I again got drafted into being the chairman of that Atlanta meeting; I don't know how or why, but I was [Note: Bill Reeves was one of the great summarizers and rapporteurs I ever met. He was constantly asked to do such tasks at meetings and always asked "Why me?" Sometimes he even accused the person who asked him to do this of being lazy. However, with only a little bit of arm-twisting, he always did the job, and did it better than anyone else could have. Often, it was difficult to recognize the proceedings from what Bill wrote about them, as he always added incisive comments and questions to the minutes.]. They agreed at that meeting that they wanted to formalize the group, not to the extent of having an organization that would be incorporated but that would have dialogues and so on. They would have a series of working groups of people concerned with certain problems, and I could serve as chairman and treasurer for this informal organization.

"Meanwhile, the W.H.O. wasn't sitting still. They put together an organized study group on arthropod-borne viruses in 1960. That was a pretty rapid development for W.H.O. Within two years they organized a group to put together their views on the total field and to review the recommendations of the Gould House [group], the Lisbon meeting, and all of these things. The W.H.O. group specifically endorsed and supported all the recommendations that had been made. Again, it was an international group which represented all the countries of the world that had a concern with arboviruses. As a matter of fact, they had too many people to fit in as members of that committee. The W.H.O. is limited in how many people they can have from any one country.

"[Telford] Work and I were drafted to be in the secretariat of the organization. I'd never recommend to somebody that they do that unless they like to work, because what happens is that the major members of the committee sit and talk, and the secretariat puts it all together and makes sense of it. We had an excellent group of people. We worked very hard day and night.

"A report came out of that committee which emphasized that arthropod-borne viruses represented an acknowledged field of effort. It recognized that there were both official approaches to the problem by organized groups like the Rockefeller Foundation worldwide reference center, which would soon be at Yale, and the regional laboratories that would be developed. ACAV activities would include a newsletter, to be developed by the American group, and would not be limited to news from the United States; it would collect information from all over the world from anyone who wanted to submit information, and it would not be a publication that could be cited as a scientific reference source. Also, meetings would be held in association with major international and national meetings of scientists concerned with virological and tropical disease research. There would be enough people interested in this particular group of agents to have meetings held within formal meetings and congresses. This would allow arbovirologists to be kept up to date on what was going on."

Organized by the ACAV Executive Committee, subcommittees were established: Subcommittee on Arbovirus Laboratory Safety (SALS), Subcommittee on Information Exchange (SIE), Subcommittee on InterRelationships (formerly "Immunologic Relationships") Among Catalogued Arboviruses (SIRACA), Subcommittee for Evaluation of Arthropod-borne Status (SEAS), and Subcommittee on Low Passage Viruses (SLPV).

Figure 68. (standing l. to r.) Thomas Aitken, Herb Barnett, Robert McKinney, Roy Chamberlain; (seated l. to r.) Archie D. Hess, Carl Eklund, Richard Taylor, Leslie Spence at the BushBush Forest field station of the Trinidad Regional Virus Laboratory, 1963
(image courtesy of Leslie Spence)

The Subcommittee on Arbovirus Laboratory Safety took on the most important task of all, keeping laboratory workers and others safe from infections with newly and previously recognized viruses. In 1967 Robert P. Hanson, S.E. Sulkin, Edward L. Buescher, William McD. Hammon, Robert W. McKinney (Figure 68), and Telford H. Work of that subcommittee published in Science a very detailed and well written summary of what was known about arbovirus infections of laboratory workers. By 1980, this subcommittee was populated by William F. Scherer, Gerald A. Eddy, Thomas P. Monath, Thomas E. Walton, and John H. Richardson (except for ad hoc member Richardson, who was the CDC Safety Officer at the time, all were arbovirologists). The 1980 summary reported that 19 deaths had occurred among 499 laboratorians working with arboviruses and "certain other viruses". These reports showed just how dangerous working with these viruses could be, being particularly dangerous to laboratorians who were inadequately trained, were careless, or who worked in laboratories that were inadequately equipped. From that time to this, arbovirologists have not only been aware of the potential hazards of working with these viruses but have taken much more care in handling them. Vaccination programs for laboratory workers and improved training, plus the elimination of "mouth pipetting" and inhibitions against smoking and eating in laboratories, also have helped. The United States National Institutes of Health and the United States CDC now post safety information and handing restrictions on their web sites.

For many years the Subcommittee on Information Exchange (Richard M. Taylor (Chair), Telford H. Work and William F. Scherer) published a printed newsletter, the "Arbovirus Information Exchange", as well as a published catalogue of all these viruses, eventually totaling more than 500, at least 150 of which are known pathogens. The catalogue is now on-line, so that anyone anywhere can obtain the available information. The now-defunct "Arbovirus Information Exchange", edited first by Richard Moreland Taylor, then by Telford H. Work, then by me, Adrian Chappell, Barry Miller, and Laura Chandler, respectively, was a remarkable tool for arbovirologists to remain in contact with one another and as a reference source. Through this publication and the people who supported it, an international community of like-minded arbovirologists formed. That quarterly (then semi-annual, then annual, now defunct) publication served as a newsletter and forum for presenting unpublished data. I know of no other such publication and, given the ease with which information now can be exchanged by people who want to exchange information, I expect we will not see its like again.

The Subcommittee on InterRelationships (formerly "Immunologic Relationships") Among Catalogued Arboviruses first was chaired by Jordi Casals, then by Robert Shope, then by me, and now by Scott Weaver (Figure 69). These tenures, covering altogether more than a half century, have seen discoveries large and small and, one at a time, useful pieces added to the puzzle.

Figure 69. Scott Cameron Weaver (1957 -)
(image courtesy of Scott Weaver)

The Subcommittee for Evaluation of Arthropod-borne Status examines the data on a virus registration sheet (formerly for the printed Catalogue, now for the on-line version) and determines as best as possible whether the virus is an arbovirus. This is not nearly as straight-forward as it might seem and sometimes the only conclusion is a "maybe".

For many years the Subcommittee on Low Passage Viruses maintained a growing collection of viruses that had not been passed in laboratory hosts or had only been passed once or twice (or, anyway, available material with the least number of passages). For reasons more due to the decreasing rate of virus isolation and the increasing rate of detection of viral nucleic acids, this group no longer functions as such but the collection is maintained by Robert Tesh at the University of Texas Medical Branch at Galveston.

Particular expert non-United States arbovirologists were asked to join ACAV as international collaborators and contributors to the Catalogue, whose editors maintained the necessary details and published and distributed periodic reports to anyone interested in them. Richard Moreland Taylor was the first editor of the printed catalogue, Trygve O. Berge its second editor and Nick Karabatsos (Figure 70) the last editor of the published (on paper) edition. The current editor is the Chair of the Subcommittee on Arbovirus Information Exchange, now Ann Powers (Figure 71), at CDC. The catalogue, now continuously up-dated, continues to be invaluable <http://wwwn.cdc.gov/arbocat>.

In earlier days, national virological laboratories could and did call on the resources of the W.H.O. Collaborating Centres for virus iden-

Figure 70. (l. to r.) Elena A. Vladimirtseva, Nick Karabatsos and Alexander M. Butenko
(photo by Charles Calisher)

tifications, tests of sera for diagnostic or survey purposes, and for any other reasons they might have. Those collaborating laboratories were in Bratislava (Czechoslovakia), Brisbane (Australia), Dakar (Senegal), Entebbe (Uganda), Fort Collins (United States), London (England), Moscow (U.S.S.R.), Paris (France), Pune (India), Tokyo (Japan), and Zagreb (Yugoslavia).

According to the 1985 (last printed) edition of the catalogue, the number of registered arboviruses grew until the 1970s. The printed catalogue was last published in 1985.

Period	Number of arboviruses registered
1900-1929	6
1930-1939	10
1940-1949	19
1950-1959	109
1960-1969	209
1970-1979	129
1980-1985	22

Figure 71. Ann Marie Powers (1968 -)
(image courtesy of Ann Powers)

As funding priorities changed and the great arbovirologists of earlier days retired or otherwise left the field, fewer new viruses were registered in the catalogue, although the existence of many previously unrecognized viruses has been documented elsewhere. Increasingly, polymerase chain reaction and other techniques were being used to detect virus nucleic acids but less effort was made to isolate and biologically characterize them. In addition, many other viruses were being recognized as "emerging" and as causing serious human and livestock diseases, including filoviruses and hantaviruses, which are not transmitted by arthropods but which were isolated or detected by many of the people who were arbovirologists

Thus an internationally-oriented and cooperative group of people began the field of arbovirology and continued to extend knowledge about arboviruses. What came after that was unexpected but, in retrospect, followed logically.

CHAPTER 5

Arbovirology comes of age

This chapter profiles some of the people and events that moved the field forward during the late 1950s to the 1970s and who continue to move it forward. It also highlights some of the viruses that were key to understanding various aspects of arbovirology and reviews information that brought arbovirus research into the modern era. Improvements in use of experimental animal models, serologic reagents, and laboratory tests aided researchers. An increasing number of arboviruses were isolated and studied, and new antiviral strategies were devised. Electron microscopy was used to further our understanding of viral pathogenesis and aided in rapid classification of arboviruses and viruses that cause hemorrhagic fever and other illnesses.

Some semblance of order began to appear not only in the classification of arboviruses but also in their taxonomy and the taxonomy of viruses in general by 1960. Researchers recognized that eastern equine encephalitis virus, western equine encephalitis virus, and certain other arboviruses were related. These were designated the "Group A arboviruses", now known to comprise the genus *Alphavirus* of the family *Togaviridae*. Because yellow fever, Japanese encephalitis, Murray Valley encephalitis, St. Louis encephalitis, West Nile, louping ill,

Russian Spring-Summer encephalitis and other viruses also were known to be interrelated antigenically, they were placed in what was termed the "Group B arboviruses", now known to comprise the genus *Flavivirus* of the family *Flaviviridae.* With improved recognition of antigenic relationships of viruses, many became recognized as members of the families *Togaviridae, Flaviviridae, Bunyaviridae, Rhabdoviridae* or other virus families.

Elegant electron microscopic studies by Frederick Murphy and his co-workers demonstrated that all arboviruses that had been placed in given antigenic groups also shared similar morphologies and similar ways in which the structure of a virus develops (morphogenesis), providing partial but sufficiently confirmatory evidence of the earlier antigenic studies. That is, if two viruses were found to cross-react antigenically they were also found to look alike and to have other physical and biological properties in common.

Over the decades, Murphy's meticulously obtained photographs of rabies, bovine ephemeral fever and other rhabdoviruses, of bunyaviruses, orbiviruses, alphaviruses, flaviviruses, phleboviruses, arenaviruses, filoviruses, and other viruses furthered our understanding of viral pathogenesis and the pathogenetic mechanisms by which viruses attack and injure cells. These discoveries and observations relieved many frustrations for investigators who had worked for years to understand disease mechanisms and served as an impetus for additional studies. A bit of background regarding Murphy and some other key individuals is provided below, so the reader can see how scientists developed intellectually, how the work and field developed, and how personal relationships developed.

Bernard Fields arrived at CDC as an Epidemic Intelligence Service officer with an interest in viruses. It was soon recognized that he not only possessed the usual high intelligence of Epidemic Intelligence Service officers but something more. Beginning his tour of duty with identifications of newly recognized viruses previously isolated from mosquitoes and rodents collected in the Florida Everglades National Park, he went on to investigate a 1965 epizootic of vesicular stomatitis in horses and humans in New Mexico, the causative agent of which was vesicular stomatitis Indiana virus. With Murphy he examined the structure of Kern Canyon rhabdovirus by electron microscopy, and with Murphy, Dorothy Reese and Pekka Halonen, a visiting scientist at the time, he discovered that rabies virus and certain other rhabdoviruses agglutinated erythrocytes, a phenomenon that was soon turned into a diagnostic assay. Leaving CDC, Fields eventually headed the division of infectious diseases at the Brigham and Women's Hospital in Boston and the Albert Einstein Medical School in the Bronx, New York and finally chaired the Department of Microbiology and Molecular Genetics at Harvard Medical School.

A charming, sympathetic, and creative scientist, Fields worked there first with reoviruses, pioneering strategies for studying viral pathogenesis. With his students and associates, he then took viruses apart and identified the functions of specific genes, eventually getting back to the basic mechanisms of infections. He was editor-in-chief of the now standard textbook Virology (later editions were renamed Fields Virology). Tragically, Fields died at age 56, his career not nearly complete and hundreds of students not yet advised. Remember that the good start this brilliant virologist had received was in arbovirology. When he was assigned to help investigate that outbreak of vesicular stomatitis in New Mexico, he became "hooked".

Antibodies are proteins that are generated by white blood cells (lymphocytes) in the immune system. These cells circulate in the blood and attach to foreign proteins called antigens in order to bind and/or destroy them. Monoclonal antibodies are laboratory produced substances that recognize a single epitope on a single protein and which can locate and bind to specific molecules, including virus proteins. The idea of a "magic bullet" was first proposed by the German polymath Paul Ehrlich who, at the beginning of the 20th century, proposed that if a something could be found that selectively targeted a disease-causing organism then a toxin for that organism could be delivered along with the selective agent. Ehrlich and Élie Metchnikoff received the 1908 Nobel Prize for Physiology or Medicine for this and

Figure 72. Charles Moen Rice III (1952 -)
(image courtesy of Charles Rice)

other work which eventually led to an effective treatment for syphilis. By the 1970s a cancer known as B-cell multiple myeloma was recognized and that the cells of this cancer produce a single type of antibody; however, production of large amounts of such antibody had not been developed. Through a tortuous series of efforts, successes, and conflicting claims of priority, eventually it became possible to culture cells that produced antibody to a single protein or peptide, a monoclonal antibody using hybridized human and mouse cells. This was done by George Pieczenik and put into routine useage by Georges Köhler and César Milstein, who shared a 1975 Nobel Prize in Physiology or Medicine with Niels Kai Jerne for this discovery.

After fundamental findings had been made of the relationships among viruses of various antigenic groups and the relationships between groups, studies of flaviviruses using monoclonal antibodies against the envelope protein supported the previously held premise that flaviviruses evolved from a single ancestral virus. However, it was not until the appropriate computer programs and molecular biological techniques became widely available that extensive nucleotide sequencing could be exploited to reveal more precise genetic relationships between viruses. For the first time, a rational, genetics-based taxonomy of arboviruses was in place. Numerous comparative assessments of flaviviral genomes contributed to our understanding of its replication strategy and of the structure and function of its various genes. For example, the crucial work done by Charles Rice (Figure 72) and colleagues of the phylogenetic relationships among these viruses provided a greater understanding of the molecular epidemiology of viruses. Rice, Edith M. Lenches, Sean R. Eddy, Shyi-Jang Shin,

Figure 73. (l. to r.) Joel McKeith Dalrymple (1939 - 1992), Tatjana Avšič Županc, Peter Jahrling
(image courtesy of Peter Jahrling)

Figure 74. Barry Russell Miller (1950 -)
(image courtesy of Barry Miller)

Rebecca L. Sheets, and James H. Strauss sequenced the entire RNA genome of a wild-type yellow fever virus, the West African Asibi strain. This was a seminal finding that provided a description with which other flavivirus genome sequences could be compared. Two years later Chang S. Hahn, Joel Dalrymple (Figure 73), James Strauss, and Charles Rice compared that sequence with the sequence of the highly passaged 17D vaccine strain, observing 68 nucleotide position differences (32 amino acid substitutions), but they could not determine which differences correlated with virulence. In 1990, Mary E. Ballinger-Crabtree and Barry R. Miller (Figure 74)

Figure 75. Ottis Causey (1905 - 1988)
(image courtesy of the Rockefeller Archive Center)

Figure 76. Calista Causey (1898 - 2000)
(image courtesy of the Rockefeller Archive Center)

partially sequenced the genome of a South American isolate of yellow fever virus, showing that the greatest number of non-conserved differences (variations) occurred in the viral envelope protein, which may very well account for differences in biological functions.

The Rockefeller Foundation's arbovirus program was first headed by Richard M. Taylor. Born in 1887 in Kentucky, where he did his undergraduate studies, Taylor obtained his medical degree from the University of Michigan. Leaving a faculty appointment at New York University, he served as medical director of the Red Cross for two years in post-World War I Poland. There he used innovative methods to distribute resources, helping to bring about a dramatic decline in child mortality and attracting the attention of Rockefeller Foundation personnel in Paris. He soon joined their staff and was quickly assigned to Montpellier to investigate an epidemic of brucellosis. In 1936 he was sent to Hungary to establish "the first influenza listening post", an office that collected data regarding influenza so that at least some predictions of its spread could be made, the initial step in establishing a Rockefeller Foundation-supported series of institutes of hygiene

Figure 77. John Clifford Bugher (1901 - 1970)
(image courtesy of the Rockefeller Archive Center)

and epidemiology in Eastern Europe. When his home was destroyed by German bombs he was reassigned to South America. There he worked under the celebrated entomologist and mosquito control expert Fred L. Soper, who had led an effective campaign against yellow fever in Brazil. Taylor successfully studied the mechanisms of jungle yellow fever virus transmission. This was a new concept at the time - that forest animals could participate in the natural cycle of yellow fever virus. Martine Jozan Work, a friend of Taylor's and the wife of Taylor's protégé, Telford Work (who hired me to work at CDC), has said that Taylor was a charismatic and nurturing leader to future prominent virologists, such as John Fox, Ottis Causey (Figure 75) and Calista Causey (Figure 76), David Davis, Edward Lennette, Hilary Koprowski and many others, all of who showed a growing interest in the characterization and investigation of newly discovered viruses.

At the end of World War II, little was known about arthropod-transmitted pathogens. At the Rockefeller Foundation laboratories in New York City, Taylor established as a priority the study of infectivity and pathogenicity of viruses for chicken embryos and made efforts to create or improve diagnostic techniques. With collaborators Harald Norlin Johnson, the rabies expert (working on histopathology), John Austin Kerr (addressing complement-fixation), John Clifford Bugher (filtration, ultracentrifugation, electron microscopy; Figure 77), Kenneth C. Smithburn (cross-neutralization) and Alexander John Haddow (medical entomology; Figure 78), a global research program

Figure 78. Alexander John Haddow
(1912 - 1978)
(image courtesy of Andrew Haddow)

for arbovirus diagnosis and research emerged.

Born to immigrant farmers in Nebraska in 1907, Harald Johnson first pursued his interest in music at a conservatory in Minneapolis, then obtained a bachelor's degree at the University of Nebraska, Lincoln, and then graduated from the medical school at the University of Nebraska, Omaha. He trained in internal medicine, infectious diseases, and pathology at Harvard, at Peter Bent Brigham and Children's Hospitals. In 1938, he joined the Rockefeller Foundation, where Max Theiler was testing yellow fever vaccines in the hope of protecting its field researchers. There he developed the strain of rabies virus used in the vaccine, which by the late 1960s in the United States brought that disease under control in dogs, and dealt with rabies and other public health problems around the world. In Alabama he helped control a serious rabies outbreak (1938-1945), in Mexico he traced a cattle epidemic to rabid vampire bats (1944), and in India he established a field station for studying arbovirus diseases (1950s). His laboratory later became the Indian national virus laboratory.

In 1954, the Rockefeller Foundation sent him to the Berkeley laboratory of the California Department of Health Services to investigate an encephalitis outbreak and to work on other arthropod-borne virus diseases. Johnson captured deer mice (*Peromyscus maniculatus gambeli*), from which he isolated Modoc flavivirus. Even though he suffered from a quadriplegic paralysis, perhaps caused by infection with rabies virus (his diagnosis) or by having been too often vaccinated against rabies virus (his physicians' opinion), Johnson recovered sufficiently to continue his field studies, being undeterred by the harsh working conditions of the field. Interested in overwintering mechanisms of viruses, he went so far as to dig in the snow in mountainous northern California to find deer mice and examine them for evidence of Modoc virus.

Johnson retired in 1972 but continued to work in the Berkeley laboratory part time. Edwin H. Lennette, who headed the Viral and Rickettsial Disease Laboratory in Berkeley during the nearly two decades Dr. Johnson worked there, described Johnson as a Renaissance man: "He was an accomplished pianist. He could walk into an open field and tell you the Latin and common names of the flowers, trees, shrubs, birds and other animals - besides being a superb physician and researcher."

In addition to his discovery of and work with Modoc virus, Johnson had a strong interest in bats. He obtained three isolates of a virus (Rio Bravo flavivirus) from Mexican free-tailed bats (*Tadarida brasiliensis mexicana*) collected at at trapping site in Kern County, California, at the Rio Bravo school. Both Modoc virus and Rio Bravo virus have been shown to be non-vector borne. That is, there is no evidence that these viruses are transmitted by means other than through passage of saliva or other excreta from infected bats. In addition, they possess certain characteristics in common that indicate they do not replicate in arthropods. This is surprising because they are closely related to flaviviruses that clearly are mosquito-borne or tick-borne. Dennis Constantine and Dora Woodall later showed that Rio Bravo virus was excreted in bat saliva for as many as seven months after infection. Rare laboratory infections with these viruses have been documented.

Johnson was interested in a large population of Yuma myotis (*Myotis yumanensis*) bats at power stations in Kern Canyon, located in the southern Central Valley of California. In 1956 he collected 15 of these bats, and from tissues of one of them he isolated Kern Canyon rhabdovirus. He isolated another rhabdovirus, Klamath virus, from brain and lung tissues of a montane vole (*Microtus montanus*) that he had dug out of the snow in southern Oregon in 1962. He also isolated rickettsial bacteria and another new virus from voles collected there. In 1965 he isolated Farallon virus, named for the islands of the same name, which lie just west of San Francisco Bay. This virus (family *Bunyaviridae*, genus *Nairovirus*), which was isolated from *Ornithodoros denmarkii* ticks, is related to Hughes virus, which was isolated from ticks collected from bird nesting areas of the Dry Tortugas, a small group of islands off the Florida Keys. Johnson also isolated the related Punta Salinas virus from ticks in Peru; others have isolated it from bird ticks collected in Cuba and in the Persian Gulf. Members of the Hughes group (Hughes, Farallon, Punta Salinas, Soldado, and Zirqa viruses) were all isolated from *Ornithodoros* species ticks collected from bird colonies essentially world-wide. Whereas none of the Hughes group viruses is known to cause illness in humans, and might be considered of lesser importance than those that do cause illnesses, these viruses are worth noting, if only to point out that one might not know where one is going until one arrives.

John C. Bugher was a staff member of the International Health Division of the The Rockefeller Foundation, beginning in 1938, and director of the Yellow Fever Laboratory in Bogota, Colombia, and the Yellow Fever Research Institute in Lagos, Nigeria. Bugher was director of the Division of Biological and Medical Sciences of the Atomic Energy Commission before becoming Director for Medical Education and Public Health of the Rockefeller Foundation in New York City. However, it was long before he held these influential administrative positions that Bugher made his essential discovery – that baby mice could be useful for studies of yellow fever virus. While at the Yellow Fever Laboratory in Villavicencio, Colombia, he found that baby mice were not only equal to adult mice in their susceptibility to the virus but had the advantage of being more easily handled and maintained when used for mosquito feeding in virus transmission studies. This finding led to expanded use of baby mice by Edwin Lennette and Hilary Koprowski (for neutralization tests of arboviruses), Melnick and Ledinko (for isolation and amplification of coxsackieviruses), and Casals, Olitsky and Anslow (for arbovirus reagent production, arbovirus characterization and arbovirus serosurveys).

A physician-zoologist who had studied methods to control malaria in Kenya, Alexander John Haddow joined the Rockefeller Foundation's Yellow Fever Virus Research Institute in Entebbe, Uganda, in 1942. During the next decade, Haddow, Kenneth Smithburn and A.F. Mahaffy discovered Semliki Forest virus (1944) and Bunyamwera virus (1946). The three studied Bwamba and numerous other viruses during their successful and seminal studies of the ecology of yellow fever in Uganda. For the latter they ingeniously used sentinel monkeys as human surrogates, monkeys housed on platforms built onto trees at various heights, so they could sample arthropods at various levels of the forest, from floor to canopy. These methods were successfully adapted and used at other Rockefeller Foundation field stations in other parts of the world and are still being used with excellent results at the Institute Evandro Chagas in Belem, Brazil, and perhaps elsewhere. At the same time that the Entebbe laboratory was renamed the East Africa Virus Research Institute, Haddow became its Director.

When Richard Taylor reached mandatory retirement age, Max Theiler was put in charge of the New York laboratories, having worked with Hugh Smith to develop the celebrated yellow fever vaccine. Taylor deferred his retirement and instead went to Egypt to establish a scientific program at the Naval Medical Research Unit-3 in Cairo. In Egypt he worked with John Paul to investigate poliomyelitis but coincidentally isolated West Nile virus from febrile children. With Telford Work, Herbert S. Hurlbut, Harry Hoogstraal (Figure 79), and other colleagues, he conducted epidemiologic studies leading to the isola tion of mosquito- borne and tick-borne viruses (Quaranfil, Chenuda, and Nyamanini viruses), the elucidation of the transmission cycle of West Nile virus in birds, the isolation of Sindbis virus, and the first isolates of coxsackieviruses from blood. In 1956 Taylor joined John Paul's group of epidemiologists at Yale University. A 1958 and 1960 survey of the Everglades National Park yielded a new alphavirus,

Highlands J virus, and further serological investigations of Native Americans there led to the discovery of Venezuelan equine encephalitis virus type II (Everglades virus) by Telford Work, Roy Chamberlain and Daniel Sudia. As increasing numbers of arboviruses were being isolated, identified and characterized, some as pathogens, Taylor realized that these viruses needed to be catalogued. To accomplish this, a better means of communicating among arbovirologists world-wide was becoming imperative and so Taylor founded the Arbovirus Information Exchange newsletter.

Figure 79. Harry Hoogstraal (1917 - 1986)
(image courtesy of Susan M. Woodfin, U.S. Naval Medical Research Unit No. 3, Cairo, Egypt)

The first issue of this newsletter appeared in print in 1960, and in 1966 the Rockefeller Foundation published the first edition of the International Catalogue of Arboviruses Including Certain Other Viruses of Vertebrates (Figure 80), with Taylor as its editor. He continued editing that catalogue until he passed that job to Trygve O. Berge (Figure 81) who, after a career in the military characterized by many accomplishments, had "retired". As Martine J. Work has written, "In a career that spanned more than six decades, Taylor authored fewer than 50 publications, yet he was the epitome of chivalry and stood as a thoughtful perfectionist seeking worthy goals, the hallmarks of a critical scientific mind."

A noted physician, naturalist and virologist, Wilbur G. Downs (Figure 82) succeeded Taylor as Director of the Rockefeller Foundation's arbovirus program. That program was responsible for studies of many viruses in many countries of the world and Downs' background and intellect prepared him for this work. He studied tropi-

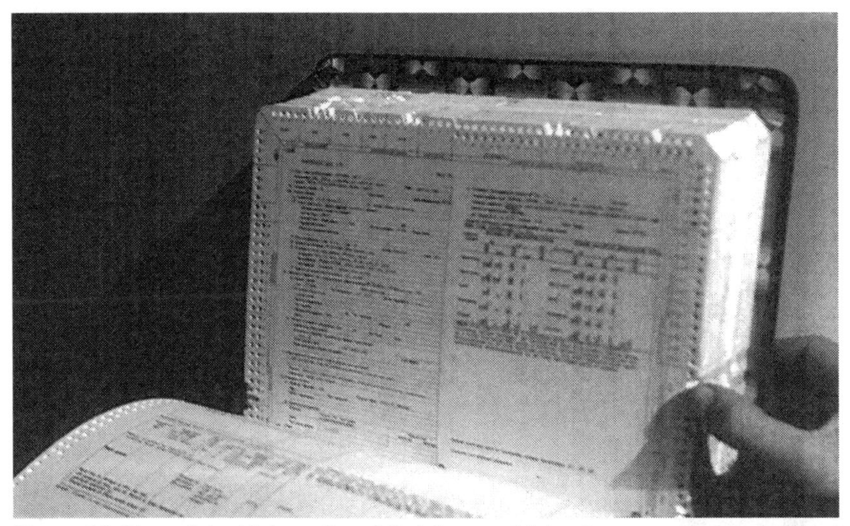

Figure 80. The original International Catalogue of Arboviruses, edited by Richard M. Taylor and Telford H. Work. Note the perforated cards on which the data were printed. Long needles, much like knitting needles, were inserted through these cards to allow only certain cards to be selected. Computerized data came later.
(image courtesy of Trygve Berge)

Figure 81. Trygve Obert Berge (1909 - 1995)
(image courtesy of Patricia Berge Muckle)

Figure 82. Wilbur George Downs (1913 - 1991)
(image courtesy of the Rockefeller Archive Center)

cal parasitology with Pedro Kourí at the University of Havana, Cuba, then graduated from Cornell Medical College in 1938. Downs studied malaria in Trinidad and Tobago in 1941, producing a series of classical papers on that disease, after which he was inducted into the United States Army (1943). He served as Malaria Control Officer in the South Pacific, served in Bougainville, and became Acting Chief of Preventive Medicine in Okinawa in 1945, also spending time in Guam. By the end of World War II, he was recognized as a world expert in tropical diseases, including not only malaria but also filariasis, intestinal parasites, fungal infections, venereal diseases, dengue fever, leprosy, tuberculosis, and scrub typhus. After Downs retired from the military, he joined the Rockefeller Foundation, which sent him to Mexico to direct a malaria control program (1946-1952), then back to Trinidad to establish the Trinidad Regional Virus Laboratory (now the Caribbean Epidemiology Center) in Port-of-Spain. Under his guidance, that laboratory became a center of excellence for teaching young Trinidadians, attracting exceptional researchers to assist with the work, and overseeing the isolation and studies of yellow fever virus and scores of newly recognized viruses. Collaboration with investigators in northern South America and elsewhere proved exceptionally productive. The published reports of those studies are classics in the field. In 1961 Downs became Associate Director of the Medical and Natural Sciences Division in charge of the Foundation's arbovirus program.

Downs was an avid reader with a huge private library, including works in Spanish, French, German, and Russian. He had a large collection of tropical orchids and performed a number of hybridization experiments. A hybrid genus of orchids, *Downsara,* was named after him. He was a keen fisherman (he tied his own flies) and expert marksman (he had once been a member of the National Rifle Team of Trinidad & Tobago), an accomplished photographer, stamp collector, guitarist, and bookbinder. From 1963 to 1971 he was Director of the Yale Arbovirus Research Unit and Professor of Epidemiology. After he resigned that position, he stayed on as a lecturer and Clinical Professor of Epidemiology. In 1969, he collaborated with Jordi Casals and Sonja Buckley (Figure 83) in discovering and describing the deadly Lassa fever in Nigeria and the virus that causes that disease. In later years he advised health officials of African countries regarding prevention of

Figure 83. Sonja M. Buckley (1919 - 2005)
(image courtesy of the Rockefeller Archive Center)

river blindness (onchocerciasis), caused by infection with the parasitic nematode *Onchocerca volvulus,* which is transmitted by black flies (*Simulium* species). However, it is not the nematode itself, but its endosymbiont, the bacterium *Wolbachia pipientis,* that causes the severe inflammatory response that leads to blindness. The building of dams in Australia, Brazil, and elsewhere raised concerns about exposure to many potential disease agents. Downs was asked to consult on these potential problems.

Wilbur Downs was the archetype of the sort of person who attracted me to arbovirology. His eclectic interests were fascinating in and of themselves, but, more important they were a practical necessity, for understanding the many complex political, ecological, sociological, economic, religious, climatic/meteorologic, botanic, mammalogic, entomologic, virologic and medical components of arthropod-borne disease transmission. He was supportive of many students, faculty, social programs, and much more.

In 1964, the Rockefeller Foundation arbovirus laboratories were moved from New York City to the Department of Epidemiology and Public Health at Yale University, with the Foundation funding a major part of the construction of a necessarily expanded facility. Some of the scientific and technical staff moved to Connecticut, others maintained their homes in and near New York City. Although the commute was somewhat inconvenient for those who rode the train to New Haven, at least they could get in some writing, reading, and cogitating (or, perhaps, even sleeping). Coincidental with the institutional move, the personnel who continued and extended their work at Yale included Thomas Henry Gardner Aitken, Charles Anderson (Figure 84), Sonja Buckley, Jordi Casals, Delphine H. Clarke, Wilbur G. Downs, Nick Karabatsos, Peter Olitsky, Albert Sabin, Robert Shope, Robert B. Tesh, Max Theiler, Gregory Tignor (Figure 85), Leslie Webster, Loring Whitman (Figure 86), and others. In 1973, Theiler and Downs published a book, a marvelous review of arbovirus research funded by the Rockefeller Foundation. The merged organization was named the Yale Arbovirus Research Unit and the merging of the expertise of each was synergistic.

Figure 84. Charles R. Anderson (1915 - 1984)
(image courtesy of Thomas P. Monath)

Combining methods used by others and their own modifications of those methods, Delphine Clarke and Casals prepared suspensions of the brains of suckling mice infected with one or another of various arboviruses and then used acetone to extract the non-specific inhibitors (mostly phospholipids) that might be in those suspensions. This procedure rendered most of these antigens non-infectious, adding a safety feature to the process. The antigens also were dispensed in small quantities for later testing, use and distribution. With potent, standardized reagents in sufficient quantities now available, the stage was set for a series of remarkable discoveries. These serologic techniques became the accepted standard for preparation and quality control of arbovirus antigens and antibodies and for diagnosis of arbovirus diseases and allowed laboratories world-wide to reproduce their own

Figure 85. Gregory Hayes Tignor (1938 -)
(image courtesy of Gregory Tignor)

Figure 86. Loring Whitman (date of birth unknown [graduated medical school 1930] - died 1987)
(image courtesy of the Rockefeller Archive Center)

results and those of others to produce reliable and meaningful epidemiologic data.

With Rockefeller Foundation support and under the aegis of Downs, laboratories were established or enlarged in collaboration with existing national laboratories in many locations. In Port-of-Spain, Trinidad, the Caribbean Epidemiology Centre, directed at the time by the inspired and enthusiastic Downs, investigations of arboviruses were conducted at several sites, including the Bush Bush forest, the Nariva Swamp, the Vega de Oropouche rainforest, and elsewhere in Trinidad. In addition, study sites were established in what was then British Guiana (now Guyana) and in the British territories of Montserrat in St. Kitts and elsewhere. With Leslie P. Spence (epidemiologist), Andries H. Jonkers, Thomas Aitken (entomologist), Charles Anderson (virologist), C. Brooke Worth (mammalogist-ornithologist) and Downs in the field and the laboratory, the presence of arboviruses was documented and the details of cycles of transmission of yellow fever virus, eastern equine encephalitis virus, St. Louis encephalitis virus, and other arboviruses investigated.

A young physician from the British territory of St. Vincent in the Caribbean, Leslie Percival Spence (Figure 87) was recruited in 1954 by Downs to join the Rockefeller Foundation staff at the Trinidad Regional Virus laboratory. Downs left for the New York laboratories in 1961, and in 1964 the Trinidad laboratory was moved to new and better facilities in Port-of-Spain and became part of the Department of Microbiology of the University of the West Indies with Spence as its director. It is now part of the Caribbean Epidemiology Center in Port-of-Spain.

Yellow fever was well known in Trinidad in the 18th and 19th centuries, with the last urban outbreak occurring in 1907. In 1914 a cluster of cases of yellow fever occurred among oil field workers in southern Trinidad. These workers lived in bungalows with screened windows and doors and mosquito control measures were applied in the general area, but their work was in the forest. Downs suggested that the vector might have been a jungle species of mosquito, rather than *Aedes aegypti*. Results of a fortuitous survey of humans in 1953 and early 1954 had revealed the occurrence of only a few infections with yellow fever virus, all non-fatal. Yet more than 15% of humans surveyed had antibody to the virus, such that more serological surveying was needed before the Trinidadian government could initiate a program to clear large areas of the forest in 1954. Plans for the expanded survey were interrupted in April 1954 by the recognition of a mild case of yellow fever in a young forest worker living in northeastern Trinidad. Yellow fever virus was isolated by Spence from the patient but the virus rapidly spread among humans, transmitted by the peridomestic *Aedes aegypti* mosquito.

From August through October of that year four fatal and 12 non-fatal cases of yellow fever were seen. The fatal cases were diagnosed either by virus isolation or by pathological examination of patient liver; the non-fatal cases were diagnosed by serologic testing. Spence isolated yellow fever virus from hunter-collected dead red howler monkeys (*Alouatta seniculus*). Work then focused on the red howler monkey and results of additional studies suggested that these primates served as a reservoir for yellow fever virus and demonstrated that the virus was being transmitted among them by *Haemagogus spegazzini* mosquitoes at both ground and treetop levels in the rainforest, a definite jungle yellow fever cycle.

Figure 87. Leslie Percival Spence (1922 -)
(image courtesy of Leslie Spence)

An imminent epidemic was forecasted, and, amid public warnings to that effect, Downs initiated a program to vaccinate health workers and to stockpile vaccine. Trinidad health authorities began a large-scale vaccination campaign and an anti-*Aedes aegypti* campaign, which included education, inspection of potential breeding sites, and dichlorodiphenyltrichloroethane (DDT) spraying of residences. Notwithstanding that an estimated 80% of the human population of Port-of-Spain now had antibody to yellow fever virus and to dengue viruses, more cases of yellow fever were documented. But because of the preventive measures that had been taken there was no Trinidad-wide epidemic. Nonetheless, in spite of an attempt to quarantine the island in 1954, yellow fever spread to the Venezuelan mainland just a few kilometers away and eventually to southern Mexico, killing many thousands of people along the way.

Given the impetus and background information which had been gathered during that epidemic and because of other viral discoveries there, the Trinidad virus laboratory under Spence was prepared to conduct further studies of arboviruses and other viruses, and they did so. Eventually, Spence became professor of Microbiology at the

University of the West Indies, then at McGill University, and the University of Toronto, where he served as chairman of the Department of Microbiology and Microbiologist-in-Chief at Toronto General Hospital, and held a number of important advisory posts in Canada. Spence also made contributions to research on respiratory viruses, rotaviruses, and other viruses but, throughout his career and into retirement, he continued his active support of all things arboviral.

The mammalogist-ornithologist C. Brook Worth of the Rockefeller Foundation began his career as an assistant in animal pathology at the Rockefeller Institute for Medical Research in Princeton New Jersey, while on leave of absence from the Department of Biology, Swarthmore College. Working under the direction of Carl Ten Broeck, one of the co-discoverers of eastern equine encephalitis virus in 1933, Worth discovered and reported the detection of juncopox virus (family *Poxviridae*, genus *Avipoxvirus*) in a slate-colored junco (*Junco hyemalis*). With H.E. Paterson and the noted South African entomologist Botha de Meillon, he documented the occurrence of arboviruses in mosquitoes in Tongaland (KwaZulu-Natal), South Africa (1956-1960). Worth, Bruce M. McIntosh, and Robert H. Kokernot isolated Semliki Forest virus from mosquitoes collected in Portuguese East Africa (now the Republic of Mozambique), that virus having been isolated previously only in Uganda. Worth eventually worked with Downs, Anderson, Spence, and Aitken in Trinidad, conducting experimental infection studies with arboviruses isolated there. Worth, a true naturalist, wrote several superb books on natural history (*A naturalist in Trinidad, The nature of living things* [with Robert K. Enders], *Mosquito safari: a naturalist in South Africa,* and *Nature living*).

Succeeding Spence as director, Elisha Seujit Tikasingh (Figure 88) continued and extended the work begun years before. He trained in entomology, parasitology, and zoology and focused these interests on arbovirology. Having worked at both the Trinidad Regional Virus Laboratory and the Caribbean Epidemiology Centre, he was responsible for studies of malaria and other vector-borne diseases of the

Figure 88. Elisha Seujit Tikasingh (1927 -)
(image courtesy of Elisha Tikasingh)

Caribbean area, but his work with arboviruses became his first love. His contribution to the development of more readily available antibody reagents secured his reputation. With Spence and Downs, they described a technique for the production of large volumes of antibody using a transplantable ascites-producing carcinoma (Sarcoma-180 TG cells) in laboratory mice. They discovered that as the malignancies developed in mice, these rapidly multiplying cells produced ascites, an accumulation of fluid in the abdominal cavity. They then modified that method to prepare inocula that included Freund's complete adjuvant (inactivated and dried mycobacteria in oil emulsified with water) for production of large quantities (up to 30 ml per mouse) of immune ascitic fluids, rather than simply immune serum (1 ml maximum per mouse). That technique is no longer in use because it can cause necrosis of tissues at the site of injection, which results in considerable distress to the mice. Today, researchers use other, less hazardous adjuvants instead.

Before that method was available, antibodies were produced painstakingly (for the laboratory worker) by immunizing a few laboratory animals at a time, which resulted in only relatively small volumes of serum containing antibody. The production of larger volumes allowed for greater uniformity and greater volumes distributed for use in quality control studies. Tikasingh's book on arbovirus studies in the Caribbean area is well worth reading, as it documents the history of that laboratory and its many findings.

Figure 89. John Payne Woodall (1935 -)
(image courtesy of John Woodall)

One of the many viruses discovered by Anderson, Spence, Downs, and Aitken during the arbovirological surveys at the Trinidad Regional Virus Laboratory in Trinidad was Oropouche virus, first isolated from a forest worker with a mild and brief febrile illness in 1955. The virus was isolated from mosquitoes of various species in the forest where the patient was living and later was shown to be related to Simbu virus, the prototype virus of the Simbu group of African and Asian orthobunyaviruses. Antibody surveys indicated that humans and monkeys had been infected with Oropouche virus.

Over time since then, thousands and sometimes tens of thousands of human cases of Oropouche virus infection have been recorded in outbreaks and epidemics in urban and rural population centers in many states of Brazil, in Panama in 1989, and in the Amazon region of Peru in 1992 and 1994. The virus has been isolated in Surinam and some evidence suggests its presence in Amazonian Ecuador. Further investigations have shown that *Culicoides paraensis* is the principal urban vector and that it persists in a sylvatic cycle involving primates and possibly wild birds and sloths. Larvae of these midges develop in water trapped in husks of coconuts and stalks of bananas either under cultivation or after being harvested. Such information could lead to the development of programs to control the vector and, therefore, the virus and the disease.

Several others laboratories were in the Rockefeller system. A laboratory in Belém, Brazil, established jointly with the Special Service for

Figure 90. (l. to r.) Jordi Casals-Ariet (Yale University), Francisco de Paulo Pinheiro (Evandro Chagas Institute, Belem, Brazil), Charles Calisher (Centers for Disease Control and Prevention), and Paul Bres (World Health Organization) at the International Symposium on Tropical Arboviruses and Hemorrhagic Fevers, Belem, Brazil, 1980.
(image courtesy of Barry J. Beaty)

Public Health of Brazil at the Institute Evandro Chagas, was directed first by Ottis and Calista Causey, thereafter by Robert Shope, John P. Woodall (Figure 89), Francisco de P. Pinheiro (Figure 90), Amelia Paes de Andrade Travassos da Rosa (Figure 91), and now Pedro Vasconcelos (Figure 92). Other laboratories included those in Cali, Colombia, at the Universidad del Valle, (Guy Hayes, Patrick Owens, and Farzam Arbab); Ibadan, Nigeria, at the University of Ibadan and the Federal Ministry of Health, Abuja (Akinyele Fabiyi; Figure 53), Abdulsalam Nasidi, Oyewale Tomori (Figure 93), and Peter M. Tukei); Poona (now Pune), India (Khorshed M. Pavri; Figure 94); with offices also in Johannesburg, Republic of South Africa (formerly the Union of South Africa), Rio de Janiero, Brazil, and Cairo, Egypt. Workers in each of these laboratories made seminal discoveries, with the individuals who labored on all this providing more and more information. By appropriating funds for many efforts outside the United States, the

Figure 91. Amélia Paes de Andrade Travassos da Rosa (1937 -)
(image courtesy of Amélia Travassos da Rosa)

Figure 92. Pedro Fernando da Costa Vasconcelos (1957 -)
(image courtesy of Pedro Vasconcelos)

International Health Commission (later Board), was launching the basis for foundation activities in international public health.

In Canada, arbovirologists have collaborated closely with other virologists and with physicians, epidemiologists and entomologists for many years to diagnose, survey, and otherwise investigate the many aspects of the many arboviruses found there. Harvey Artsob (Figure 95), Serge Belloncik, Reinhart A. Brust, Althea N. Burton, Max A. Chernesky, Michael A. Drebot (Figure 95), John O. Iversen, G. Donald Kettyls, Robbin Lindsay, John A. McKiel, Donald M. McLean (Figure 96), Odosca Morgante, and many others directed or participated in these studies. Some continue to pursue answers to diagnostic and epidemiologic questions such that now at least 18 arboviruses and other arthropod-associated viruses, some associated with human, livestock or wildlife disease, others not (yet?), have been found in Canada: St. Louis encephalitis, West Nile, Powassan, eastern equine encephalitis, western equine encephalitis, California encephalitis, snowshoe hare, Jamestown Canyon, Northway, Cache Valley, Turlock, epizootic hemorrhagic disease 2, Colorado tick fever, Avalon, Bauline, Great Island, Flanders, Manitoba, the recently detected Calbertado,

Figure 93. Oyewale Tomori (1946 -)
(image courtesy of Oyewale Tomori)

Figure 94. Khorshed Minocher Pavri (1927 -)
(image courtesy of Korshed Pavri)

Figure 95. Mike Alexander Drebot (1959 -) and Harvey Artsob (1945 -)
(image courtesy of Mike Drebot)

and bluetongue, dengue and Lassa (the latter imported only) viruses. Many of these viruses were first detected in Canada, and some have been found only in Canada. Canadian researchers have, of course, a particular interest in whether viruses found in Canada cause human

Figure 96. Donald Millis McLean (1926 -)
(image courtesy of Donald McLean)

disease there and in determining the Canadian virological burden, how to diagnose diseases they cause, and the effects of these diseases on wildlife and livestock. In land area, Canada is the second largest country in the world, its range of habitats, ecosystems, and climatic conditions present interesting challenges to those who conduct field studies there.

Born in Melbourne, Australia, Donald M. McLean obtained a doctorate of medicine from the University of Melbourne in 1950, and later became a Fellow of The Royal College of Physicians of Canada and a Fellow of the Royal College of Pathologists in England. During his virology training with Nobelist Sir Frank Macfarlane Burnet at the Walter and Eliza Hall Institute at the University of Melbourne, he was first to demonstrate mosquito transmission of the then recently isolated Murray Valley encephalitis virus. McLean worked with Max Theiler and Loring Whitman at the Rockefeller Foundation, with Carl M. Eklund (Figure 68) at the Rocky Mountain Laboratories of NIH, and with Jerome T. Syverton at the University of Minnesota. At Cambridge University, England, with Michael Stoker, McLean was first to identify human echovirus 9 as a cause of aseptic meningitis. Shortly after his appointment as virologist at the Hospital for Sick Children in Toronto in 1958, he isolated and identified Powassan virus as the cause of encephalitis in a human and as the first tick-borne flavivirus in the Western Hemisphere, after which he demonstrated its transmission in a tick-mammal natural cycle. He tirelessly studied numerous viral agents as possible causes of aseptic meningitis, taught virology at the University of Toronto and later at the University of British Columbia and wrote textbooks for students and others regarding the history of virology, laboratory diagnosis of viral infections, and methods used for diagnosis.

His elucidation of the transmission cycle of snowshoe hare orthobunyavirus and of its transovarial transmission confirmed earlier studies with other California serogroup viruses and reflected a classic example of a researcher's persistence and stamina. In May 1974 McLean collected *Aedes communis* larvae from water of the frozen Marsh Lake in the Yukon Territory (daily maximum temperature 13.1°C) and isolated snowshoe hare virus from some of them, a landmark finding because it made clear at least one over-wintering mechanism for this virus

A native of Germany, Heinz Feldmann received his B.Sc. in 1981 from the University of Giessen, Germany, then graduated from Medical School at the University of Marburg in 1987 and earned a Ph.D. in 1988 from that University. His postdoctoral research was on filoviruses and hantaviruses at the Institute of Virology, University of Marburg, Germany, and later at the Special Pathogens Branch, CDC Atlanta, where he held a fellowship from the United States National Research Council. In Atlanta he worked on molecular characteristics and diagnostics of hantaviruses and other dangerous pathogens, later moving to the Department of Medical Microbiology at the University of Manitoba to work with viruses requiring high or maximum containment. He was chief of the Special Pathogens Program at the National Microbiology Laboratory, Public Health Agency of Canada and holds an adjunct appointment with the Department of Pathology at the University of Texas Medical Branch, Galveston. A laboratory expert on high containment (exotic, hazardous) viruses, he serves as a consultant on viral hemorrhagic fevers to the W.H.O., is a member of national and international professional societies, edits for *Archives of Virology* and other journals, and serves on the editorial board of several virology journals. As do many others, he also acts as an invited reviewer for journals from related fields. He is an external scientific reviewer for national and international organizations and serves as a scientific consultant for high containment laboratories. His professional interest is the pathogenesis of hemorrhagic fever viruses, such as the ebolaviruses, Lassa virus, and hantaviruses, and other viruses requiring high security. He has been awarded several honors including the Loffler-Frosch Award from the German Society for Virology and the Arnold Wedum Memorial Lecture Award from the American Biological Safety Association. At this time Feldmann is Chief of the Laboratory of Virology at the National Institutes of Health facility in Hamilton, Montana, continuing to study the pathogenetic processes of these important and hazardous pathogens and how to diagnose them.

Robert E. Shope was the fulcrum of arbovirology for more than three decades. Born in Princeton, New Jersey, the son of Richard E. Shope, the internationally renowned virologist mentioned previously. He received B.A. and M.D. degrees from Cornell University and completed an internship in internal medicine at Grace-New Haven Hospital (Yale University School of Medicine). He then spent three years in the U.S. Army Medical Corps where he was initially assigned to Camp Detrick (now the U.S. Army Medical Research Institute for Infectious Diseases) and later to the U.S. Army Medical Research Unit in Kuala Lumpur, Malaysia. The latter experience included studies of the etiology of fevers of unknown origin among British soldiers and the local Malaysian civilian population. This experience had a profound effect on his subsequent research interests and career decisions. As most of the senior staff of the Rockefeller Foundation's overseas virus program were relocating to Yale University and were establishing the Yale Arbovirus Research Unit, it became the pre-eminent arbovirus research center for the benefit of the world.

After beginning a residency in internal medicine at Yale and then studying under the guidance of Max Theiler, Shope took a staff position with the Rockefeller Foundation's International Virus Program at its laboratory in Belém, Brazil, now the Evandro Chagas Institute,

Figure 97. Rebeca Rico-Hesse (1955 -)
(image courtesy of Rebecca Rico-Hesse)

Figure 98. Thomas Wallace Scott (1950 -)
(image courtesy of Thomas Scott)

remaining there for six years and eventually serving as Director of the laboratory. Returning to the Yale laboratories, Shope worked with Aitken, Anderson, Buckley, Casals, Clarke, Downs, Theiler, Whitman and Woodall. He later served as mentor or advisor (usually both) to many of the subsequent generation of arbovirologists, including Barry Beaty, Rebecca Rico-Hesse (Figure 97), Dennis Knudson, Peter Mason, Barry Miller, Thomas Schwann, Thomas Scott (Figure 98), Robert Tesh and Mark Wilson. Shope remained at Yale for 30 years, rising to full professor and serving for many years as director of the Yale Arbovirus Research Unit.

In 1995, Shope and Robert Tesh left Yale and moved to the University of Texas Medical Branch at Galveston to begin a new phase in their remarkable careers. At the Galveston laboratories Shope expanded his interests from arboviruses to include other emerging infectious diseases, global warming and biodefense. At the time of his death in 2004, he held appointments as professor in the Departments of Pathology, Microbiology and Immunology, and Preventive Medicine and Community Health. Shope also was an active member of the W.H.O. Collaborative Center for Tropical Diseases, the Sealy Center of Structural Biology, and the Center for Emerging Infectious Diseases and Biodefense and held the John S. Dunn Distinguished Chair in Biodefense. In November 2003, the Galveston medical center inaugurated a new biosafety level 4 maximum security laboratory, the first at an academic institution in the U.S.A., and named it in his honor ("Robert E. Shope, M.D., Laboratory"). Shope's long-time associate, Robert Tesh, wrote the following obituary for Shope:

> "It is difficult to succinctly describe Shope's many contributions to infectious diseases, public health and biomedical research, because they are so numerous and varied. During the past 50 years, he has played leadership roles in the fields of virology, tropical medicine, infectious disease epidemiology, and international health. Perhaps his most important contribution was co-chairmanship, along with Nobelist Joshua Lederberg, of the U.S. Institute of Medicine's Committee on Emerging Microbial Threats to Health. This effort resulted in the publication in 1992 of the book entitled Emerging Infections: Microbial Threats to Health in the United States. This seminal publication, which was co-authored with Drs. Lederberg and Stanley C. Oaks, Jr., reported on the committee's deliberations and outlined the factors that were implicated in the emergence of infectious diseases in the U.S.; publication of that book initiated much of the current worldwide interest in emerging and reemerging infectious diseases.
>
> Although the concept of "emerging diseases" was new to many in the scientific, medical and public health communities at that time, it was always a major focus of Shope's research, since he began his career as a young staff member with the Rockefeller Foundation. His first assignment with the Foundation in New York in 1954 was to study the etiology of "epidemic polyarthritis", a disease characterized by fever, arthralgia and rash that occurred mainly during the summer months in Australia. In a classical retrospective serologic investigation, he and S.G. Anderson demonstrated that the disease was caused by an alphavirus. Ten years later, Australian scientists isolated

Ross River virus and confirmed the association with epidemic polyarthritis.

After assignment to Brazil, he succeeded Ottis Causey as director of the Rockefeller Foundation's program of arbovirus research in the Amazon region. During his tenure, the laboratory in Belém isolated and characterized more than 50 tropical arboviruses, including some that were completely new to science. Several, such as the viruses of groups C and Guama caused human disease. Not only did he play a role in isolating and characterizing these agents and their diseases, but his team was instrumental in studying and understanding the role of forest reservoirs [of the viruses]. He refined the capture-mark-release-recapture technology for rodents, marsupials, and birds, and applied these methods to the Amazon fauna. His team also correlated the vertebrate ecology with virus infection of the Amazonian mosquitoes. He personally identified Oropouche virus when the first epidemic caused by this virus struck the city of Belém. This disease has since emerged as a major scourge, not only in the Brazilian Amazon, but also in cities in Panama and Peru.

In this same six-year time span, he also completed classic serological studies showing for the first time, the existence of a Venezuelan encephalitis complex of viruses and the group relationships of Junin virus, the etiologic agent of Argentine hemorrhagic fever, with other arenaviruses.

During his early tenure at Yale, Shope was involved in a collaborative project with the Smithsonian Institution and discovered multiple new arboviruses transported by birds migrating through the Nile River delta. He continued to be directly involved in the characterization of emerging pathogens. Lassa fever and yellow fever emerged in Nigeria in 1969, occupying his research efforts; and he played a major role in the establishment of the W.H.O. World Reference Center for Arboviruses during the 1960's. For a time, Yale became known as the preferred site for training in arbovirology, and a generation of students and post-doctoral fellows followed during the period when he was director of the Yale Arbovirus Research Unit.

Viruses and newly recognized diseases continued to emerge. Among other pioneering discoveries and concepts by Shope was that of the rabies virus-related viruses. In 1970, he and Murphy showed the diversity of the lyssaviruses and recognized Mokola and Duvenhage, two new human pathogens that were rabies virus-like with regard to morphology and pathogenicity. In 1971, Shope, Murphy and Ernest Borden of the CDC described the bluetongue related viruses as a new taxonomic group; this subsequently became the *Orbivirus* genus. In 1971, Shope was also co-author on a rather obscure paper in the Indian Journal of Medical Research describing Thottapalayam virus, a presumed arbovirus isolated from a shrew in India. Thottapalayam virus was subsequently shown to be a hantavirus and actually was the first hantavirus to be isolated. Hantaan virus, the type species of the Hantavirus genus was not isolated until 1976 and was first reported in 1978.

In 1977, a post-doctoral fellow working in Shope's laboratory discovered the first ovine bluetongue virus in northern Australia, while studying a viral agent isolated from midges. This discovery caused economic turmoil in the Australian sheep industry, but it was seminal in the initiation of an intensive research program in Australia, where sheep are a major export product.

That same year, Shope and James Meegan identified Rift Valley fever virus as the cause of an epidemic in Egypt in which 200,000 people and a much greater number of sheep and cattle were infected. There were at least 600 human deaths. This disease emerged in virgin territory and in an immunologically naïve population. Shope also was the first to demonstrate that Rift Valley fever virus was a member of the genus *Phlebovirus*.

It is noteworthy that in 1977, Shope also co-authored the first description of Lyme disease in the U.S. This was a brief sojourn into bacterial diseases of Connecticut with Allan Steere, then a young rheumatologist at Yale School of Medicine, who had just completed two years as an EIS officer at the CDC. Lyme disease has subsequently emerged as the most important tick-borne disease in North America, and its complex course and varied clinical manifestations are now well known to most vector biologists and specialists in infectious diseases.

During the last two decades of his life, Shope and his associates continued to discover new viruses. These included Lassa virus, Sabia virus, the cause of Brazilian hemorrhagic fever, and Guanarito virus, the cause of Venezuelan hemorrhagic fever. The latter arenavirus disease has a case fatality rate of about 30%. In addition, he worked extensively in developing an attenuated dengue vaccine. For 12 years, he chaired the W.H.O. Peer Advisory Committee on dengue vaccine development in Thailand, where a new candidate tetravalent vaccine was developed and field-tested. During the mid-1990's he chaired the Flavivirus Steering Committee of the W.H.O. Programme for Vaccine Development in Geneva. After moving to Galveston, he embarked on a new phase of his career with the support of the U.S. Defense Advanced Research Project Agency and the CDC. He and colleagues started new programs to develop countermeasures to combat bioterrorism and to develop novel anti-viral approaches to diseases caused by alphaviruses, flaviviruses, and arenaviruses. This research is a novel blend of classical virology, cutting-edge molecular biology, and structural biology for the discovery of new strategies for the control of these agents.

Shope was also an outstanding, devoted and beloved teacher. He cared deeply about education and training; infectious viral diseases, epidemiology and public health were his expertise. His extensive knowledge, honesty, humility and supportive manner endeared him to his students, who had come from all over the world to learn at the elbows of the master. He treated everyone with respect and was never too busy to meet with a student or to offer guidance for he saw students as the future.

> In addition to his research and teaching, he also served as consultant and advisor to many national and international organizations. During the decade before his death, he served on expert committees advising the U.S. Government on such major public health issues as emerging infectious diseases, bioterrorism and the potential health consequences of global climate change. Throughout his career he was a frequent advisor on infectious diseases and virology to the NIH, CDC, Department of Defense, U.S. Department of Agriculture, U.S. Agency for International Development, Institute of Medicine and American Type Culture Collection. He also was a frequent consultant to the W.H.O. and the Pan American Health Organization as well as to a large number of foreign governments. Because of his broad experience and knowledge, as well as his enthusiastic and supportive demeanor, he was much in demand and highly effective as an advisor and lecturer. His enthusiasm and love for his chosen field were as infectious as the viruses he studied, and he made a lasting and positive impression on his colleagues and students. Those of us who know him and worked with him were very fortunate."

Shope had an encyclopedic knowledge of arboviruses, rodent-borne viruses, and many other viruses and he enthusiastically shared what he knew with anyone who inquired. It is likely that everyone who met Shope recognized his scientific acumen and remarkable personality, such that he was elected President of the American Society for Tropical Medicine and Hygiene, and was given the Bailey K. Ashford Award, the Richard M. Taylor Award, (nine of whose recipients had been or were to be Presidents of the American Society for Tropical Medicine and Hygiene), and the Walter Reed Medal, among other prestigious awards and citations. Still, no words and titles could begin to describe this honest, charming, and unfailingly pleasant man. A list of hundreds of publications, hundreds of consultations, thousands of collaborations, and endless hours writing, editing, and providing a level head and excellent ideas at all-too-often boring and unproductive committee meetings, would not describe him. Shope was the gold standard for two generations of arbovirologists and for humans in general.

Many years ago, Shope and I were invited to Bogota, Colombia, by the Colombian Government and the Pan-American Health Organization to present a course on methods for diagnosis of arbovirus infections. One evening, while we were walking to a restaurant in a crowded part of the city, someone bumped into Bob and stole his passport. Soon after Bob realized the loss and we went to a police station to make a report. The police were very kind but not very helpful, so the next day I taught the course while Bob attempted to find out what to do when a passport and visa have been stolen: report the loss to the United States Embassy. I accompanied Bob while he was interviewed by an Embassy staff member, who asked Bob questions that would likely be answerable by U.S. citizens: How many home runs did Babe Ruth hit in his record year? Can you name one of Elvis Presley's recorded hit songs? Who is the U.S. Secretary of State? Can you name any model of a Buick automobile? Bob did not know the answer to any of those questions and told the man that if that was what it would take to certify him as a United States citizen he likely was not going to get back home. Bob asked the gentleman to name 25 Nobel Prize winners in Medicine or Physiology. He did not know; Bob did, and obtained his new passport and visa after that.

Shope told me that when he was a child in Princeton, New Jersey, where his father worked for the Rockefeller Foundation, his next door neighbor was a nice gentleman with wild hair who tossed a baseball with him from time to time. Of course, it was only later that he learned the neighbor was Albert Einstein and what he represented.

John P. Woodall is another of the many experienced, resourceful and accomplished arbovirologists. He was born in what was then British territory in Tientsin (Tianjin), China, a third generation member of a British family in China. After graduating from Cambridge University, in 1958 he obtained a Ph.D. degree from the London School of

Hygiene and Tropical Medicine at London University. Her Majesty's Overseas Research Service appointed him to the East Africa Virus Research Institute in Entebbe, Uganda, where he stayed long enough to help describe the epidemic of fever caused by o'nyong-nyong alphavirus with Miles C. Williams and Alexander J. Haddow and the isolation of Congo virus (now Crimean-Congo hemorrhagic fever nairovirus) with Williams and David I. Simpson. In 1963 Woodall traveled to the Rockefeller Foundation virus laboratories in New York City for additional training, remaining to become a staff member of the Foundation. Later he was appointed director of the Foundation's virus laboratory in Belém, Brazil. His arbovirological accomplishments there included not only virus isolations, but summarizing and documenting the distribution of the arboviruses of Brazil.

After spending another year with the Foundation when it moved its arbovirus laboratories to Yale University, the peripatetic Woodall moved to the New York State Department of Health Laboratories in Albany, New York, as head of its arbovirus laboratory. Then, from 1975 to 1983 he worked for the United States Centers for Disease Control and Prevention, being stationed in Puerto Rico as the director of the San Juan Laboratories, then taking an assignment at W.H.O., Geneva. He returned to Albany in 1994 as director of the state arbovirus laboratory, but eventually settled at Brazil's Federal University of Rio de Janiero in its Institute of Biomedical Sciences. Woodall was one of the founding members of ProMED-mail, the Program for Monitoring Emerging Diseases, an invaluable internet-based reporting system that rapidly and globally disseminates information on outbreaks of infectious diseases, and which appears in many of our mailboxes each day. He remains an active editor of ProMED-mail and an enthusiastic supporter of the need for rapid, accurate (honest), and complete disease reporting.

Francisco de Paulo Pinheiro became the Pan-American Health Organization's Chief of Viral Diseases, and Travassos da Rosa moved to the University of Texas Medical Branch at Galveston. Before they left Belém, however, they sustained and considerably expanded the work of their Rockefeller Foundation predecessors by continuing the virus isolation work that has been so fruitful, by investigating outbreaks of human disease and by formulating epidemiological hypotheses as to how these viruses emerge from their natural cycles to cause disease. Pedro Vasconcelos put all this on a more forward-looking basis, incorporating molecular methods, while at the same time continuing in the grand tradition of that institute.

Other arbovirologists in Brazil have included Oscar de Souza Lopes and Terezhina Lisieux M. Coimbra of the Instituto Adolfo Lutz, São Paulo, Lyggia B. Iversson of the Department of Epidemiology, Faculty of Public Health, University of São Paulo and Luiz Tadeu Moraes Figueiredo of the Faculty of Medicine of Ribeirão Preto, Universidade de São Paulo, Ribeirão Preto. Not only did they discover many previously unrecognized arboviruses, including the human pathogen Rocio flavivirus, but they also followed up with epidemiologic studies of those virus infections and investigated the molecular characteristics of some of them, principally those of yellow fever virus.

Amélia Paes de Andrade Travassos da Rosa was the mainstay of the arbovirological competence in Brazil through many years and all the recent as well as remote administrative changes. She is now a research associate in the Department of Pathology, Center for Tropical Diseases, University of Texas Medical Branch at Galveston. Devoted to her work and to her supervisors and mentors, Travassos da Rosa was born in Belém, obtained a B.S. in Pharmacy at the Federal University of Para in Belém, and then specialized in medical microbiology and general immunology at the Federal University of Rio de Janiero. Beginning her professional career as an employee of the Evandro Chagas Institute in Belém in 1959, she rose from serologist to Chief of the Virology Section, the person responsible for the W.H.O. Collaborating Centre for Arbovirus Reference and Research. During those years she was directly involved in tens of thousands of isolations of viruses from mosquitoes, ticks, culicoids, birds, rodents, bats, livestock and, of course, humans. Her meticulous care for the records in pre-computer days, her knowledge of the biological characteristics and geographic origins of the viruses is legendary, and her devotion to virus taxonomy is appreciated by all. Perhaps one day she will write a history of Brazilian arbovirology.

The impact of the Rockefeller Foundation, on public health as well as on medical education, food production, scientific advancement, social research, the arts, and other fields world-wide should not be minimized. The Foundation was established to "promote the well-being of mankind throughout the world." In keeping with this commitment, the Foundation gave important assistance to its International Health Division, expanding the work of the Sanitary Commission worldwide, which had so much to do with the control and, in some areas, eradication of yellow fever. The Foundation eventually found itself working on diseases in 52 countries on six continents and many island groups. It has been recognized as the foremost organization publicizing the need for international efforts to improve public health and environmental sanitation. Its early field research on yellow fever, hookworm, and malaria provided basic techniques intended to control these diseases and established a template for modern public health services. The Rockefeller Foundation built and endowed the world's first School of Hygiene and Public Health at The Johns Hopkins University in Baltimore, Maryland, and then spent millions of dollars to develop public health schools in the United States and in 21 other countries. Its agricultural development program in Mexico led to what has been called the Green Revolution in the advancement of food production around the world, and the Foundation provided much of the funding for the International Rice Research Institute in the Philippines. Scientists and scholars from all over the world have received Rockefeller Foundation funding for advanced studies in many fields. The Rockefeller Foundation's search for yellow fever in far-flung places yielded new knowledge and developed techniques that were valuable to many disease studies.

Gilbert Dalldorf, Bugher, Casals, Lennette, Koprowski, Theiler, and Webster each made contributions that were central to the generation of assays that allowed much more precise measurements of the amount of virus in samples than were previously possible. A relatively inexpensive and simple tool became available with the discovery of hemagglutination by Hirst and its application to both hemagglutination-inhibition tests for antibody to viruses and to the study of virus-cell attachment mechanisms. Subsequently, Sabin and Buescher and Clarke and Casals applied this method as well as complement-fixation and neutralization to epidemiological and laboratory studies of arboviruses and arboviral diseases. Worldwide studies of arboviruses, supported by the Rockefeller Foundation, led to the discovery of newly recognized viruses and their geographic distributions. Later, electron microscopic studies by Ian H. Holmes and Murphy corroborated the antigenic studies of Casals, Shope, and others, and the cascade of information about the molecular characteristics and genomic sequences of viruses subsequently provided powerful additional analytical tools.

The Middle East has been the location of many arboviral epidemics. Therefore, arbovirological expertise exists in a few Middle Eastern countries, notably in Israel and Egypt, but also in Saudi Arabia, Iraq, and Iran (where a Pasteur Institute, founded more than 90 years ago, continues to function as a diagnostic and research center). In addition to Medhat A. Darwish at Ain Shams University School of Medicine, Cairo, and Imam Z.E. Imam at the Egyptian Organization for Biological Preparations and Vaccines, Cairo, the great entomologist Harry Hoogstraal at the United States Naval Medical Research Unit No. 3, Cairo, made major contributions..

In Israel, studies of a wide variety of viruses affecting humans, livestock and wild life have been carried out for decades. Newly and previously recognized arboviruses have been detected and studied by Natan Goldblum at the Hebrew University-Hadassah Medical School, Jerusalem; Yehuda Nir and Robert Goldwasser at the Israel Institute for Biological Research, Ness-Ziona; Yechiel Becker at the Hebrew University of Jerusalem; Yehuda Braverman, Mertyn Malkinson, and Ben Ami Peleg at the Kimron Veterinary Institute, Bet Dagan; and Steven A. Berger at the Tel Aviv Medical Center. Although not widely publicized, it is a poorly kept secret that informal consultations and material aid frequently has been exchanged between otherwise adversarial neighbors in the Middle East, to the benefit of all sides.

An extensive epizoodemic appeared in five governates of Egypt in 1977, causing abortion storms and increased mortality in domestic animals, as well as severe disease and many fatalities in humans. Rift Valley fever virus was identified as the cause of this epidemic, which was characterized by patients with acute febrile illnesses, encephalitis, ocular manifestations, and fatal hemorrhagic illnesses. At least 200,000 human cases were estimated to have occurred, causing at least 598 deaths and leaving many survivors blind. A group led by James M. Meegan with the considerable assistance of Harry Hoogstraal, both of the United States Naval Medical Research Unit No. 3, Cairo, as well as many Egyptian and other investigators worked to address the problems. They reported clinical findings, developed antibody detection tests, and conducted experimental transmission studies and field isolations of Rift Valley fever virus, implicating *Culex pipiens* as the principal arthropod vector of the virus. Their studies determined the antigenic relationship of Rift Valley fever virus and other phleboviruses. Furthermore, using retrospective serologic surveys, they accumulated data suggesting not only that this virus had been introduced to Egypt recently, likely coming from Sudan, which had experienced an outbreak of Rift Valley fever in 1976. It is believed that environmental changes in Egypt, including the building of the Aswan High Dam and the subsequent inundation of 800,000 hectares for agricultural development between 1970 and 1977 contributed to ecologic alterations that established habitat in which Rift Valley fever virus could be amplified.

At first, the virus did not appear to have become enzootic in Egypt. However, in the summer and fall of 1978 epizootic Rift Valley fever reappeared in Egypt and spread to previously unaffected areas. Sporadic infections were reported to have occurred in 1980 but after that it was not detected again in Egypt until 1993 and again in 1997. As is usual in post-epidemic periods, a great deal of additional information has been accumulated regarding the geographic distribution of the virus, its reservoirs, the competence of potential vector arthropods to become infected and transmit the virus, virus persistence, virus genome sequencing, and so on. Rift Valley fever vaccine research is on-going and promising. The number of countries where Rift Valley fever virus has been reported has increased greatly, perhaps due to better surveillance, perhaps to incursions of the virus. At present, evidence suggests that Rift Valley fever virus likely occurs in all of tropical Africa.

As regards the persistence of the virus, it is now recognized that "dambos", shallow depressions in complex wetlands in certain parts of Africa, allow mosquito eggs to survive dry seasons and, if they were transovarially infected with Rift Valley fever virus, to initiate epizootics when they hatch, quest for blood meals, and feed on nearby sheep and cattle pastured in grasslands. Enormous numbers of virus-infected mosquitoes can be produced in this way. Thus the mosquito vector can be considered the reservoir of Rift Valley fever virus. In many parts of Africa, heavy rains occur only every few years, which may coincide with the intermittent appearance of Rift Valley fever virus because mosquito eggs require water to hatch.

The first confirmed Rift Valley fever outbreak outside Africa occurred in September 2000, in the Arabian Peninsula and ended in early 2001. In Saudi Arabia 884 patients were hospitalized, of whom 124 died. In Yemen 1,087 cases with 121 deaths occurred; however, it was estimated that the hospitalized cases represented only a small proportion of the actual cases and infections. A constellation of modern diagnostic methods and molecular tools allowed not only serologic diagnoses but comparisons of RNAs from many isolates of the virus. These indicated that little genetic variation existed among the isolates and showed that the viruses in Saudi Arabia and in Yemen were essentially identical to those associated with earlier Rift Valley fever epidemics in East Africa, suggesting that the virus had been introduced into the Arabian Peninsula shortly before the epidemics there. How the virus was introduced into the Arabian Peninsula is unknown, but via the commercial livestock trade from East Africa is a distinct possibility.

Other outbreaks of this disease have occurred in East Africa. During a 2006-2007 epidemic, researchers conducted spatial mapping of the outbreaks across Kenya, Somalia, and Tanzania and isolated and genetically characterized viruses from human cases, livestock cases, and mosquitoes. Seven geographical foci reporting hundreds of livestock and more than 25 cases in humans between December 2006 and June 2007 were identified. The onset of cases in each epidemic focus was recognized to occur after heavy rainfall and flooding that lasted for at least 10 days. Full-length genome analysis of 16 Rift Valley fever virus isolates recovered in five of the seven outbreak foci revealed three distinct lineages of the viruses within and across outbreak foci. The findings indicated that multiple lineages of the virus, either independently activated or introduced to distinct outbreak foci, caused the sequential Rift Valley fever epidemics in the region. Natural introductions of this virus to livestock and humans in the Middle East and Europe and unnatural introductions of the virus elsewhere remain a threat.

Meegan went on to work at the Yale Arbovirus Research Unit and Yale University School of Medicine, headed the program for research on emerging viral diseases and viral vaccines at the World Health Organization and, after 13 years with the National Institute of Allergy and Infectious Diseases (NIAID) at the National Institutes of Health, headed the research team at Invitrogen's Biological Defense Systems.

In the 1930s it was found that young or adult albino mice were susceptible to many viruses. When inoculated with virus directly in the brain, they became sick, with paralysis of the limbs and other signs of encephalitis. Workers at the Rockefeller Foundation not only studied the pathology of these viruses but used the mouse model to devise a test that would detect antibody in humans and other vertebrates. They mixed measured amounts of virus with serum from patients or healthy people or wild animals, inoculated the mixture into mice, and waited to see whether the mice would die. If they died, then the serum did not contain antibody to the virus. If they did not die, then the serum had "neutralized" the virus.

In this way they not only determined the presence of antibodies, the sign of previous infection with that virus, but determined how much virus the undiluted serum would neutralize, i.e., the potency of the antibody, a "virus-dilution neutralization" test. Later, however, "serum-dilution neutralization" tests were employed. This change was diagnostically useful as well as historically significant. The virus-neutralization test determines how much virus is neutralized, the serum-dilution neutralization test determines how much a given serum can be diluted and still neutralize a particular virus; the two should not be confused. The serum-dilution neutralization test required far less serum than did the virus-dilution neutralization test, which made it more convenient and more practical and adaptable to modern dilution tools. However, it should be understood that virus-dilution neutralization test results are more "real world" in that those results give an indication of the protective capacity of a serum (a clinically-relevant index), rather than a dilution (a diagnostically-relevant titer). It matters much more that a patient's undiluted serum can neutralize 1,000 infectious virions than that that serum can be diluted 1:10,000 and still neutralize 100 infectious virions, the standard dose used in such tests. For diagnosis, however, serum-dilution neutralization test results are more clear-cut and more sensitive.

Armed with the neutralization test, Rockefeller Foundation workers surveyed human populations as well as monkeys and other vertebrates and determined where yellow fever virus occurred, in which species it occurred, when it occurred, and under what circumstances it amplified to cause outbreaks or epidemics. Workers surveyed populations throughout the world. The results showed that the original observations of the United States Army Commission in Cuba were correct: *Aedes aegypti* mosquitoes were infected with and could transmit yellow fever virus and mosquitoes of other species also could become infected and transmit the virus.

A bonus was that this technique could help make a "serodiagnosis" of infection in patients with yellow fever. Paired serum samples, the first taken in the acute phase of illness (within a week or so after onset) and the second taken in the convalescent phase of illness (usually at least two to three weeks after onset), were tested by this "constant serum-virus dilution" method and significant changes in potency of the antibody were considered diagnostically meaningful. A problem with the "constant serum-virus dilution" method was the volume of (undiluted) serum needed and the fact that the technique was not terribly useful for diagnosis, although it provided a measure of protectivity, i.e., indicated how much virus this patient's serum could neutralize. It was not long before a "constant virus-serum dilution" assay was developed, because it is much easier to amplify virus than to obtain blood from patients (humans, small vertebrates, and others). Today, researchers use cell cultures rather than laboratory mice or other indicator vertebrate hosts for virus neutralization tests.

One of the first arboviruses that had been isolated was a member of the bluetongue serogroup. This virus was isolated from pooled ("combined") sheep bloods collected in 1901-1902 in South Africa, which at the time was called "Cape Colony". In the 1920s, yellow fever virus was isolated in Nigeria, louping ill virus in Scotland, and vesicular stomatitis Indiana virus in the United States. In the 1930s, as virus isolation techniques became more widely used and more uniform, Rift Valley fever, African horse sickness, West Nile, Japanese encephalitis, Russian Spring-Summer encephalitis, eastern equine encephalitis, western equine encephalitis, Venezuelan equine encephalitis, St. Louis encephalitis, and Bwamba viruses were isolated for the first time. Clearly, disease in humans, in livestock and in other vertebrates spurred attempts to isolate these viruses and, coincidentally, other viruses were found. Investigators throughout the world worked in relative isolation from one another. Contacts and communications were infrequent and difficult, and scientific exchange was accomplished mostly by letter. Given these circumstances, irregularly held scientific meetings afforded the most regular contact.

From the early days of yellow fever studies and for many years after, arboviruses were nearly always isolated in adult or weanling mice. Gilbert Dalldorf, using suckling (1-day-old or 2- to 4-day-old) mice, successfully isolated viruses from stool samples of humans in Coxsackie, New York. As some of the people from whom these viruses were obtained had had signs and symptoms analogous to those of people with poliomyelitis, it was clear that these coxsackieviruses (which are enteroviruses, not arboviruses) were causing a poliomyelitis-like disease. This finding opened a Pandora's box of enteroviruses, some associated with illnesses in humans and other vertebrates, some not. It became abundantly clear that the surface had been merely scratched and that the numerous viruses identified at the Rockefeller Foundation laboratories in the Americas and in Africa had demonstrated just how many viruses might still be unrecognized.

With Rockefeller Foundation-supported laboratories in Rio de Janeiro, Bahia, and Belém (Brazil), Yaba and Ibadan (Nigeria), Port-of-Spain (Trinidad), Johannesburg (South Africa), Entebbe (Uganda), and Bogota (Colombia), attempts to isolate yellow fever virus often resulted in the isolation of other, previously unrecognized, viruses, many of which were associated with human illnesses.

At the laboratory in Belém, Ottis and Calista Causey, who were investigating yellow fever, adapted virus isolation techniques to include use of intracranial inoculation of suckling mice. With the increase in sensitivity provided by use of this laboratory host, researchers isolated hundreds of previously unrecognized viruses from mosquitoes and other arthropods, mammals, birds, cold-blooded vertebrates, and humans in the Old and New Worlds. The Belém laboratory alone has isolated thousands of viruses from field-collected specimens. Other Rockefeller Foundation laboratories isolated other viruses from other samples collected from nature. Fortuitously, the plethora of viruses isolated created another problem: Who would identify them all?

By 1944, when Edwin Lennette and Hilary Koprowski reported that suckling mice could act as hosts for neutralization tests for antibodies to eastern equine encephalitis, western equine encephalitis, and

Venezuelan equine encephalitis viruses, reliable diagnostic tools had been devised to track yellow fever and other, newly emerging, arboviral diseases. Collaborative efforts with French, Brazilian, Colombian, British, and other investigators revealed the geographic distribution of yellow fever and the presence of hundreds of other viruses.

Born in Viladrou, Spain, in 1936 Jordi Casals-Ariet obtained a fellowship from the City Council of Barcelona to study at the Rockefeller Institute in New York City. Francisco Duran-Reynals, a Spanish scientist working at the Rockefeller Institute, had become well known for the fundamental discovery of "spreading factor", hyaluronidase, which is responsible for increasing the permeability of connective tissue by depolymerizing its basic substance, hyaluronic acid, and thus for increasing the diffusion and passage into lymphatic capillaries of water, salts, metabolic products, and any bacteria that might be within range. Duran-Reynals tried to recruit Casals to return to Spain and assist in starting an institute similar to the Rockefeller Institute but Casals had arrived in New York City only months before the Spanish Civil War began and, for political reasons, could not return home after that. Instead, he stayed on and worked with Leslie Webster, which proved fortunate for arbovirology, virology, and science in general.

Casals and Webster found that, whereas antibody to rabies, poliomyelitis, and other viruses did not react serologically with each other or with other viruses that caused encephalitis, antigens and antibodies to Russian Spring-Summer encephalitis and louping ill viruses reacted with each other and with St. Louis encephalitis, Japanese encephalitis, and Murray Valley encephalitis viruses. But, Casals noted, antigenic proximity between these viruses varied; that is, though all were related, some were more distantly and some more closely related one to another.

Thereafter, Casals, along with Robert Shope, and others at the Rockefeller Foundation laboratories began to sort the numerous viruses arriving almost daily. Field laboratories did the best they could under the circumstances, identifying viruses that had been isolated by them previously and sending the others to New York. It quickly became obvious that more rapid techniques were required.

Long before he developed the live-attenuated poliomyelitis virus vaccine, Albert Sabin had produced hemagglutinins of yellow fever virus and dengue viruses and showed by hemagglutination-inhibition that these viruses were related to each other. Later, with Edward Buescher of the Unites States Army, Sabin demonstrated that the hemagglutination-inhibition test could be applied in the same way to other arboviruses. When Theiler suggested using hemagglutination-inhibition as a simple, rapid, and inexpensive serologic test for evidence of infection by arboviruses (J. Casals, personal communication, 1972), Casals and Lenore Brown fine-tuned the test and applied it to the general diagnosis of arbovirus infections, creating the *sine qua non* of serologic testing at the time by providing a method for simply and rapidly assessing antigenic similarities as well as differences between the viruses themselves. Rapid, simple, safe and effective, the hemagglutination-inhibition test served as a standard tool in arbovirology for many years, until it was superseded by other, more specific tests. It has not, however, been surpassed for simplicity or low cost.

Viruses, antigens, and antibodies of high titer (potency) are essential for detecting distant antigenic relationships between viruses. Therefore, following Dalldorf's findings, the report by Joseph Melnick and N. Ledinko in 1950 that coxsackieviruses replicate to high titer in newborn mice led Jordi Casals, Peter Olitsky and Ralph Anslow of the Rockefeller Foundation, to replace adult mice with newborn mice for production of arboviral reagents.

By 1951 Casals and coworkers adapted human poliomyelitis virus type 2 to replicate in newborn mice and developed a complement-fixation test to detect it. Similar applications of newborn mice to studies of arboviruses resulted in shorter incubation periods, higher titers, and more satisfactory polyclonal (multiply reactive) antibodies. Newborn mice and serologic tests became invaluable tools for studies of the many insect and vertebrate viruses being sent to the New York laboratories by investigators at the Rockefeller Foundation outposts throughout the world. Casals, Shope, Loring Whitman and their co-workers were in the unique position of having available not only a large number of viruses but superb reagents with which to compare them. They thus began the classical investigations so integral to our knowledge of the interrelationships among arboviruses and other viruses. In the hands of these now-legendary people, production of polyclonal antibodies was a meticulous task: amplify the virus in the brains of suckling mice, harvest the brains, and prepare the reagents.

As many as 50 litters of suckling mice were used for the production of a single virus, antigen or antibody reagent. Brains from some of these infected mice were pooled, and 10% suspensions of part of the pool prepared in a solution containing protein, to stabilize the virus. The suspensions were centrifuged to remove the larger particles and debris and the supernatant fluid dispensed in small quantities and frozen at very low temperatures. This was considered "stock" virus, with which subsequent work and further virus passage was done. Some of these original stocks still exist and are quite valuable because they were prepared at low mouse passages and therefore are most similar to the original virus isolates (portions of which were stored neat, as mouse brain tissue). Virus stocks were titrated in suckling mice by one or more routes of inoculation (intracranially, intraperitoneally, intramuscularly, and subcutaneously). In this way, basic biological characterization of the virus (pathogenicity, titer, stability, etc.) was determined and standard pools were available for further studies, either at the Rockefeller Foundation laboratories or at other collaborating research facilities. This was considered a "reference" activity and the products of the Rockefeller Foundation laboratories were considered the "gold standards" for the world.

Other portions of the brain pool were used for production of antibody to the virus. Antibody was produced in mice with mature immune systems (10- to 12-weeks of age) and immunization was by the intraperitoneal route. If the virus was pathogenic for older mice, the virus was inactivated using beta-propiolactone. More recently, beta-propiolactone has been recognized as a carcinogen and is suspected to be a gastrointestinal, liver, respiratory, and skin or sense organ toxicant. It has properly fallen into disuse, for the most part replaced by various other inactivating agents.

Unless a virus was extraordinarily pathogenic, subsequent doses of virus were not inactivated. Virus, killed or not, was administered to mice on days 0, 7, 14, and 21 (or a similar schedule), the mice sacrificed, and bloods collected from these "hyperimmunized" mice. These bloods were pooled, allowed to clot and centrifuged. The serum containing antibody was then collected, dispensed in small quantities, and frozen for storage and later use, such as determination of antibody titers by hemagglutination-inhibition, complement-fixation, and neutralization tests. Again, these sera served as reference reagents for investigators.

A further modification of the technique used for immunizing mice was that used to produce hyperimmune antibodies in mice given more than one virus. That is, mice were immunized with multiple viruses that were related to each other ("groups" or "serogroups"). In actuality, these groups reflected antigenic relationships, which in turn reflected differing genetic expressions (phenotypes) that were suspected but not known at the time. These antibody preparations, called "grouping fluids", could be used to detect the presence of antigens of viruses already recognized or of unrecognized viruses that were distant members of that particular group. For example, if mice were immunized with eastern equine encephalitis virus, western equine encephalitis virus, Venezuelan equine encephalitis virus, and Highlands J virus (all Group A arboviruses, now recognized as members of the family *Togaviridae*, genus *Alphavirus*) an alphavirus isolate could be recognized as such using this polyclonal grouping fluid, even though the mice used to prepare this immune fluid had not been immunized with the isolate.

When antibodies from mice immunized against viruses using Freund's adjuvant were still being produced, researchers could prepare large volumes of fluid containing antibody. These also were dispensed in small quantities for later testing, use, and distribution.

Tests such as hemagglutination-inhibition and complement-fixation require both antibody and viral antigens. The antibodies detected can be from humans or other vertebrates, as such tests are not host-specific. They can be collected during surveys ("serosurveys") or from patients, human or otherwise, for diagnostic purposes. With standardized and reliable reagents in hand, and led by Casals and Shope, workers began attempts to categorize scores of viruses and many hundreds of isolates of some of these viruses, which had originated in laboratories in the Rockefeller Foundation system.

The paucity of women mentioned in these summaries of arbovirology may be cause for dismay but should surprise no one. In the very early days of arbovirus discovery and investigation, women were excluded because of the social and professional traditions of the time. Field work was lonely and arduous, and women were not considered up to such tasks. As time passed and customs finally changed in many places, as wars took men away from home to fight and women replaced them in scientific fields as in all other fields of endeavor, an increasing number of women became involved in this research. Today, women play a central role in science, virology in general, and arbovirology in particular. If women are not as numerous in this field as are men, they are at least as prominent. These women include: Fatima Begum (Pakistan), Gilberta Bensabeth and Amelia P. Travassos da Rosa (Brazil), Jelka Vesenjak-Hirjan and Volga Punda (Croatia), Vlasta Danielova (Czech Republic), Patricia A. Nuttall (England), B. Rhese-Küpper (Germany), Khorshed Pavri (India), Paola Verani and Loredana Nicoletti (Italy), Dorothy King (Jamaica), Milota Grešíková, Helena Libíková, Magdalena Sekeyová, and Doubravka Málková (Slovakia), Sophia Gaidamovich (Russia), Barbara P. Hull (Trinidad), Carol D. Blair, Delphine H. Clarke, Laura D. Kramer, Ann M. Powers, Rebecca Rico-Hesse (United States), Marta S. Sabattini (Argentina), Martine Jozan Work (United States), and others mentioned elsewhere in this book. Their contributions, not as women but as arbovirologists, include discovering new viruses, conducting field work, sorting out the details of virus epidemiology, addressing clinical concerns, answering entomologic questions regarding virus transmission, adding to our knowledge of the molecular biology of viruses, and administrating laboratories, There are still other women, quite young and new to all this, who already are making contributions and who will undoubtedly make many more contributions in the future.

CHAPTER 6

Seminal discoveries

The fundamental concepts and early technical developments having been put in place, the time was right for arbovirologists to apply what had been learned to the epidemiologty and prevention of arboviral and other diseases. This not being an encyclopedia, there is no way for me to list all the critical, creative and influential findings that impacted the progress of arbovirology without turning this into a 2,000-page tome. Besides, Murphy has already listed many of them (see *Suggested Readings*).

The most significant findings had been the recognition of (1) diseases and the viruses associated with them, (2) the vectors of those viruses, (3) the epidemiologies of the diseases, and (4) the means to control the diseases and to prevent the suffering they cause. One of the early attempts to control disease through the control of disease vectors arose from the discovery that dichloro-diphenyl-trichloromethylmethane (DDT), which had been found by workers in the Swiss textile industry to kill moths, was effective in killing other insects, including lice, which were the known vectors of the bacterial pathogen causing louse-borne typhus. For this and more, Paul Hermann Müller received a Nobel Prize in Physiology or Medicine in 1948.

Used to control not only the mosquito vectors of malarial parasites but also the arthropod carriers of viruses causing sandfly fevers, DDT provided hope to all who desired a means of controlling the vectors of viruses and other pathogens. Unintended consequences of the use of DDT, including bioaccumulation and toxicity, would cause governments to ban its use, but the benefits of safely distributed pesticides were obvious.

Attempts have been made to produce vaccines to protect against infection with yellow fever, eastern equine encephalitis, western equine encephalitis, Venezuelan equine encephalitis, Japanese encephalitis, Rift Valley fever, and tick-borne encephalitis viruses. Recent molecular discoveries allow the construction of novel vaccines now being tested for efficacy. Ribavirin, a nucleoside analogue, is recognized as an effective antiviral against some disease agents. In addition, researchers have elucidated the pathophysiologic mechanisms of yellow fever, chikungunya, and other diseases caused by arboviruses. The critical role of the case-control study, used in 1854 by John Snow to study epidemic cholera in London, which served as the foundation of the field of epidemiology, has been applied to arboviral and hemorrhagic fever outbreaks. Other important advances were the invention of various traps to collect insects for viral studies, which permitted collections tailored to particular situations, and the development of numerous laboratory tests for diagnosis of viral infections. It is not the intent of this book to enumerate every advance, large or small, but it is instructive to mention some of the discoveries specific to arbovirology.

Virus Overwintering

One of the hallmarks of arboviruses is that they must be able to replicate in organisms with widely differing biological characteristics (the arthropod vector and the vertebrate host). Such biological flexibility, however, does not come without a price. That is, the virus is forced to subjugate its own reproductive (replicative) activity to that of the seasonally influenced vector. Because by definition arthropods transmit arboviruses, those arthropods must be questing for a blood meal from hosts during the period when they can transmit the viruses. However, if they are not questing for blood, then they might serve as a passive repository for viruses during conditions that allow the virus to persist for relatively long periods. This is the basis for a mechanism called "overwintering" by which arboviruses persist long enough to be viable and to amplify themselves when more favorable conditions arise.

In the early days of arbovirology, overwintering of arboviruses was not a consideration because most recognized arboviruses, including yellow fever virus, were from tropical locales, where winter means "dry" rather than "cold". As more and more arboviruses were found in subtropical, dry, temperate, cold, and even polar climates, questions arose as to how these viruses could persist during conditions unfavorable for persistence or transmission. Clearly, little was known about mechanisms that could allow viruses to persist, to "overwinter".

William C. Reeves was one of the first to give serious consideration to the question of virus overwintering because of his interest in St. Louis encephalitis virus persistence in California. He and his colleagues studied the biology of overwintering *Culex pipiens* mosquitoes, the principal vector of this virus, and they published their speculations concerning the possible mechanisms by which overwintering occurs.

In the 1960s, Louis P. Gebhardt and collaborators at the University of Utah obtained evidence for the persistence of western equine encephalitis virus in garter snakes (*Thamnophis* spp.) that were found to be naturally infected with western equine encephalitis virus. They hypothesized that the snakes had been infected with the virus by mosquitoes that had fed on them and that the snakes could then serve as reservoirs of virus to infect mosquitoes that subsequently fed on them. Gebhardt et al. and others showed that enough virus persisted in the blood of experimentally-infected garter snakes to infect *Culex tarsalis* mosquitoes allowed to feed on them when the snakes emerged from hibernation. They showed that the snakes exhibited a fluctuating viremia (detectable virus in the blood, then no detectable virus, then again detectable virus), that these snakes do not move much more than 100 m from their origin, and that climatological conditions influence when mosquitoes will feed on snake blood (spring, late summer, and early fall but not early or mid-summer in Canada). They found that snakes infected about a week before hibernation (they placed them in a refrigerator to induce hibernation) will maintain their viremia through the winter but snakes infected 19 days or more before hibernation will not. Gebhardt and associates also reported isolation of western equine encephalitis virus from naturally infected snakes of three species. Althea N. Burton, John McLintock and Jacob G. Rempel isolated western equine encephalitis virus from snakes and leopard frogs (*Rana pipiens*) in Saskatchewan. Note that although on two occasions Ho-Wang Lee isolated Japanese encephalitis virus from wild-caught snakes in South Korea, that this is not definitive evidence that the virus overwinters in reptiles.

Other observations suggest that at least certain arboviruses can overwinter in their overwintering arthropod or vertebrate hosts. Charles L. Bailey, Bruce F. Eldridge, David E. Hayes, Douglas M. Watts, Ralph F. Tammariello and Joel Dalrymple, isolated St. Louis encephalitis virus from hibernating (overwintering) *Culex pipiens* mosquitoes in Maryland, and others have isolated viruses from other overwintering mosquitoes. Most of those findings have been in areas where climatic or microclimatic conditions are appropriate to allow activity of the insects during the winter months. Reeves and his group isolated Turlock virus (family *Bunyaviridae*, genus *Orthobunyavirus*) from the spleen of a bird captured in mid-winter in California, and western equine encephalitis virus was isolated from hibernating Texas tortoises (*Gopherus berlandieri*) during an epizoodemic of Venezuelan equine encephalitis in 1971.

G. Steven Bowen provided experimental evidence that tortoises may be viremic for as long as 105 days, that peak viremias are very high, that environmental temperatures affect maximum titer and duration of viremias and that neutralizing antibody was detectable in

Figure 99. Wayne H. Thompson (1922 - 2000), using a "turkey baster" to collect mosquito larvae from discarded automobile tires (image courtesy of Barry J. Beaty)

only 11 of 16 viremic tortoises. These and other laboratory studies of experimental infections of mosquitoes of various species suggest that at least some arboviruses can persist during conditions otherwise deleterious to them. Given the wide ecologic and biologic disparities among arboviruses, multiple mechanisms probably are in play. These findings may be unrelated or may be provisional evidence that the viruses mentioned may persist only locally.

Transovarial Transmission

Another mechanism by which many arboviruses have been shown to persist through both time and generations is that of transovarial ("vertical") transmission, by which a virus is transmitted from an infected female mosquito to her eggs and, therefore, to her offspring. The classic studies of this phenomenon were those of La Crosse

Figure 100. Thomas McKay Yuill (1937 -)
(image courtesy of Thomas Yuill)

Figure 101. Leon Rosen (1926 - 2008)
(image courtesy of National Institute of Allergy and Infectious Diseases, National Institutes of Health)

orthobunyavirus in *Aedes triseriatus* mosquitoes by Douglas Watts, Wayne Thompson (Figure 99), Thomas Yuill (Figure 100), Gene R. De Foliart, Somsak Pantuwatana, Robert Hanson, and Barry Beaty. Robert Tesh, Leon Rosen (Figure 101), Donald McLean and others have shown that transovarial transmission can occur with many California serogroup orthobunyaviruses as well as with yellow fever virus, dengue viruses, Kunjin virus, St. Louis encephalitis virus, Japanese encephalitis virus, West Nile virus, and some of the phleboviruses. Whether this is an important feature of the natural cycles of these viruses has not been fully determined, except for Rift Valley fever virus and for the California serogroup viruses. The latter viruses have been shown to be transmitted vertically in mosquitoes and to overwinter in the egg stage; their culicid vectors overwinter in the adult stage. Nonetheless, vertical transmission between generations brings with it additional peculiarities, which in turn bring about further opportunities for virus persistence. For example, male mosquito larvae can develop into transovarially-infected adults and, although they do not take blood meals, these males can venereally infect females during copulation, as has been shown for Sindbis, St, Louis encephalitis, dengue, and chikungunya viruses as well as for La Crosse virus. Such a mechanism might not be directly responsible for virus recrudescence or for epidemic amplification, but it certainly would provide an alternate means by which viruses can persist during otherwise challenging times.

Another form of vertical transmission (or partial vertical transmission or even horizontal transmission, depending on one's perspective) is transstadial transmission. This occurs when a virus or other parasite remains with the vector from one life stage ("stadium") to the next. For example, when a virus infects its tick vector when it is in the larval stage, the infection is maintained when the tick molts to a nymph and to an adult. Transstadial transmission is a critical means of maintenance of such viruses as flaviviruses that cause tick-borne encephalitis.

Introduction of Viruses by Migrating Birds

Studies of birds migrating between Africa and the Middle East, between South America and North America, between Russia and more southerly locations, and along the eastern seaboard of the United States have shown that a small proportion of such birds are viremic. A critical issue is whether these birds arrive at times when conditions are amenable to virus amplification (presence of active vectors, adequate food supplies for the birds). For example, South American subtype eastern equine encephalitis virus in migrating birds has been shown to enter the United States in the spring but too early to become established in local mosquitoes. Although this may not be the case with other viruses in other circumstances, it is quite clear that specific genotypes of St. Louis encephalitis virus have been found consistent with the flyways over which birds of certain species move, i.e., the Pacific, Central, and Atlantic flyways. Viruses of ticks transported long distances by birds have been demonstrated to be disseminated from their arrival points, an observation that has important epidemiologic implications.

Alternate Vectors and Hosts

Isolations of viruses from non-principal hosts may indicate either that spill-over has occurred in times of virus amplification or indicate that a virus has taken advantage of a competent secondary vector. Although many medical entomologists consider the most important virus vectors to be those found to have the highest virus titers, it has also been shown that mosquitoes with lower titers that are in great abundance also serve as important vectors during epidemics.

Genomic studies of viruses isolated from mosquitoes of non-principal species may be necessary to fully understand this quandary. Moreover, studies of blood-feeding individuals other than mosquitoes, ticks, and culicoids might provide information regarding other sources of virus. In the past arthropods of many families and genera were tested for virus without success, but the application of more modern techniques might now be successful.

At one time researchers thought mites were possible vectors of arboviruses because they are quite commonly found on birds and other wildlife and because they blood-feed. But only mechanical transmission by mites was ever demonstrated. Distinguishing between mechanical (physical) and biological (replication) transmission of viruses is usually an arduous task; until evidence for the presence of an arbovirus in a non-traditional arthropod host is presented, little is likely to be done in this regard.

Researchers have isolated arboviruses from ticks collected from non-viremic mammals, which suggests nothing so much as that there are many ticks feeding on many vertebrate hosts. Whether insusceptible vertebrate hosts simply serve as blood meal sources for infected ticks or whether the ticks serve as reservoirs of viruses has yet to be investigated fully.

Whereas studies of bats undoubtedly have yielded some intriguing results, their roles as possible significant hosts of arboviruses have not been studied adequately. For example, John R. Herbold, Werner P. Heuschele, Richard L. Berry, and Margaret A. Parsons reported a series of experimental infections of big brown bats (*Eptesicus fuscus*) with St. Louis encephalitis virus in Ohio. Bats maintained the virus through a 70-day hibernation period, and the bats became viremic within four days after arousal from hibernation, which was 105 days after they were infected. A field survey of big brown bats and little brown bats (*Myotis lucifugus*) in Ohio caves and abandoned mine shafts during a non-epizootic period showed that 9% of the bats had neutralizing antibody to St. Louis encephalitis virus. *Culex pipiens* mosquitoes, known vectors of St. Louis encephalitis virus in Ohio, were found cohabiting with the bats, suggesting that these bats may be involved in the maintenance and possibly the amplification of the virus.

S. Edward Sulkin, Ruth A. Sims, and Rae Allen of the Southwestern Medical School of the University of Texas at Dallas reported the isolation of St. Louis encephalitis virus from Mexican free-tailed bats (*Tadarida brasiliensis mexicana*) collected during and for several months after epidemics of St. Louis encephalitis in Houston, Texas in 1964 and in Corpus Christi, Texas, in 1966. The virus was detected in virtually every month of the year, indicating virus persistence. Other evidence of virus persistence and transmission in bats has been found, including vertical transmission of rabies virus in Mexican free-tailed bats and transplacental transmission of Japanese encephalitis virus in bats of the same species. In addition, Louis LaMotte detected viremia in big brown bats subcutaneously infected with Japanese encephalitis virus and showed that when the bats that had been held at the hibernating temperature of 10 degrees C were removed to a warmer temperature they became viremic. More recently, it has been shown that Japanese encephalitis virus was transmitted from black flying foxes (*Pteropus alecto*) to *Culex annulirostris* mosquitoes even though the bats were not detectably viremic. Bats, unique in many ways, clearly are a potential subject for further studies of virus transmission.

Adaptation of Arboviruses to Non-traditional or Unique Niches

Most of the first arboviruses isolated and identified were from mosquitoes, chiefly because the investigators who found them were focused on mosquitoes collected for yellow fever studies. As it became increasingly apparent that mosquitoes of many species other than *Aedes aegypti* were also infected with viruses and that mosquitoes were not the only blood-feeding arthropods associated with arboviral infections of vertebrates, investigators began collecting arthropods in general. This, of course, opened yet another door to even larger possibilities. Most arboviruses continued to be found first in mosquitoes, but collections were soon being made in non-tropical areas, first in temperate climes and later in what could be considered "unusual", or at least non-traditional, zones, such as in sub-Arctic and even Arctic areas. C.E. van Rooyen in Halifax, Nova Scotia, conducted serologic surveys of humans in Arctic populations; Russian investigators isolated arboviruses from ticks collected from birds and by flagging (dragging a piece of cotton flannel or other fabric across the ground) in Arctic areas (Sakhalin Island, Murmansk, Kamchatka regions). Donald McLean isolated California serogroup orthobunyaviruses in the Yukon Territory of Canada; Donald Ritter and Katherine Sommerman isolated Northway virus from mosquitoes in Alaska; and Terke Traavik isolated California serogroup orthobunyaviruses from mosquitoes in Arctic Norway. Reidar Mehl and Richard Wiger accumulated serologic evidence indicating that arboviruses could be found even at far northern latitudes. All this evidence indicates the remarkable capacity of these viruses to adapt to climatic and microenvironmental conditions distinct from conditions in tropical and subtropical areas. Arboviruses may need vertebrates with elevated core body temperatures as a host in one stage of their life cycle but they can also, in a single step, adapt to replication in arthropod hosts that are exposed to much lower external temperatures.

Many viruses have been isolated from arthropods but have not been shown to be pathogens. We know little of their natural cycles, arthropod-vertebrate host relations (if any), or overall significance. These include Cascade virus from adult *Dermacentor occidentalis* ticks in Montana; Calbertado virus from *Culex tarsalis* mosquitoes in Alberta, Canada, as well as from mosquitoes of the same species collected in Colorado and California. Many other insect-specific flaviviruses have been detected elsewhere in the United States, Mexico, Trinidad and Tobago, Japan, and other locations. Densoviruses (family *Parvoviridae*), which are not arboviruses, also have been detected in mosquitoes. This appears to be a burgeoning field of research that may lead to clues to the evolution of arboviruses and other viruses, to the production of vaccine candidates, and to biological control of pathogens.

The Group C orthobunyaviruses, can serve as an example of closely related viruses that have adapted to different ecologic niches and that have biogeographical limitations. Discovered in forested areas near Belem, Brazil, these viruses infect humans, mosquitoes, and wild animals (principally rodents, marsupials, and bats), and have been found from Ecuador to Florida. They are transmitted by infected mosquitoes that specialize in feeding on vertebrates living at different levels of the forest. With few but important differences, they are so ecologically similar to each other and so dependent on specific habitats inhabited by their vectors, that they may very well be recently evolved and have yet to expand their geographic distribution from the Western Hemisphere. Geographic expansion may not occur due to the relatively limited geographic distribution of their arthropod hosts.

Fort Morgan virus and Buggy Creek alphaviruses, each related closely to western equine encephalitis virus, have been isolated from nestling birds and from swallow nest bugs (Cimicidae, *Oeciacus vicarius*) in the western United States. A novel alphavirus was isolated from the blood-feeding louse *Lepidophthirus macrorhini,* collected from southern elephant seals, *Mirounga leonina,* on Macquarie Island, Australia.

Whether these viruses fit into an evolutionary scheme for the alphaviruses has not yet been determined but these viruses are not found in the classic mosquito-bird cycle we accept as "usual" for most alphaviruses. In sum, many arboviruses and related viruses as well as other viruses occur in non-classic niches, and many more likely could be found, if only we searched for them.

Genome Sequencing, Infectious Clones, and Dissection of Virulence Factors Leading to Production of Useful Chimeras

By now, no one doubts the usefulness and significance of polymerase chain reaction (PCR) assays in allowing us to multiply and copy small quantities of nucleic acid sequences and to then analyze those sequences. When automated, the entire process can be accomplished within a few hours. Before this method was devised, sequencing could be done but was tedious, time-consuming, and expensive. Added advantages of the contemporary methods are that novel applications are providing answers to questions not even dreamed of previously. For example, a virus that in the past was known to occur but to cause only one or a few cases or small clusters of cases of a disease might suddenly be found to cause hundreds or many more cases of that disease. Application of PCR to analyze the genomes of the original virus isolate and comparison with viral sequences of the recent isolates might reveal nucleotide substitutions (mutations) responsible for differences in pathogenicity. The finding of a well-recognized virus in an unusual arthropod vector also might be attributed to such a mutation.

Arboviral molecular epidemiology, the study of the contribution of viral genetics to the etiology of a disease or to knowledge of the geographic distribution of arboviruses, is used to track the movement of viruses in epidemic situations. It might be possible to predict outbreaks of these viruses if the scientific community had the support it needs to detect viruses where they are not already known to occur.

For now though, all we can do is track the movement of viruses after they have moved, using human, livestock or wildlife populations as sentinels, rather like closing the barn door after the horse has left. Nonetheless, if all we have are molecular epidemiologic data, then at least we can use our understanding of viral genetics in our attempts to understand the mechanisms or progression and possible routes of such movement. It is rather exciting to find that the genotype of a virus is exactly the same as or slightly distinct from the genotype of that same virus newly found in a location distant from where it had been cycling for many years, such as was shown by Chen, Rico-Hesse, and Tesh for Japanese encephalitis virus. Genotypic comparisons of viruses now is the *sine qua non* of diagnosis and epidemiology. Such data are useful in understanding not only virus distribution but origin, evolution, and mechanisms of emergence as well.

Many other viral applications of PCR have been devised. It can be used to determine whether a virus is a newly recognized virus or a natural reassortant or both, or to provide provisional evidence as to whether a particular virus genotype could only have been devised artificially, perhaps by a bioterrorist – information that is useful in understanding the distant origins of a virus and its evolution and in determining the proper taxonomic placement of a virus (although I do not suppose a bioterrorist is much interested in the taxonomy of a virus he concocted).

We can passively observe such changes, and we also can actively modify viral genomes, alterations that might very well be useful for studying the effects of such modifications or even to construct viral genomes that are less virulent for the host and that could therefore serve as vaccines with the capacity to immunize but not to cause disease. This is an approach being actively exploited.

In 1970 Howard Martin Temin and David Baltimore independently discovered the enzyme reverse transcriptase, an RNA-dependent DNA polymerase. Using reverse transcriptase and adapting other technologies, it became possible to insert a mutation at any location in a viral genome. The technology necessary for producing infectious viral clones first appeared in 1973 when Stanley N. Cohen, Annie C.Y. Chang, Herbert W. Boyer, and Robert B. Helling devised methods to produce recombinant DNA. This remarkable series of brilliant insights and elegant studies led to a cascade of innovations and novel applications. The key element in this technology was production of an infectious DNA clone, a double-stranded copy of the viral genome, and its insertion into a bacterial plasmid, a usually circular, sometimes linear extra-chromosomal element capable of replicating independently of the chromosomal DNA.

A series of ingenious applications of this technology has been applied to the production of vaccines against various flaviviruses. Using the backbone of yellow fever 17D vaccine virus, Monath and his collaborators produced live, attenuated chimeras of yellow fever and dengue viruses, yellow fever and West Nile viruses, and yellow fever and Japanese encephalitis viruses. They used a recombinant cDNA infectious clone of the yellow fever virus into which they inserted the pre-membrane and envelope genes of one or another of selected viruses. These viruses were then amplified in Vero cells transfected with the viral RNA transcripts. Intracerebral neurovirulence was evaluated in adult mice and both viremia and protectivity were determined with wild-type virus. These chimeras were shown to be attenuated, immunogenic, host-protective and genomically stable - a remarkable and useful application of plasmids and of modern arboviral technology. As a bonus, accessory studies allowed these investigators to determine the molecular basis for attenuation (decrease in pathogenicity) of neurovirulence. Interestingly, but not surprisingly, the yellow fever-West Nile virus recombinant protected mammals (both viruses infect mammals) but did not protect birds (yellow fever virus does not infect birds) against West Nile virus infection.

Virus Persistence

Among the responses of most vertebrates to virus infections is production of various types of antibody against the infecting virus and, often, against viruses closely related to the infecting virus. These antibodies quench the viremia and eliminate the virus from the vertebrate host. As shown by the use of monoclonal antibodies, which are produced against specific antigens, rare variants of the infecting type may not be neutralized by certain antibodies produced against the infectious virus. These "immunologic escape mutants" have been shown to be valuable in defining dominant immunogenic and pathogenesis domains and in determining other aspects of the antigenic structure of viral proteins. This is really getting down to the heart of the matter, so that additional knowledge about immunologic escape mutants may serve to provide answers to many questions.

Arthropods do not produce immunoglobulins or antibodies, but they do have an innate immunity, RNA interference (RNAi), which can act as a potent intracellular anti-viral in vector arthropods. This mechanism, triggered by the presence of virus-specific, double-stranded RNAs, has been shown to reduce vector competence. RNAi destroys messenger RNAs that carry information regarding proteins to be synthesized as part of the viral replication mechanism. Because of the potential for using RNAi as a means of controlling virus replication in arthropods, many groups now are exploring its practical aspects. Anthony A. James at the University of California at Irvine, among the leaders in this field, is attempting to engineer resistance of mosquitoes to viruses as well as to other parasites. Kenneth Olson, Carol Blair and Barry Beaty at Colorado State University and their former students Zach N. Adelman and Kevin M. Myles at Virginia Tech University pursue such studies in an effort to decrease the competence of mosquitoes to support the replication of viruses and therefore to prevent their transmission. Under usual conditions, however, female mosquitoes become persistently infected for all of their relatively brief lives, perhaps a few days to a few weeks for most.

Alternatively, most vertebrates infected with viruses produce antibody to the virus, which eventually quenches the viremia, and then recover completely. That is the usual and optimal condition, but there are exceptions. Certain viruses have evolved mechanisms to counter the immune response of the host either by suppressing it (filoviruses) or by evolving so quickly as to evade that response (human immunodeficiency virus). Other viruses, such as arenaviruses and hantaviruses become sequestered and continue to replicate in tissues not exposed to blood, which contains antibodies. The sequestered virus continues to proliferate and to be excreted, a remarkable adaptation for a parasite.

It is not yet understood how bats respond to virus infections as do other vertebrates. It is likely that they do however, simply based on Occam's razor (the simplest explanation is likely to be correct). However, many bats have been shown to be viremic or to have virus or viral nucleic acids in their tissues and yet appear healthy (a carrier state) and have no detectable antibody to that particular virus, suggesting that they may possess a somewhat different mechanism for dealing with viruses. We simply do not yet know enough about the biology of bats to speculate with confidence at this time. Painstaking studies of the biology of bats are being done by Lin-Fa Wang, a molecular virologist with the CSIRO in Geelong, Victoria, Australia, and Tony Schountz, an immunologist at the University of Northern Colorado; these certainly will provide us with further insights as to how bats manage virus infections.

Ecologic Factors Determining Amplification

In arctic habitats characterized by very short periods suitable for mosquito breeding, it is common for huge populations of mosquitoes of various species to appear quickly and simultaneously. In habitats characterized by a landscape that is mostly flat but with shallow depressions containing water from melted snow, large populations of mosquitoes hatch nearly simultaneously and must find vertebrate hosts from which to take blood meals in order to lay their eggs and produce offspring. Rabbits, hares, wolves, musk ox, birds and other vertebrates in the area, including humans, may serve as blood meal sources, depending on the feeding habits of the mosquitoes. Under such conditions, virus amplification is likely to be sudden and intense, guaranteeing the continuance of both the mosquitoes and the viruses they transmit. Transovarial transmission, whereby the adult mosquito that emerges from the infected pupal stage is already infected and ready to transmit the virus, is another remarkable adaptation in favor of the virus.

Under more temperate climatic conditions, mosquito breeding may begin for those of some species as soon as the snow melts and water is available in which to lay eggs. As the ambient temperature increases, both mosquitoes and their virus-amplifying hosts (small mammals and birds) are more commonly available to each other and the vector-virus-vector cycle continues. Virus spillover to unlucky humans, horses, or other vertebrate hosts occurs when mosquito population density and virus prevalence are unusually high. In the tropics, particularly in rain forests, the expansive vector and potential vertebrate host populations provide extraordinary opportunities for virus transmission and for virus diversity, including opportunities for viral nucleic acid reassortment; the more diverse the landscape characteristics, the more diverse the viral flora.

Under all ecologic conditions where ticks are found (which is just about everywhere), the possibility of virus persistence in them is high. As with other arthropods, ticks become infected for life. Because ticks may live for decades and survive for long periods without taking a blood meal, female ticks may serve as the index vector of an epizootic and thence of an epidemic. The natural cycles of ticks also may be advantageous to viruses infecting them. Ticks may use one, two, or three distinct vertebrate hosts to develop into adults, taking a blood meal at each stage, thus infecting one, two or three different vertebrates on the way to adulthood. How? A virus-infected adult female lays eggs that hatch into larvae, which (1) feed on small mammals then molt into nymphs in the fall, then (2) attach to a second host the next spring, molt to adults in the fall, and (3) attach to a third host the following spring, after which they mate and the cycle begins again. In addition, because embedded and long-lived ticks may be carried long distances by vertebrates such as birds and camels, they may serve as a source of virus dissemination, even between continents.

Evolution of Viruses as a Result of Genetic Changes

Persistence by adaptation to changing environmental conditions is one of the many ways that arboviruses have maintained their parasitic uniqueness; evolution is another. The natural cycles of arboviruses depend on the occurrence and continuity of their vector and vertebrate hosts. Therefore, if the host population decreases or is decreased by humans, the natural and continued perpetuation of a virus is threatened. These viruses, however, are genetically flexible to a certain degree and can adapt to new hosts in new areas. Because they can replicate in arthropods that live at low external temperatures (e.g., arctic mosquitoes) or at high external temperatures (e.g., tropical forest mosquitoes), in other poikilotherms, or in homeotherms, arboviruses are presented with opportunities unavailable to most other viruses. Even with natural or human-made climatic and environmental changes, arboviruses likely will not disappear any time soon. Furthermore, their adaptability could be an advantage to them and a disadvantage to humans and others because arboviruses replicate at a faster rate at higher temperatures (up to a point, of course), and the range of their arthropod hosts may extend to habitat that had been unavailable previously. We shall simply have to see how this all plays out, but we would be well advised to investigate these changes as they occur and, if possible, to stay ahead of situations in which viruses emerge.

CHAPTER 7

Learning from cases, clusters, outbreaks, and epidemics

If Aristotle did not say "One case does not an epidemic make.", he should have. An epidemic (from epi- = on + dēmos = people, now sloppily used to indicate a disease outbreak among non-human vertebrates and plants as well) by definition affects or tends to affect a disproportionately large number of individuals within a population, community, or region at the same time. Terms used to refer to viral outbreaks describe who or what is affected and how large the problem is:

epizoodemic	An outbreak or epidemic among both humans and non-human vertebrates
epizootic	An outbreak or epidemic among non-human animals
endemic	A disease constantly present to greater or lesser extent in a particular locality
pandemic	An epidemic occurring over a wide geographical area
epornitic	An outbreak of disease in a bird population
epiphytotic	An epidemic among plants of a single kind

Sometimes even one case is excessive in terms of acceptability. It is not critical to distinguish among cases, clusters of cases, outbreaks of disease, or epidemics of disease, but it is useful, if only to estimate the size of the problem and to make plans to counter it. The first properly diagnosed case (index case) of an infectious disease in a particular geographic area may not be a crucial public health problem, but that single case may amplify quickly to become many cases, i.e., an epidemic.

The following examples of disease recognition in various geographic areas do not include data and are not presented in order of chronology or importance. These provide historical information and are prime examples of findings central to modern understanding of viruses and the diseases they cause. These outbreaks afforded opportunities for astute investigators to conceive the bigger picture. The reader can obtain the details by searching the scientific literature, for example by using Pubmed.

Venezuelan Equine Encephalitis in the Americas, 1969-1971

In early summer 1971, the CDC was alerted to the incursion of Venezuelan equine encephalitis into Mexico; it was expected to reach the southern states of the United States. This epidemic was first recognized in 1969, when cases of Venezuelan equine encephalitis were diagnosed in horses and donkeys in Ecuador. When the Ecuadorian government requested assistance, Robert Kissling, a veterinarian, and Thomas Monath, a physician, both working at CDC, traveled to Ecuador to help in the investigation. Although they collected samples and documented many cases of encephalitic illnesses in humans and equids, they failed to obtain tissues from which they could isolate the virus. The problem was not that they did not collect the proper tissues but that they collected them after the virus could no longer be isolated; unfortunately polymerase chain reaction assays were not available at the time. They were struck, however, by the number of cases that were occurring, including many in pediatric patients.

The origin of the virus causing this epidemic was undetermined, but the virus very quickly spread from Ecuador in February-May 1969, to El Salvador and Guatemala (moved by horses, humans, and perhaps bats) that July, to Honduras and Costa Rica in August, to Nicaragua in October, and to southern Mexico in November. By 1970 the virus was found on the eastern seaboard of Mexico and was still causing trouble in Central America. By April 1971 there was little doubt that this virus and the disease it was causing were headed north toward Texas at the remarkable rate of 10 miles per day. In early July 1971 it was found in west central Mexico and had crossed the Texas border into the United States. Soon it spread throughout central Mexico from the Pacific coast to the Gulf of Mexico.

The first dead horse near the United States border with Mexico was found in the Rio Grande River, and some of the U.S.D.A. folks who had called this "a disease of backwards countries" (probably never having been in south Texas) reported that the horse had been found in the Mexican half of the river! Trying to be helpful, certain U.S.D.A. officials informed local horse owners that all horses in certain border counties of south Texas would be given an "experimental vaccine" beginning the next day, and, if they did not want to have their horses vaccinated, they might consider moving them north, away from those counties. A long line of trucks pulling trailers with horses in them soon began to leave south Texas. Officials who tried to stop them were shocked to have guns pointed at them in defiance. The first dead horse certified to be in the United States in 1971 was found at Three Rivers, Texas, about 257 km (160 mi) north of the border with Mexico, which is the Rio Grande River.

The vaccine virus available at the time, a live-attenuated one called "TC-83", had been developed by and was available through the United States Army Medical Research Institute of Infectious Diseases in Maryland. It was soon amplified, diluted in equine serum albumen, and distributed as necessary, as requested, and as appropriate. Mexican authorities received many doses of the vaccine for their use.

Before the vaccine had been approved for use in the United States and distributed legally, ranchers in Texas who could afford it purchased the vaccine from ranchers in Mexico because they felt they had no alternative. When the United States government made the vaccine available, many of the first recipients of the vaccine in Texas were less valuable equids because it had been well publicized that the vaccine was considered "experimental", a term that frightened some horse owners. The result was that many of the less valuable equids survived while many extremely valuable horses did not. More than 1,500 equids died in Texas and Mexico during the summer of 1971 (Figure 102).

At this time, the Director of CDC was David J. Sencer, who had overseen the world-wide eradication of smallpox. Sencer had taken the risk of diverting resources to fund and provide the staff and support necessary for the success of that eradication program, although Congress had not appropriated funds for that purpose. An activist director, scientist and humanitarian, Sencer later took a strong lead in the conceptualization and establishment of the Rollins School of Public Health at Emory University, which is just down the street from CDC. As principally a "laboratory person" at CDC, my task in the summer of 1971 was to identify viruses isolated from equids, humans and mosquitoes from Texas and to do this as rapidly and as accurately as possible, so that daily up-dates could be distributed at CDC and sent by Sencer to the relevant authorities in other organizations and jurisdictions.

Identification of viruses during that epizoodemic was an onerous task because not only was the epidemic strain of Venezuelan equine encephalitis alphavirus circulating there but so was the vaccine strain of this virus, as well as eastern equine encephalitis alphavirus, western equine encephalitis alphavirus and other viruses. Distinguishing among them was a challenge.

Nevertheless, the TC-83 strain of Venezuelan equine encephalitis virus is not pathogenic for guinea pigs inoculated with it by the intraperitoneal route; the others are. Therefore, we inoculated each field and diagnostic sample into a litter of newborn mice. If the mice died we tested crude but clarified suspensions of their brains by a complement-fixation test and, at the same time, inoculated two guinea pigs intraperitoneally with the clarified material. If the complement-fixa-

Figure 102. Dead horse, south Texas, U.S.A., 1971. Venezuelan equine encephalitis virus was isolated from tissues of this horse. Note the classical "running in place" marks on the ground where the horse had unsuccessfully tried to move before it died.
(photo by Charles Calisher)

tion test indicated that the virus was either eastern equine encephalitis or western equine encephalitis, that was that, but if it indicated that it was Venezuelan equine encephalitis virus, then we looked to the guinea pigs. If the guinea pigs died, the virus with which they had been inoculated was considered to be the epidemic strain. If they did not, it was provisionally considered the TC-83 strain. That system worked well but was used for a short time only, because some uninoculated guinea pigs also died, ostensibly after aerosol exposure in the holding room. We replaced the guinea pigs with 10-to-12-week old mice and lined their cages with filter material to decrease the aerosolized virus content of the room. We did not have a Biosafety Level 4 (BSL-4) facility at CDC at that time, but I had been vaccinated with the TC-83 vaccine, and it had been certified that I had antibody to that virus. We all felt I would be well protected, particularly as I was well trained to handle exotic viruses, had already done so, and would take all the proper precautions available. Essentially, I lived at CDC for a month, going home only to change my clothes and eat something more nourishing than a candy bar. For that reason alone, if for no other, I will always remember the birth year of my youngest child as 1971; it was that impressive an epidemic.

Millions of horses, from Texas to Minnesota and into Canada, and from Mexico to California, were vaccinated. The epidemic finally ended in August 1971. When things were slowing down that month, I was able to visit the epidemic zone in south Texas. There still were some horses staggering around, blinded by their encephalitis and soon to be euthanized. I was enormously impressed by the capacity of the government to put the necessary resources into an attempt to control the epidemic. One motel had been taken over, and most of the walls between the rooms had been removed. In separate areas there were piles of automobile tires and batteries, smaller batteries for powering the light traps, piles of tape, note pads, maps, pencils, pens, and everything else that was needed (except computers, unfortunately not available at the time). Apparently, the American Quarter Horse Association had contacted President Richard Nixon and impressed upon him the need for such a response.

I accompanied Morris Schaeffer to the west coast of Mexico in 1972. Schaeffer had been Director of the Virus and Rickettsia Section at CDC and had hired Chamberlain, Sudia, Kissling, and Donald Stamm among others. He was by 1972 a consultant to the Pan-American Health Organization. We drove the back roads of western Mexico, stopping where we saw horses that were lame, blind, or wandering in circles, and seeing piles of ashes, the remains of horses cremated on site by members of the Mexican military. From information available locally, the last cases of Venezuelan equine encephalitis virus on the west coast of Mexico had occurred in late 1972.

Scores of publications resulted from the studies that were done, and our knowledge regarding epidemic Venezuelan equine encephalitis increased considerably. Substantial experience with this virus already existed when the epizoodemic began and background information was available because of the work done by many others (Wil-

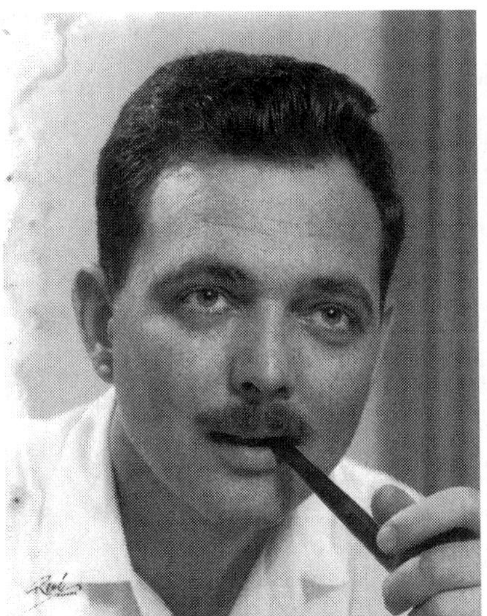

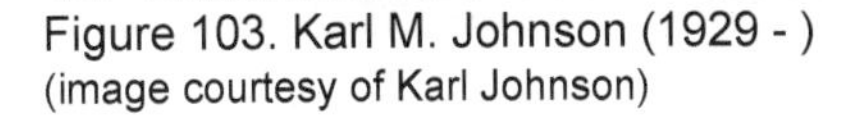

Figure 103. Karl M. Johnson (1929 -)
(image courtesy of Karl Johnson)

Figure 104. Nathaniel A. Young (1938 - 1979)
(image courtesy of Karl Johnson)

liam Scherer, Robert W. Dickerman and colleagues on pathogenicity of Venezuelan equine encephalitis virus in laboratory-bred guinea pigs and their earlier work on Venezuelan equine encephalitis virus in Mexico and elsewhere in Latin America; Karl Johnson (Figure 103) and Nathaniel Young (Figure 104) on discriminating between subtypes and variants of Venezuelan equine encephalitis virus, a study which was an enormous help in laying out the epidemiologies of these viruses; Robert W. McKinney, Trygve O. Berge, William D. Sawyer, William D. Tigertt, and Dan Crozier on devising a useful and safe vaccine against the virus for the United States Army). As Roy Chamberlain mused, "Were it not for wide-scale veterinary use of a live Venezuelan (equine encephalitis virus) vaccine, originally developed to protect laboratory workers, horses might have become a curiosity in Texas". That comment was published in a paper Chamberlain delivered as the 46th Annual Charles Franklin Craig lecture in which he demonstrated not only his knowledge of the history of arbovirology but his capacity to be reflective, insightful, and creative in regard to various basic concepts that might explain the behavior and persistence of arboviruses.

Birds are important in the spread of some viruses and not others, including the long distance movement of influenzaviruses (family *Orthomyxoviridae*). Birds are also a mechanism of movement for Newcastle disease virus (family *Paramyxoviridae*, genus *Avulavirus*) and many other viruses, including several important (and some apparently unimportant) arboviruses. This transport may occur when viremic birds migrate or otherwise move great distances or when virus-infected ectoparasites fasten themselves to migrating birds. Ticks are thought to be important sources of viruses that can take advantage of such movement. In the Soviet era, Russian symposia summarizing viruses isolated from migrating birds were quite informative. However, bird surveys are expensive and usually not terribly productive, given that millions of birds migrate and only a relative few are found viremic.

West Nile Virus Jumps the Pond

West Nile flavivirus was discovered by Kenneth L. Smithburn and others who were working for the Rockefeller Foundation in East Africa and searching (successfully) for yellow fever virus and other viruses in the West Nile District of Uganda. They isolated West Nile virus in 1937 from the blood of a person who manifested only a low-grade fever and who denied feeling ill, a relatively unexpected beginning for a virus now found to cause serious, sometimes fatal illnesses in people on five continents: Africa, Asia, Europe, North America and South America. A close relative, Kunjin virus, occurs in Australia and nearby islands. West Nile virus now has been shown to cause illnesses of varying severity, from uncomplicated fevers, to fever with rash, to central nervous system involvement with a sometimes fatal outcome.

In late summer 1999 a cluster of five human patients with illnesses characterized by fever, confusion, and muscle weakness were admitted to the intensive care unit of a hospital in the Flushing neighborhood of New York City. Four of the five went on to develop profound muscle weakness or flaccid paralysis and required ventilatory support. At about the same time, Tracey MacNamara, a veterinary pathologist with the Wildlife Conservation Society in New York City's Bronx Zoo and a keen observer, watched as not only resident, exotic zoo birds but also free-living crows (*Corvus* spp.) outside the zoo had difficulty retaining their balance while walking and were found dying or dead both inside and outside the zoo. Her persistent efforts to obtain diagnostic assistance were not immediately rewarded. However, thanks to the persistent MacNamara, it was soon recognized that the two episodes, the human illnesses in Flushing and the dead birds at the zoo, might be related. Initially, the CDC reported that blood samples obtained from human patients provided evidence for infections with St. Louis encephalitis flavivirus. Because of necessarily limited testing of bird samples, the USDA could only say what it was not, which was not helpful. It should have been relatively clear early on that St. Louis encephalitis flavivirus was not the only likely cause. There was no evidence of the presence of this virus anywhere in the United States and it had never been found in New York City. The "profound muscle weakness" of the human patients, and the unconvincing "borderline positivity" of the samples also made St. Louis encephalitis flavivirus an unlikely cause. A group under the direction of Marcelle Layton, Director of Communicable Diseases of the New York City Department of Health, continued to search for the cause of the mysterious illness.

It was not until the leading practitioners of virus discovery, W. Ian Lipkin and Thomas Briese, then at the University of California at Irvine, now at Columbia University School of Public Health, showed that brains from fatal human cases of this illness contained RNA sequences specific to West Nile virus that the true etiologic agent was recognized. Subsequent efforts by Lipkin and Briese, CDC virologists, collaborating investigators at USDA and the New York State health department, and researchers in Australia, France, and Israel confirmed and extended the initial findings. Complete sequencing of the RNA of virus from the brain of a Chilean flamingo (*Phoenicopterus chilensis*) found dead at the Bronx Zoo, supplemented by partial sequence analyses of the envelope glycoprotein genes from birds of several other species as well as from mosquitoes and humans, indicated that a particular strain of West Nile virus had caused the outbreak and that it was most closely related to a West Nile virus isolate found in Israel in 1998.

It is unknown how West Nile virus came to the Americas. A bioterrorist act was ruled out early on based on a variety of observations and facts. Movement of an infected bird that had somehow crossed the Atlantic Ocean was unlikely because West Nile virus viremias in birds are relatively brief, the flight would have had to be relatively long, and no sufficiently powerful storm had occurred within a time frame that could be consistent with such an outbreak. A viremic human arriving in New York City by air from the Middle East was a possibility, but West Nile virus viremias in humans also are brief and of very low titer, probably too low to infect a mosquito feeding on such a person. Unproven is the generally accepted supposition that a West Nile virus-infected mosquito secreted itself aboard an aircraft that landed in New York City, escaped, fed on a local bird, and initiated this remarkable epidemic.

Expert characterizations of the virus were soon complete and a great deal became known about its distribution in the New York City area. The hubbub did not end there, however. Given the time lost, any opportunity to eradicate all (or nearly all) infected mosquitoes also was lost, if indeed there ever had been such an opportunity. The virus overwintered in mosquitoes in sewerage systems and other cryptic areas in the epidemic zone and soon West Nile virus spread to areas contiguous with New York City: Connecticut, Pennsylvania, New Jersey and onward, even into Canada. Laboratory workers and epidemiologists tracked it westward to the Pacific Coast and southward to the border with Mexico, where clinical cases appeared to end. That appearance was an illusion. West Nile virus now has been shown to have moved all the way to southern South America, causing a relatively few human, equid, and avian cases of encephalitis but not on the scale that has been seen in North America, perhaps because of the presence of cross-reactive antibodies to other flaviviruses, perhaps because of a slight but significant genetic change in the virus, or perhaps for other reasons.

The mechanism by which this virus traveled so widely was the movement of infected birds. In the Americas, migratory or other, more local, movements of birds have been known for many decades but have not been clearly and simply defined. For instance, the terms "migration route" and "flyway" are somewhat distinct from each other. Migration routes are the lanes of travel from a particular breeding ground to the winter quarters of the birds that use them. Flyways are those broader areas in which related migration routes are associated in a definite geographic region; they are wide arterial highways to which the routes are tributary. Four major North American flyways have been named: Atlantic, Mississippi, Central, and Pacific. Except along the coasts, the flyway boundaries are not always sharply defined. In both the northern breeding and the southern wintering grounds there is considerable overlap. In Panama, parts of all four flyways merge.

Local, non-migratory movement of birds also occurs. In the search for food and for other not clearly understood reasons, some birds may move scores or even hundreds of miles even when not migrating; some birds do not migrate yet move over relatively large distances. Thus when West Nile virus began to be detected in areas outside of the New York City and nearby Connecticut and New Jersey areas where it was found early on, it appeared to the north, the south, and the west of that initial core area, such that it eventually spread throughout the United States into Canada and then south into and throughout Latin America. If evidence for the presence of West Nile virus has not been detected in a particular area in the Americas it is as likely that it is there, undetected, as it is that it is not there.

According to the CDC, in the United States alone, by the end of 2010 at least 12,727 human cases diagnosed as neuroinvasive West Nile virus disease, 17,165 diagnosed as West Nile virus fever, and hundreds of other West Nile virus-caused illnesses not placed in either category were reported. A total of 1,208 human deaths were attributed to this virus. According to the USDA's Animal and Plant Health Inspection Service, at least 25,765 equids were shown to be infected with West Nile virus in the United States between1999 and 2009, with cases identified in every state except Alaska and Maine. Application of vaccines useful for protecting equids against West Nile virus decreased the number of cases from the peak of 15,257 in 2002 to 276 in 2009.

West Nile virus infections of humans, birds, or mosquitoes occurred in 43 states in 2012 (through mid-August), with outbreaks of the disease in Texas, Mississippi, Louisiana, Oklahoma, South Dakota, and California; about half the nearly 700 human cases (including 26 deaths) have occurred in Texas. These are the most cases seen in a similar period since the virus was first detected in the United States in 1999. Further studies are necessary if we are to understand this sudden surge in infections. No vaccine is available yet for use in humans.

Chikungunya virus and o'nyong-nyong virus re-emerge and spread essentially worldwide

The word "chikungunya" is said to be derived from a word in the language of the Makonde ethnic group meaning "to become contorted", referring to the altered posture of people with chikungunya virus disease. Becoming contorted reflects the joint and muscle pain associated with this disease. In 1952, Marion C. Robinson first recognized the disease, observing an epidemic of fever, rash, arthralgia and photophobia among residents of the Makonde Plateau, southeastern Tanzanika (now Tanzania). W.H. Russell Lumsden of the Virus Research Institute of Entebbe, Uganda, first described it in the literature in 1955; Ronald W.N.L. Ross (not the same person as Ronald Ross) was first to isolate the virus. Since that original discovery, outbreaks of disease caused by this virus have been documented not only in Africa (1958, 1971, 1985 in Uganda; 1960, 1999–2000 in Democratic Republic of Congo; 1961, 1963 in Zimbabwe), but in south Asia and southeast Asia (1963 in Cambodia; 1960, 1962–1964, 1988, 1991–1993, 1995 in Thailand), 1963-1965, 1973, 2006 India; and others, in

Asia (1960s-1990s) in Vietnam, Malaysia, Taiwan, Burma (Myanmar), Indonesia, Philippines, Timor, Pakistan; and Africa (1960s-2003) in Senegal, Nigeria, South Africa, Kenya, Burundi, Gabon, Malawi, Guinea and many other countries.

Chikungunya virus is an alphavirus (family *Togaviridae*, genus *Alphavirus*) and a member of the Semliki Forest virus complex, which also includes Bebaru, Getah, Mayaro, o'nyong-nyong, Ross River, Semliki Forest, and Una viruses, each of which can cause fever and rash in humans. Earlier descriptions of illnesses similar to chikungunya might have been mistaken for dengue or for other Semliki Forest virus complex viruses and vice versa. Beginning in 1986, there was a resurgence of outbreaks of chikungunya, with major disease clusters documented in Senegal in 1986 and 1996-1997, Ivory Coast in 1996-1997, Democratic Republic of Congo in 1998-2000, Indonesia in 2003 Kenya in 2004, Union of the Comoros in 2005, the Seychelles, Mauritius, Madagascar, and Réunion islands in 2005-2006 and in India in 2006-2007. What was going on? What was the reason for the sudden epidemic spread of this virus? Outbreaks occurred almost continuously from 2004 to 2007 with hundreds of thousands of reported cases and new geographic areas involved. Cases were reported in Europe (Belgium, Czech Republic, France, Germany, Italy, Norway, Spain, Switzerland, and the United Kingdom), Asia (Hong Kong, Japan, Singapore, Sri Lanka and Taiwan) and North America (Canada and the United States); these were associated with the return of tourists from India and affected islands of the Indian Ocean.

Early field studies of chikungunya virus showed that *Aedes aegypti* mosquitoes were the principal vectors, with some isolates from *Aedes africanus* mosquitoes but rarely from other mosquitoes. The more recent isolates from mosquitoes were from *Aedes albopictus,* which has a wide distribution, suggesting that adaptation of the virus to a different vector had occurred. Schuffenecker et al. and Tsetsarkin et al. have shown that a single mutation, E1-A226V, significantly changed the ability of the virus to infect and be transmitted by *Aedes albopictus* mosquitoes, a remarkable and instructive finding.

That *Aedes albopictus* mosquitoes have a very wide geographic distribution is in itself something relatively recent. These mosquitoes have found their way from their native habitats in southeast Asia to North America, South America, Europe, and Africa. Because of modern modes and speeds of travel, increased commerce between producers and their distant consumers, and for other, less obvious, reasons, arthropods of many species have invaded and continue to invade areas from which they have been previously absent. Continued surveillance for these arthropods likely will provide information necessary to prevent their establishment and spread. Should any of them prove to be vectors of pathogens, this will be a public health necessity.

O'nyong-nyong virus was first isolated by Williams and Woodall from a human in 1959 in northwestern Uganda during an epidemic of a dengue-like disease (fever, headache, itching rash, and marked joint and back pains). The illness was named o'nyong-nyong, "joint breaker" (and other iterations). The epidemic quickly spread into Kenya and the total number of cases in Uganda and Kenya was estimated at the time as at 750,000, later as 2 million cases, with no deaths. Unlike chikungunya virus, which causes a similar illness, and all other alphaviruses, o'nyong-nyong virus is not transmitted by aedine mosquitoes but by anopheline mosquitoes, typically *Anopheles funestus* and *An. gambiae.* Rapid spread of this virus may be due to the common and close proximity to human habitations of its vector mosquitoes. A vertebrate reservoir for o'nyong–nyong virus has not been identified.

In 1996, after more than three decades absence, o'nyong-nyong virus reappeared in Uganda, and travelers spread it essentially worldwide. In contrast, there is clear evidence that chikungunya virus continuously circulates in Africa in sylvatic cycles. Molecular analyses of a variety of chikungunya virus isolates from Africa and Asia and of o'nyong-nyong virus isolates from 1959 and 1995 indicated that the African and Asian isolates of chikungunya virus are substantially different from each other but that the recent o'nyong-nyong virus isolates are not substantially different from the 1959 isolates. A bonus to this work is that Igbo-Ora virus from Nigeria, reported by some to be distinct from both chikungunya and o'nyong-nyong virus, was shown to be a strain of o'nyong-nyong virus.

The preceding examples merely illustrate classical investigations done by members of the arbovirology community with collaboration of others who were drawn into this fascinating field by unexpected circumstances. This book, a history rather than the history of arbovirology, could cite earlier and later outbreaks and epidemics, studies of which provided material and information. The contents are biased by the experiences of the author. Omission of mention of other disease outbreaks is not intended to minimize their significance. I suggest that the reader seek the intriguing literature describing many other fascinating arboviral epidemics, such as the classical studies of Japanese encephalitis after World War II done by William Scherer, Edward Buescher, and others. This disease is a leading cause of viral encephalitis in Asia, with 30,000-50,000 clinical cases reported annually. The distribution of Japanese encephalitis is very significantly linked to irrigated rice production combined with pig rearing. The virus causing it has now been discovered in southern Papua New Guinea and it has been shown to occur on an island 70 km (43 mi) from mainland northern Australia (probably limited by the geographic distribution of variants of its vector mosquito, *Culex annulirostris*), as studied by Scott Ritchie, Annette Broom, Andrew van Den Hurk, Cheryl Anne Johansen, John Mackenzie (Figure 105) and other investigators in Australia.

Accounts of other arboviral epidemics that are intriguing to read include those of western equine encephalitis alphavirus in horses in North Dakota and Minnesota in 1975; the continuing occurrence of La Crosse orthobunyavirus in the Upper Midwest of the United States; the reemergence of chikungunya and o'nyong-nyong alphaviruses; and the remarkable epidemic explosions of dengue in tropical and subtropical areas around the world.

The classic arbovirus, yellow fever virus, causes periodic outbreaks of disease in Africa and Latin America, where it occurs and reports of these outbreaks are always instructional. These incidents can be

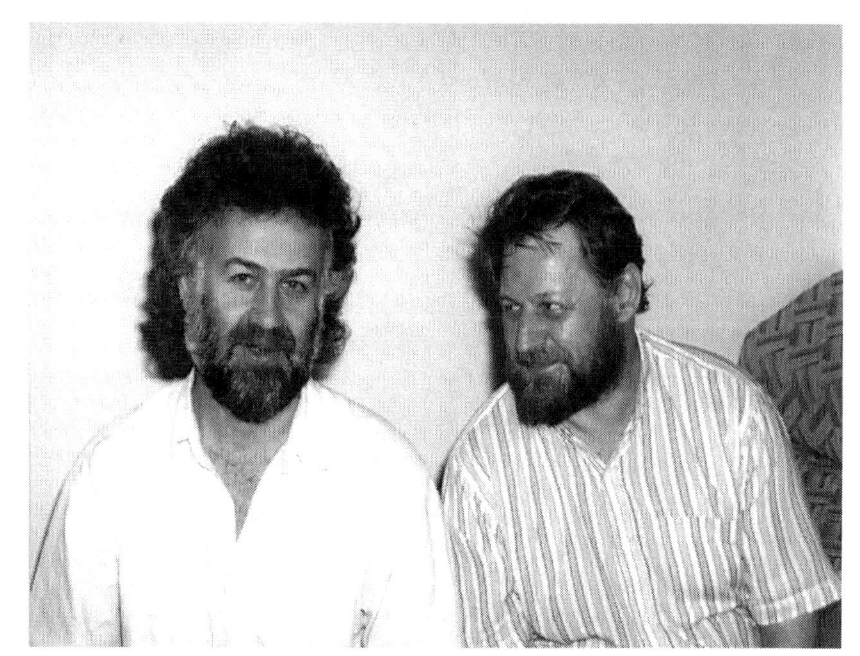

Figure 105. Richard Charles Russell (1947 -), left, and John Sheppard Mackenzie (1941 -), undoubtedly having a laugh.
(image courtesy of John Mackenzie)

attributed principally to the absence of competent governments. The virus is known to occur in rain forest habitats; primate hosts are present; competent arthropod vectors of this virus are present; yet an adequate vaccine is also available. At present, the only effective preventative measure, application of the vaccine to at-risk populations, is the *sine qua non* of combating this disease.

Dengue

Caused by any of four closely related flaviviruses, dengue now is recognized as a global scourge, being found in at least 110 countries, and is the most common arbovirus disease world-wide. Philadelphia physician and signer of the Declaration of Independence Benjamin Rush ostensibly was the first to describe dengue in 1789, describing a 1780 case. His observations on dengue (which he called "bilious remitting fever") were notable because he linked seasonal occurrence, classical onset features, classical signs and symptoms, and geographic location of cases within the city. His description of dengue cases included notes on post-illness depression. Today it is recognized that dengue is the only acute febrile illness with rash that has been associated with such depression.

Nonetheless, probable dengue epidemics had been described long before that, as far back as the 17th century, in tropical and subtropical areas. Because the signs and symptoms of mild dengue mimic those of many other diseases, without laboratory confirmation it is impossible to say what was what. Still, a description of a disease outbreak in the West Indies in 1635 may have been the first. Toward the end of the 18th century, epidemics were described in Indonesia, Egypt, India, Spain, and the United States (by Rush). In the 19th century four extensive epidemics occurred in the Americas, principally in the Caribbean region and also in Southeast Asia, with the prevalence of disease more frequently noted among foreigners than among locals. Throughout the 20th century, large epidemics of dengue have been reported from Australia, Greece, Japan, and the Caribbean region.

Because nonindigenous personnel apparently were more likely to be affected than were local residents in dengue-endemic areas, military investigators became interested in this disease. In 1907 Ashburn and Craig of the United States Army Medical Corps published a report of their proof of the viral etiology of dengue and the presence of infectious virus in the blood of military personnel stationed in the Philippines as a consequence of the Spanish-American War. John Burton Cleland, Burton Bradley and W. McDonald in Sydney, Australia, provided evidence in 1919 for experimental human-to-human transmission of the virus in blood from patients and showed that the incubation period was 5 to 9 days and that the likely vector was the *Aedes aegypti* mosquito.

In 1926 Joseph Franklin Siler and co-workers confirmed that the virus vector was *Ae. aegypti* and in 1931 James Steven Simmons and co-workers extended those research results to show that *Ae. albopictus* mosquitoes also can serve as a competent dengue virus vector. Scott B.

Figure 106. Scott Barker Halstead (1930 -)
(image courtesy of Scott Halstead)

Halstead (Figure 106), 42 years after Siler's and 48 years after Simmons' studies, bled some of the volunteers from those studies and showed that those in Siler's 1924-1925 study had had dengue virus 4 and those in Simmons' 1929-1930 study had had dengue virus 1.

It simply is not possible to take a blood sample from everyone who has frontal headache, fever, and rash during an epidemic that involves millions, hundreds of thousands, or even many fewer people; all that can be done is sample the population of sick individuals and some control (well) people and to compare the laboratory test results. Because dengue viruses may cause asymptomatic infections in half the infected people involved, reported cases in dengue epidemics are usually underestimated. Notwithstanding that fact, it is possible to estimate the least number of people involved in such widespread epidemics and the rates of infection, illness, and death.

Any of four dengue viruses (family *Flaviviridae*, genus *Flavivirus*) can cause the disease. E. Kimura and S. Hotta discovered dengue virus 1 in 1943. Because of difficulties in distributing their published findings after World War II had ended, Albert Sabin and R. Walter Schlesinger received that credit when they published their work on isolation of the virus from patients during a Honolulu epidemic. Dengue virus 2 was isolated from United States military members during an epidemic in New Guinea in 1944.

Discovery of Dengue Hemorrhagic Fever/Dengue Shock Syndrome

Descriptions of what were not serologically confirmed but which could reasonably be considered dengue hemorrhagic fever (bleeding, low levels of blood platelets and blood plasma leakage or dengue shock syndrome (circulatory failure) (DHF/DSS) cases were reported in Queensland, Australia, in 1897 and retrospective serologic studies elsewhere suggested that other DHF/DSS cases had been caused by dengue viruses. William McD. Hammon was in the Philippines to study poliomyelitis cases in 1956 when he and co-workers, Albert Rudnick and Gladys E. Sather, coincidentally isolated hitherto unrecognized dengue virus 3 and dengue virus 4 from children. Nonetheless, it was Hammon's studies in the Philippines and Thailand in 1956-1960 that demonstrated the association of secondary infections with dengue viruses and DHF/DSS. Later, as President of the American Society of Tropical Medicine and Hygiene, Hammon presented an address to the Society's annual meeting summarizing the details of their discoveries and the concepts and further planning that arose from them.

Initial serologic studies of these patients indicated secondary antibody responses in DHF/DSS patients and the fact that only indigenous residents were affected severely. The conclusion was that first infections with a dengue virus do not cause severe illness; these usually are relatively mild. But subsequent infections with a different dengue virus cause the severe illness of DHF and DSS.

The Role of Immune Enhancement ("Antibody-dependent enhancement") in the Pathogenesis of Dengue Hemorrhagic Fever and Dengue Shock Syndrome

Investigators in many areas of microbiology studied enhancement of immune responses by various stimulants. It was not until years after Royle A. Hawkes (Figure 107), working in the laboratory of Ian Mar-

Figure 107. Royle Anthony Hawkes (1937 -)
(image courtesy of The John Curtin School of Medical Research, Australia National University)

shall (Figure 108) at Australian National University laboratory, demonstrated enhanced infectivity of arboviruses by antisera that this phenomenon was more fully investigated and correctly understood by Scott Halstead and Edward J. O'Rourke and by Joseph Sriyal, Malik Peiris and James Stuart Porterfield. They found that the addition of a flavivirus to minute amounts of lower than neutralizing concentrations of antibody to that virus could potentiate the replication of the virus – an altogether new concept, which at first view seems counterintuitive because we accept that neutralizing antibodies neutralize rather than prime the immunologic pump, so to speak. It is now known that such potentiation occurs when non-neutralising antiviral antibodies enhance viral entry into host cells, which leads to increased infectivity in the host cells. There are always some cells that do not have the receptors on their surfaces which viruses use to gain entry. The enhancing antibodies bind to antibody Fc (fragment, crystalizable) receptors that some of these cells have on their plasma membranes. The viruses then bind to the antigen binding site at the other end of the antibody.

Halstead persisted in investigations of the immune enhancement phenomenon and used it to explain the historical and increasing frequency of DHF/DSS episodes. At the same time, Leon Rosen, a brilliant and outspoken physician who was quite articulate in defending his scientific positions, hypothesized that DHF/DSS might be the result of extraordinary pathogenicity by unique strains of dengue

Figure 108. Ian David Marshall (1922 - 2010)
(image courtesy of The John Curtin School of Medical Research, Australia National University)

viruses and provided some evidence to support this hypothesis. He reported the occurrence of DHF, the clinical definition of which is a subjective one, in Pacific Islanders who had had only one dengue virus infection. Rosen, a long-time NIH employee, moved to the Pacific Biomedical Research Center at the University of Hawaii, where he could be closer to Pacific island outbreaks of dengue (and SCUBA diving), and spent part of each year in Paris at the Pasteur Institute, to the end convinced that at least sometimes, a primary infection with a dengue virus can cause DHF/DSS.

Acknowledging that a primary dengue infection might precede DHF/DSS caused by a subsequent infection, Rosen suggested that this was not the only mechanism of this very serious condition and also argued that the principal site of replication of dengue viruses might not be the cells mentioned by Halstead. However, Halstead and his colleagues generated irrefutable evidence that the pathogenesis of viruses causing dengue is a complex mechanism. References to these fascinating and fundamentally important papers may be found in the *Suggested Readings* section.

Based on the findings of Hammon and his associates that secondary infections with dengue viruses precede DHF/DSS, Nyven J. Marchette, J.S. Sung Chow, Halstead, Somsak Lolekha, and Boonchob Pongpanich investigated the replication of dengue virus 2 in cultured human peripheral blood leukocytes from children with primary or secondary dengue virus infections. They found that the occurrence of dengue virus 2 replication in these cells was infrequent in leukocyte cultures from children within 10 days after onset of symptoms but more frequent thereafter. Marchette, Halstead, and Chow then showed that dengue viruses replicated in cultures of peripheral blood leukocytes from dengue-immune but not dengue-susceptible rhesus monkeys, thus demonstrating immunological dependence of in vitro replication of dengue viruses in these monkey leukocytes. Essentially simultaneously, they showed enhanced dengue virus 2 viremia in rhesus monkeys with secondary dengue virus infection. A long, detailed series of historically significant studies continued to support a hypothesis that prior infection with a dengue virus enhanced the replication of other dengue viruses, whether determined in vivo or in vitro. For example, a pool of serum from human cord bloods had a virus neutralizing titer of 40 but a titer of human monocyte infection enhancement of more than 2,000,000. When this serum was inoculated into susceptible rhesus monkeys and the monkeys were then infected with dengue virus 2, daily titers of virus were always higher in monkeys that had received antibody to dengue virus 2 than in monkeys that had received normal serum, further demonstrating antibody-dependent enhancement and showing that the severity of dengue in humans is regulated by antibody.

In 1981, Peiris, Siamon Gordon, Jay C. Unkelless, and Porterfield demonstrated that monoclonal IgG antibody to the mammalian Fc receptor blocks antibody-dependent enhancement of viral replication in macrophages. They furthermore reported that this occurred not only for flaviviruses (dengue viruses, West Nile virus) but for alphaviruses and bunyaviruses as well. They showed that cells lacking macrophage characteristics did not demonstrate antibody-dependent enhancement of viral replication and that this was due to their lack of Fc receptors. This likely explains Hawkes' findings of such enhancement because he had used a Murray Valley encephalitis virus model in chicken embryo fibroblasts (connective tissue cells) that were found to also contain functional macrophages, cells which participate in the immune process. It was also found that the antibody used in this system had to be from birds, as the Fc terminals of mammalian antibodies

Figure 109. Phillip King Russell (1932 -)
(image courtesy of Phillip Russell)

do not interact with Fc receptors of antibodies from birds. In 1983, Halstead, Linda Kay Larsen, Srisakul Kliks, Peiris, Jane Cardosa, and Porterfield reported the use of P388D1 mouse macrophage cells for larger scale studies of dengue virus-enhancing antibodies. David M. Morens, Marchette, May C. Chu, and Halstead later showed that the characteristics of replication of dengue virus 2 in human peripheral blood leukocytes correlate with severity of dengue disease. Included among the more than 100 publications by Halstead and hundreds of other papers published on the subject were co-authors William H. Bancroft, Walter Brandt, Arwin R. Diwan, Kenneth H. Eckels, Nicholas E. Palumbo, Ravithat Putvatana, Philip K. Russell (Figure 109), Robert McN. Scott, Suchinda Udomsakdi, and a host of others who made significant contributions to this body of work.

The complexity of the mechanism, the nature of the molecular participants, the evolution, and the extent of antibody-dependent enhancement of viral replication were not fully understood but, because DHF became the most important viral cause of childhood morbidity and mortality in Southeast Asia, the hunt was on to better understand these viruses, in order to control or eliminate them. That is because understanding the epidemiology of the virus and developing a suitable vaccine in such situations are always among the first thoughts of the medical community when an epidemic is recognized. In this instance, the epidemiology was fairly obvious but application of a vaccine containing antigens of a single dengue virus would only prime the immunologic pump and set the stage for DHF/DSS.

One would expect that eradicating dengue from islands where it occurs would be a first logical step in its worldwide eradication, but doing so has been a daunting task. Interisland and intercontinental travel by dengue-infected humans visiting places where susceptible human populations live, inaccessible vertebrate hosts (primates) of dengue viruses in remote forested regions, generation-to-generation (vertical, transovarial) transmission of these viruses through the eggs of their natural arthropod hosts, climatic changes, and other natural and unnatural events prevent the eradication of diseases caused by the dengue viruses.

Studies of Dengue by Other Investigators

Hundreds of people have been involved in studies of dengue wherever it occurs and in laboratories in many places where it does not occur. The prominent role of the United States military cannot be overstated, as for decades it has supported in-house and collaborative studies of all aspects of dengue diseases and of dengue viruses. Albert Sabin, at the time a member of the United States Army Epidemiological Board, Preventive Medicine Division, Office of the Surgeon general, published a summary of research results achieved by the United States military and others during World War II, including the following:

1. Proof of the existence of multiple immunological types of dengue.
2. The long persistence of immunity to homologous types of virus under conditions precluding reinforcement of immunity by subclinical reinfection.
3. The modifications of the clinical manifestations of the disease that result from reinfection with a heterologous type of virus at various periods after the primary attack.

4. The demonstration that in areas where more than one dengue virus is present, fevers of unknown origin, clinically not recognizable as dengue, are actually caused by dengue viruses.
5. The demonstration that type-specific immunity to dengue is associated with neutralizing antibodies for the virus, which can be used for diagnostic and epidemiologic survey purposes.
6. The propagation of a dengue virus in mice with the resulting appearance of a mutant or variant strain that could be used for active immunization.

Mutual interest in the various manifestations of dengue virus infections and of the viruses themselves and the need to study these illnesses in detail led the government of Thailand and the Walter Reed Army Institute of Research to establish a laboratory in Bangkok and to use the proximity of Thai hospitals caring for dengue patients of all ages. Over many years William H. Bancroft, Walter E. Brandt, Donald S. Burke, Joel M. Dalrymple, Kenneth H. Eckels, Timothy P. Endy, Mary K. Gentry, Scott B. Halstead, Erik A. Henchal, Charles H. Hoke, Jr., Bruce L. Innis, Jack M. McCown, J. Robert Putnak, Patricia M. Repik, Philip K. Russell, Franklin H. Top, Jr., and David W. Vaughn toiled in tropical and subtropical areas overseas as well as in laboratories in the United States. Their principal collaborators and colleagues have been and are in Thailand (Ananda Nisalak, Armed Forces Research Institute of Medical Sciences, Bangkok), at the University of Massachusetts Medical Center, Worcester (Francis A. Ennis, Ichiro Kurani, Alan L. Rothman), in Japan (Akira Igarashi, Institute of Tropical Medicine Nagasaki University, Nagasaki), at the University of Maryland School of Medicine, Baltimore (Robert Edelman), and elsewhere. In no way should this be considered a complete or even near-complete list of people involved in these studies done over many decades. Many of these efforts were directed towards developing a vaccine against the dengue viruses, the most wide-spread and globally important arboviruses. That they were not completely successful should not be considered a failure. The information they developed has laid the groundwork for other studies, at least some of which will eventually lead to an acceptable and useful vaccine.

At the CDC, investigators at the Division of Vector-Borne Infectious Diseases in Fort Collins and its predecessor organizations oversaw the Dengue Branch in San Juan, Puerto Rico, developed assays, conducted epidemiologic surveys, studied the molecular evolution of dengue viruses, determined risk factors for acquiring dengue virus infections, and otherwise provided training and resources to governments of Caribbean and Central and South American countries. At one time or another, David Pimentel, Charles S. Gerhardt, Frederick F. Ferguson, Barnett L. Cline, John P. Woodall, Ernesto Ruiz, Roslyn Q. Robinson, Duane Gubler, Gary G. Clark, Wellington Sun, Kay Tomashek, and now Harold Margolis directed the San Juan Laboratory. A host of exceptional staff members participated in the studies, including Graham E. Kemp, Goro Kuno, Chester G. Moore, Paul Reiter, Jose Rigau-Pérez, Gladys E. Sather, Steven Waterman, and A. Vance Vorndam. Gubler's application of the method he and Leon Rosen developed for amplification of dengue viruses, which was to inoculate clinical samples of material known to contain a dengue virus into *Aedes albopictus* mosquitoes, later adapted by Rosen for use with *Toxorhynchites amboinensis,* an unusually large, non-hematophagous mosquito (therefore safe to use, even if an infected mosquito somehow became free), was used to detect, propagate and store dengue viruses.

Numerous other groups of investigators have been working in multiple countries to understand the epidemiology of the dengue viruses so that they might prevent the illnesses they cause. In the 1970s N. Joel Ehrenkranz, Arnoldo K. Ventura, William L. Pond, and Raul R. Cuadrado studied dengue and its many manifestations in Jamaica, Haiti, and elsewhere in the Caribbean area. Their historic overviews and epidemiologic reports helped establish a foundation for subsequent studies. Albert Rudnick of the George William Hooper Foundation, University of California School of Medicine at San Francisco, labored for decades in Kuala Lumpur, Malaysia, studying the ecologic parameters of dengue outbreaks, clinical aspects of hemorrhagic dengue, and entomologic characteristics of the vector (and non-vector) mosquitoes of the area. He further hypothesized a jungle cycle for these viruses, an idea supported by data from A. H. Fagbami, Thomas Monath, and A. Fabiyi in Nigeria and proven by Francois Rodhain of the Pasteur Institute.

Results of studies of dengue epidemics in Jamaica, Brazil, and elsewhere in Central America and South America have contributed nicely to the scientific record but a great deal of detailed information also emerged from the interest garnered by Cuban investigators when a series of dengue epidemics occurred there, first in 1977 when 500,000 cases of fever caused by dengue virus 1 swept through the island. A subsequent serologic survey indicated that 44.5% of the urban population had been infected with this virus. In May 1981 simultaneous reports of dengue came from three areas and the epidemic spread within a few days to the rest of the country. In all, 344,203 cases were reported, 10,312 of them were severely ill, and 158 people (101 children and 57 adults) died of dengue hemorrhagic fever caused by dengue virus 2. Led by Gustavo P. Kourí, Director of the Virology Department of the Pedro Kourí Institute of Tropical Medicine in Havana, Maria G. Guzman and others, including Pedro Más Lago, Marta Soler, and Nereida Cantelar, they investigated the clinical, epidemiologic, virologic, and diagnostic aspects, conducted serologic surveys, developed rapid and accurate diagnostic techniques, formulated and carried out (with the help of others, of course) mosquito control programs that continue, and determined the economic impact of the disease.

In 1975, I went to Havana at the request of the Cuban government to participate in the testing of human serum samples in order to study and better understand the arthropod-borne virus situation there. The results of the serologic survey indicated that Cuba was vulnerable to the spread of dengue viruses. In fact, two years after we completed the serologic survey Cuba experienced an outbreak of dengue, followed a few years later by a much more deadly epidemic, with many cases of dengue hemorrhagic fever caused by dengue virus 2. Subsequently, the Cuban government, in an attempt to cover their own oversights and failures, alleged that the U.S. government was involved and publicly and falsely implicated me in this human disaster. A summary of my views on this has been published.

While in Havana I had a beautiful room with a beautiful view in a hotel whose glory had passed. One evening after dinner I took a bus to a baseball field where there was a game between teams of excellent Cuban players. The next day I was invited to attend a baseball game at the same park. When I told the inviter I had already done that, I was told I should not have.

No one had advised me to take my meals in the hotel dining room, but I now suppose that I was expected to. I had preferred to find a nice little restaurant elsewhere and soon found one, but when I tried to pay the bill I was told there was no bill and that this was a restaurant for people with identifications that I did not have. Thanking the staff for dinner and nice service, I left to walk back to my hotel.

On the way I saw a woman leaning out the window of a room in an apartment from which smoke was escaping. There were fire trucks up and down the street but no one was paying the least bit of attention to the poor woman, so I entered the building, ran up the stairs, found and entered the apartment, and tried to get her to leave with me. She refused, vehemently, so I went to the window and, given that I was not in a crowded theater, shouted "Fuego!". The firemen soon arrived and one of them informed me that this was an exercise only, but she thanked me politely and led me back to the street. I learned a valuable lesson from that experience but I cannot recall what that was.

Notwithstanding all the efforts to prevent and control dengue and of the approximately 2.5 billion at-risk people living in the tropical and subtropical areas where dengue occurs, W.H.O. estimates that 50 million people acquire dengue each year, that an estimated 500,000 people (mainly children) with dengue hemorrhagic fever require hospitalization each year, and that about 2.5% (12,500) of them die. Without proper treatment, dengue hemorrhagic fever case-fatality rates can exceed 20%.

W.H.O.'s "DengueNet" web site indicates that about 884,000 reported cases occurred between 2000 and 2005. That is bad enough news, but worse when one considers that the number of dengue and dengue hemorrhagic fever cases appears to be doubling each 10 years (1955-1959 ≈ 900, 1960-1969 ≈ 15,000, 1970-1979 ≈ 122,000, 1980-1989 ≈ 295,000, 1990-1999 ≈ 481,000, and 2000-2005 ≈ 884,000). Global climate change may bring about an increase of this disaster, and the interval 2000-2005 is not 10 years. It is clear that unless we find a way to control or reduce the prevalence of this disease, the situation may soon become even more appalling. There is more work for arbovirologists than ever before.

CHAPTER 8

The arbovirologic community: a collaborative endeavor

With so much work being done by a few recognized centers of arboviral research, it was possible that they would become no more than amoeba-like institutions which did research but did not share their results in a collegial and timely manner, which is somewhat of a problem today. Nothing could be further from the truth. From its earliest days as a focus group, the arbovirologic community ensured that because international communication was essential, it should be a hallmark of the field. Even beyond scientific findings, emphasis was placed on communication and collaboration. Unfortunately, political realities prevented even more partnerships, but personal friendships often found a way. As Arnold S. Relman said, "Research is a collegial activity that requires its practitioners to trust the integrity of their colleagues."

In addition to the initial field work and fundamental virus collecting by Rockefeller Foundation and CDC investigators, first-class state health departments and universities in the United States and elsewhere conducted virus and vector surveillance in an effort to accumulate useful predictive data. Predicting what nature has in store is never completely successful but application of field and laboratory protocols and techniques held out the promise that accumulated data would eventually provide some clarity to epidemiologic situations. Eventually, thousands of observational papers were published, expertise established, reputations made, and jobs secured, so that funding was provided and further hypotheses devised.

Contributions by California Scientists

Researchers in the California Department of Health/University of California at Berkeley/George Williams Hooper Foundation (Richard W. Emmons, William McD. Hammon, James L. Hardy, Edwin H. Lennette, Karl F. Meyer, Marilyn M. Milby, Lyndon S. Oshiro, Sally B. Presser, William C. Reeves, William K. Reisen, Nathalie J. Schmidt, and their students) developed virus and antibody detection methods. They investigated the biology, epidemiology, pathology, and natural history of western equine encephalitis, St. Louis encephalitis, Colorado tick fever, and other human pathogens, and they studied the biology of the arthropods that transmitted them. By communicating openly with other arbovirologists and entomologists, researchers exchanged useful information, and improved their techniques, sharpened their skills, and shared tools. Reeves and his associates S. Monica Asman, Hardy, Milby and Reisen published a summary of entomologic and virologic studies done between 1943 and 1987. That publication includes remarkable details and useful ideas.

La Crosse virus and other California serogroup viruses

Often in conjunction with state university researchers, investigators at the Florida, Iowa, New York, Ohio, Texas, Wisconsin and other state health departments concerned themselves with studies of the arboviruses that affected their human and livestock populations, principally eastern equine encephalitis, western equine encephalitis, St. Louis encephalitis, and La Crosse encephalitis. Investigations of

La Crosse encephalitis alone provide an excellent example of work done principally at a university but in close collaboration with a state health department. The cause of this illness is La Crosse virus, a California serogroup virus, now recognized as a member of the genus *Orthobunyavirus* of the family *Bunyaviridae*. Isolated in La Crosse, Wisconsin, from the brain of a child who had died in nearby Minnesota in 1960, this previously unrecognized virus occurs not only in the Upper Midwest of the United States but essentially in all states east of the Mississippi River. The first virus of the California serogroup had been isolated in 1943 and a few human illnesses caused by that virus, California encephalitis virus, were recognized somewhat later by Hammon, Reeves and Gladys E. Sather. La Crosse virus came to be seen as a larger problem than was California encephalitis virus, causing scores of cases each year in and around its epidemiologic epicenter in Wisconsin. According to the CDC, between 1964 and 2009 a mean of about 90 cases (range = about 30 to 170) of neuroinvasive La Crosse virus infections were detected each year in children living primarily in the Upper Midwest (Minnesota, Wisconsin, Iowa, Illinois, Indiana and Ohio). More recently cases have been reported from mid-Atlantic and southeastern states (West Virginia, Virginia, Kentucky, North Carolina, and Tennessee). This is an under-reported illness, as are infections with other California serogroup viruses, including Jamestown Canyon virus.

How La Crosse virus persists through harsh Midwestern winters was a prime question. Through efforts led by Wayne Thompson, an outstanding group was formed to take on this clinical and virological challenge, with Ralph O. Anslow, Barry J. Beaty, Gene R. DeFoliart, Robert P. Hanson, Bernard Kalfayan, Laura D. Kramer, S. Pantuwatana, Daniel O. Trainer, Douglas M. Watts, Thomas M. Yuill, and many graduate students and assistants. The earliest investigations demonstrated that the principal mosquito vectors of this virus are those of the tree-hole breeding species *Aedes triseriatus*. Further studies showed that eastern chipmunks (*Tamias striatus*) were the natural vertebrate hosts of the virus and that it was transovarially and venereally transmitted (both female to male and male to female) among mosquitoes, answering the question regarding over-wintering persistence. These and other classical observations regarding La Crosse virus changed the landscape in terms of determining the natural history of many arboviruses. Moreover, information gained from those studies proved particularly valuable, especially the observation that other tree-hole breeding mosquitoes could serve as virus vectors and that these same mosquitoes could be found in mountainous piles of used automobile and truck tires in rural areas, the tires serving as gigantic breeding sites for some of them.

Soon after those early discoveries in Wisconsin, Donald M. McLean and his colleagues at the University of British Columbia, Vancouver, Canada, isolated snowshoe hare (California serogroup) virus from mosquitoes collected at Marsh Lake in the Yukon Territory. As a young physician at the Walter and Eliza Hall Institute, McLean had been introduced to field research by William Reeves (of California) in 1952, when Reeves was invited to Australia to put together a field and laboratory team to determine the arthropod vector of Murray Valley encephalitis virus. After his initial findings at Marsh Lake, McLean returned there in winter and collected mosquito larvae from beneath the ice-covered surface of the lake, from which larvae he also isolated snowshoe hare virus, adding further support to the hypothesis that transovarial transmission of California serogroup viruses is a general phenomenon, at least in temperate and subarctic habitats.

Richard Berry, Margaret Parsons and others at the Ohio Department of Health soon demonstrated that another California serogroup virus, Jamestown Canyon virus, was transmitted transovarially. Robert B. Tesh and many colleagues (Thomas Aitken, Barry Beaty, Byron Chaniotis, Bedsy Dutary, Duane Gubler, Karl Johnson, Govind Modi, Pauline Peralta, Leon Rosen, Donald Shroyer, and others) showed that transovarial transmission of many California serogroup viruses and other arboviruses could occur in laboratory-bred mosquitoes or sandflies.

Also contributing greatly to our knowledge of arboviruses has been the United States Army. At the Walter Reed Army Institute of Research and its overseas laboratories, Walter E. Brandt, Edward L. Buescher, Donald A. Burke, Joel M. Dalrymple, Charles H. Hoke, Phillip K. Russell, Albert Sabin, William F. Scherer, Joseph Smadel, Franklin Top, Jr., Thomas M. Yuill, and a host of others conducted field and laboratory studies of yellow fever, Japanese encephalitis, dengue, and other viruses. They produced and evaluated experimental vaccines, devised and improved methods and applied them, and pushed the frontiers of arbovirology toward an unseen horizon.

Investigators Elsewhere

In Europe, Australia, Africa, Asia, and South America, many noteworthy (and personally memorable) investigators, some working under nearly impossible conditions studied arboviruses in their countries and in nearby countries. Of particular note are investigations by those at the far-flung laboratories of the Pasteur Institute system who have produced some classic observations and conducted applied research leading to many practical applications, including anti-venom serums and vaccines against tuberculosis, plague, and yellow fever.

Contributions of Scientists from France: In 1890, M. Etienne, Under-Secretary of State for the (French) Colonies, asked Louis Pasteur to create a center in Saigon (now Ho Chi Minh City), Vietnam (at the time the French colony of Cochin-China) to develop vaccines against smallpox and rabies. Pasteur agreed and offered the directorship position to senior colonial physician, Albert Calmette, who immediately accepted the job. Another Pasteur Institute laboratory was established in Nha-Trang, Vietnam, that one headed by Alexandre Yersin who, while in Hong Kong, had discovered the plague bacillus, now named *Yersinia pestis*. Additional laboratories were established in Senegal, Madagascar, (Republic of the) Congo, Martinique, Cambodia, New Caledonia, Guyana, Iran, Guadeloupe, China, Cameroon, Central

African Republic, and Ivory Coast. Many of these laboratories are still in operation and function well. Their workers isolated numerous previously unrecognized arboviruses and other viruses and made many fundamental discoveries and medical advances; Laveran, Charles Jules Henri Nicolle, François Jacob, André Lwoff, Jacques Monod, of the Pasteur Institute system received Nobel Prizes. In the early 1930s, intensive collaboration between the Pasteur Institute Dakar (Constantin Mathis, Jean Laigret) and Harvard University (Andrew Sellards) allowed the development of a vaccine against yellow fever, called FNV (French Neurotropic Vaccine), which was used in West Africa from the early 1960s until 1982.

The accomplishments of Pasteur Institute scientists such as Pierre Ardoin, Michèle Bouloy, Paul Bres (Figure 90), Claude Chastel, Alain Chippaux, Roger Cordellier, Michel Cornet, Vincent Deubel, Jean-Pierre Digoutte, Max Germain, Jean-Paul Gonzalez, Claude Hannoun, Jean-Pierre Herve, Michel Lhuillier, Jean Mouchet, Bernadette Murgue, Yves Robin, Francois Rodhain, Jean-Francois Saluzzo, Jean-Louis Sarthou, Pierre Sureau, Hervé Zeller, and scores of others working in remote regions of the tropics played an important role in our understanding of the geographic distributions of arboviruses and of their epidemiologies, molecular peculiarities, and physico-chemical characteristics. These contributions cannot be overstated. To this day, many of these laboratories keep us apprised of virus emergences, including studies of ebolaviruses in Gabonese non-human primates and bats and of many other viruses that occur in areas served by the 32 institutes in the Pasteur system, scattered throughout Africa, the Americas, the Asia-Pacific Region, Europe and Iran.

Another of the many innovative and noteworthy contributions of the Pasteur Institute over the years has been its policy of providing experience to multiple investigators, allowing them to spend time at overseas institutes situated in tropical locations while maintaining contact with France itself and with Pasteur Institute resources.

Contributions of Scientists from South Africa: In Africa, laboratories established by national or international organizations can be found in many countries, but the principal ones include the Pasteur Institute laboratories, the former Rockefeller Foundation laboratories (now administered locally), both a veterinary research laboratory and the Kenya Medical Research Institute in Kenya, and the Uganda Virus Research Institute in Entebbe. Another important facility is the world-class Special Pathogens Unit at the National Institute for Communicable Diseases of the National Health Laboratory Service, Sandringham, South Africa. From 1980 Robert Swanepoel from Zimbabwe directed the development of and applied diagnoses and epidemiologic investigations for severe viral illnesses, with both clinical and pathologic studies emphasized. The Special Pathogens Unit now is headed by Janusz T. Paweska.

Researchers at the Sandringham facilities study diseases including Marburg virus disease, diseases caused by ebolaviruses, Crimean-Congo hemorrhagic fever, Rift Valley fever, West Nile virus encephalitis, rabies virus, Lujo virus (a newly recognized arenavirus causing a hemorrhagic fever), Lassa virus and other terrifying diseases in South Africa, Angola, Gabon, Republic of Congo, and elsewhere on that fascinating, gigantic, and ecologically varied continent. When a previously unrecognized virus or other disease agent suddenly crops up in Africa, the people at Sandringham are the first to be contacted. Their accumulated experimental studies of viruses add to the body of information regarding these viruses. It is unfortunate that we no longer have Dr. Margaretha Isaäcson (Figure 110) at the National Institute for Communicable Diseases of the National Health

Figure 110. Margaretha Isaäcson (1929 - 2001)
(image courtesy of the South African Institute for Medical Research)

Laboratory Service, Sandringham, South Africa, to add her expertise and efforts to what is being done, but Felicity J. Burt, Marietjie Venter and others carry on the superb work done there.

To augment the efforts of such laboratories, W.H.O. has a Neglected Tropical Diseases Department. The Foundations Initiative for African Research into Neglected Tropical Diseases is supported by European foundations. There is also a Global Network for Neglected Tropical Diseases, a program of the non-profit Sabin Vaccine Institute. The United States Agency for International Development has established a Global Network for Neglected Tropical Diseases. The long-needed journal PLoS Neglected Tropical Diseases is devoted solely to focusing on such viruses and the diseases they cause. To preempt the emergence of viruses before they become uncontrollable, many countries have established laboratories to research heretofore less well-studied viruses.

In France, the Emerging Virus Unit, University of the Mediterranean, Marseille, is such a laboratory, employing the most modern techniques and insights to confront modern problems. There Xavier de Lamballerie, Remy N. Charrel, and others have illuminated areas that had been in the dark regarding scores of viruses. Their interest in viruses that previously had been poorly studied has opened new avenues of knowledge.

Contributions of Scientists from Germany: From the very beginnings of virology, German virologists have been involved in fundamental and practical aspects of the field. A prime historical example of this is the now-classic research on foot-and-mouth disease virus on the Island of Reims in eastern Germany conducted by Friedrich Loeffler, a collaborator of Robert Koch, the great German bacteriologist, and Paul Frosch. Recognizing that Ernst Ruska of the Fritz Haber Institute, Max Planck Society, Berlin, was an inventor of the transmission electron microscope provides further perspective on fundamental achievements of German scientists. Ruska was awarded a Nobel Prize in Physics in 1986. More recently, however, most German arbovirologists have focused on diagnosis and treatment of immediate clinical problems, on disease and virus surveillance, and on the molecular biology of viruses, a very strong aspect of their work.

Volker Moennig, Irene M. Greiser-Wilke, and Oscar R. Kaaden: These scientists from the Institute of Virology, Hannover Veterinary School, contribute greatly to our understanding of hog cholera (classical swine fever) pestivirus and bovine viral diarrhea pestivirus, both members of the family *Flaviviridae*. They developed monoclonal antibodies to study the pathogenesis of these viruses as well as of Semliki Forest alphavirus and to develop sensitive and elegant diagnostic assays for them.

Rudolf Rott: From the Institute for Virology, Justus Liebig University, Geissen, Rott worked mostly with influenzaviruses and Borna disease virus but also with Semliki Forest alphavirus. Collaborating with Christoph Scholtissek, he demonstrated that the optimal gene constellation necessary for pathogenicity of influenzaviruses functions only through the genes coding for the polymerase complex (1979). This was as fundamental a finding as any with regard to influenzaviruses and to the possibilities of epidemics and prevention.

Gernot Hildebrand Bergold: After he left the University at Tübingen in 1948, Bergold moved to Canada and became what could be regarded as the founder of biochemical insect virology because of his research with polyhedrosis and other insect diseases. Later, Bergold became head of the Venezuelan Institute of Scientific Investigations, Caracas. There he collaborated with Octavio M. Suarez, Raúl Walder, and others in Venezuela and elsewhere on molecular and biological studies of arboviruses and other viruses. Bergold was an influential author of seminal papers describing and defining the biology and taxonomy of arenaviruses.

So many other viruses were identified and so many infections by viruses were diagnosed by German virologists that Rott has hesitantly called virology "one of the jewels of German research". In fact, however, arbovirology in Germany has been not as much a field of virus discovery as a practical area of medicine and as a common ground for cell molecular biologists. B. Rehse-Küpper (Medical Diagnostics Laboratory, Cologne), Gerhard Dobler and Martin Pfeffer, now at the University of Leipzig, (German Federal Defense Force Institute of Microbiology, Munich), Renate Ackermann (Max Planck Institute for Infection Biology, Berlin), Hans R. Gelderblom, the now-retired exceptional electron microscopist at the Robert Koch Institute, Berlin, and hundreds of others have used arboviruses themselves as tools to study an assortment of aspects of the natural history of viruses and to develop simpler and more specific diagnostics, all intended to reduce the human disease burden caused by these viruses.

Contributions of Scientists from Croatia and Other Former Yugoslavian states:

The former Yugoslavia comprised the states of Slovenia, Croatia, Bosnia and Herzegovina, Montenegro, Serbia and Kosovo, formerly part of Serbia, and Macedonia; you may have read of this in a newspaper. Artificially created by various governmental agreements, that country was always at some level of disarray but was controlled politically, playing one side against the other during the Cold War. Now established as separate republics, the chaos has lessened and each country is independently, but cooperatively, involved in virus research.

Tatjana Avšič-Županc: From the Institute for Microbiology and Immunology, Ljubljana, Slovenia, Avšič-Županc (Figure 73) teamed with Jelka Vesenjak-Hirjan early in her career and has become one of the leading arbovirologists of Europe. Her field and molecular studies of tick-borne encephalitis virus in Slovenia and Crimean-Congo hemorrhagic fever virus in Kosovo have been useful, but it is the investigations of hantaviruses by her and her co-workers that have made her a recognized leader in hantavirology. Cross-training with colleagues in the United States and elsewhere, Avšič-Županc has isolated or otherwise detected many hantaviruses, including Dobrava virus, a human pathogen causing severe illness, and has studied the natural history of these viruses in European rodents.

Contributions of Scientists from the Czech Republic and Slovak Republic:

Studies of arboviruses in what was Czechoslovakia (now the Czech Republic and the Slovak Republic) have for many decades provided the arbovirus community with fundamentally significant information regarding both the natural history of arboviruses and arthropod biology.

Vojtech Bárdoš: Born in Trencin, Slovakia, in 1914, Vojtech Bárdoš graduated from the medical school of Comenius University and then served as the head of the regional Bacteriology Institute in Presov, where he conducted extensive epidemiologic studies of paratyphus, spotted fever, and malaria. In 1945 he became chief epidemiologist of Slovakia, a position he held until 1952. During 1946-1947, Bárdoš attended Johns Hopkins University School of Public Health where he received training in virological techniques and a Master of Public Health degree. From 1952 to 1971 he headed the Department of Virology of what is now the Institute of Preventive Medicine Research in Bratislava and spent the rest of his life focused on the biology, ecology, and epidemiology of arboviruses in Czechoslovakia. His investigations of tick-borne encephalitis led to the first isolation of the virus in Slovakia, epidemiologic evidence of human infections acquired by drinking raw goat milk, investigations of large outbreaks of the disease, and preparation of immune globulin for disease therapy.

Studies of mosquito-borne viruses with the renowned entomologist Vlasta Danielová of the National Institute of Public Health in Prague led Bárdoš to the discovery of Tahyna and Čalovo (Batai) viruses. He later demonstrated viremia and illness in humans naturally infected with Tahyna virus and isolated that virus from larvae of *Culiseta annulata* mosquitoes, reinforcing our knowledge of transovarial transmission of California serogroup orthobunyaviruses.

Bárdoš received the Louis Pasteur Medal from the Pasteur Institute and two awards from the Institute of Virology, Moscow. In later years he organized the highly successful international symposia at Smolenice and served W.H.O. as a consultant in microbiology and virology in Kabul (Afghanistan), Colombo (Sri Lanka), and Rangoon (Burma, now Myanmar). An honest, vibrant, witty, and dedicated scientist, Bárdoš lectured on his favorite topic, arboviruses; authored numerous papers, book chapters, and monographs; and otherwise contributed greatly to arbovirology world-wide. He edited an early and classic book summarizing the proceedings of an international meeting on viruses of the California and Bunyamwera serogroup viruses (family *Bunyaviridae*, genus *Orthobunyavirus*), a 1966 meeting that brought together investigators from both sides of the so-called Iron Curtain.

Dionýs ("Dino") Blaškovič: In response to the occurrence of many cases of severe central nervous system disease, Blaškovič, a knowledgeable, charming and well-organized scientist-administrator at the Institute of Virology, (Czechoslovak) Academy of Sciences, Bratislava (now Slovakia), directed concentrated efforts to study tick-borne encephalitis and the virus that causes it. Through the detailed efforts of physician-virologists and in the grand tradition of basic European entomology, fundamental studies of arboviruses and other viruses were scrutinized, revealing many fascinating differences among them.

Milota Grešíková: A number of exceptional investigations were made by Grešíková (who had spent time with William C. Reeves at Berkeley studying California serogroup orthobunyaviruses) and her staff, including Elo Ernek, Oto Kožuch, Milan Labuda, Helena Libiková, Jozef Nosek, Julius Rajcáni, Magdaléna Sekeyová, and others. They developed useful cultures of cells from arthropods, isolated West Nile virus from birds, and showed that tick-borne encephalitis virus could be passed in the milk of infected livestock. They provided results of detailed studies of *Ixodes ricinus*, the principal tick vector of tick-borne encephalitis virus in western Europe. They also isolated Sindbis virus from birds, from ticks in Slovenia and Italy, and from black-bellied hamsters (*Cricetus cricetus*) and marsh frogs (*Rana ridibunda*); conducted experimental infections with viruses of Slovakia; isolated Tribec virus; and demonstrated the presence of hemorrhagic fever with renal syndrome in Slovakia. They also searched for arboviruses in Hungary in collaboration with Elisabeth Molnár of the Department of Virology, State Institute of Hygiene, Budapest, Hungary.

Zdenek Hubalek: The Czech Republic (and its predecessor) has also produced a number of fine arbovirologists whose primary interest was preventing disease but who also realized that knowledge of the underlying mechanisms of virus-host interactions would provide useful insights regarding virus replication, epidemiology, and, ultimately, effective prevention and treatment. One of these biologists-theoreticians is Zdenek Hubálek, now at the Institute of Vertebrate Biology, Academy of Sciences of the Czech Republic, Brno. A collaborator and student of Bárdoš, Hubálek began his career in mycology but soon changed to arbovirology. His interests include surveillance and epidemiology of virus diseases, the occurrence of West Nile virus in Europe, effects of weather and of human activities on virus prevalence, and biogeography. He has authored publications, either alone or with multiple European collaborators, on subjects ranging from virology to bacteriology, including Lyme disease. Well trained and imaginative, Hubálek is an inveterate list-keeper and academic.

Contributions of Scientists from Finland:

Finns are a practical people. Therefore, their arbovirological research has focused on detection and diagnosis of infections. Investigators at the University of Helsinki and the University of Turku, as well as the Finnish Forest Research Institute in Vantaa and various

Figure 111. Nils Christian Edgar Oker-Blom (1919 - 1995)
(image courtesy of the University of Helsinki)

other organizations throughout Finland have contributed significantly to our knowledge of arboviruses and rodent-borne viruses.

Nils Oker-Blom: First to mention, of course, is Nils Oker-Blom (Figure 111), a physician-virologist who worked at the University of Helsinki. Oker-Blom was born in Helsinki and obtained M.D. and Ph.D. degree from the University there. He became its first professor in virology, then Chair of the Department of Virology, Dean of the Medical School, and finally Chancellor of the University (a position third in line to the Presidency of Finland). He was as interested in promoting international science as he was interested in anything. In fact, he organized the first International Congress of Virology (1968). A kind, honest, charming person, and adept administrator, he built a world-class Finnish capacity in virology, while at the same time holding chairs and other leadership positions in various international organizations.

His interest in virology had begun in 1948 when he met with Sven Gard, the "Grand Old Man" of Swedish virology, in Stockholm, and Francisco Duran-Reynals in 1949-1950 at the Rockefeller Foundation in New York City. (Recall that Duran-Reynals was the very person who was trying to convince Jordi Casals to leave the Rockefeller Foundation laboratories and return to Spain to establish a Rockefeller Foundation-like institute there when the Spanish Civil War broke out.) Oker-Blom studied Rous sarcoma retrovirus in Duran-Reynals' laboratory, discovering acute chicken leucosis virus along the way. Because of his conversations with Casals and others, when he returned home he continued exploring his interest in virus epidemiology and of the possibility of devising vaccinations against polioviruses. In the late 1950s and early 1960s, supported by the Rockefeller Foundation, Oker-Blom and his colleagues carried out a major survey for the presence of arboviruses in Finland. This led to the first isolation of a tick-borne encephalitis virus in Finland (named Kumlinge virus, after the name of the island in the Gulf of Bothnia where it was found), and the disease it causes, named "Kumlinge disease". We now know that Kumlinge virus is a variant of Central European encephalitis (European subtype) flavivirus. Oker-Blom and co-workers also discovered Inkoo and Uukuniemi viruses, members of the family *Bunyaviridae*. During the early 1980s, he promoted the establishment of recombinant DNA technology in Finland. All this led to the Finnish recruitment of excellent laboratory and field personnel, consummate scientists: Olli Vapalahti, Antti Vaheri, Heikki Henttonen, Alexander Plyusnin, Levi Kääriäinen, Carl H. von Bonsdorff, Pekka Saikku, Markkus Brummer-Korvenkontio, and more.

Pekka E. Halonen: Another of the great Finnish physician-virologists, Halonen (1927-2001) was born in Helsinki and obtained his medical degree from the University of Helsinki. His interest in research motivated him to complete a thesis in virology at that university in 1955. Awarded a Rockefeller Foundation Fellowship, he used it to continue his training, this time at the United States National Institutes of Health. After serving as a lecturer at the University of Helsinki, he was appointed Professor and Chairman of the Department of of Virology at the University of Turku. Halonen, and his accomplished colleagues Perti P. Arstila, Timo Hyypiä, Olli Meurman, Aimo A. Salmi, Hanu K. Sarkkinen, Theodore Zeigler, and others focused on development of rapid and specific diagnostic methods for virus infections. A forward-looking peculiarity of the Finnish health system is that it provides additional funding for additional testing. Halonen used this funding to develop additional tests. With unparalleled facilities and devoted and well-trained personnel, he and his colleagues developed rapid tests for viruses from gastrointestinal, central nervous system, respiratory and other diseases and a laboratory that served the world as a training center, taking in many visitors and sending them home to spread the word and apply the methods.

Halonen had spent 1966-1967 as Visiting Scientist in the virology section at CDC in Atlanta, and it seemed he did not waste a minute. First he participated in improving the preparation of La Crosse virus hemagglutinin using BHK-21 cells in suspension cultures. Rubella virus (family *Togaviridae*, genus *Rubivirus*) was first isolated at that time, congenital rubella syndrome had been recognized, and rapid diagnostic tests were needed to make timely medical decisions. Halonen developed the first hemagglutination-inhibition test for antibody to rubella virus and then evaluated the various serologic techniques for measurement of antibody to rubella virus. Using an electron microscope and working with Frederick Murphy, he characterized the development of that virus in BHK-21 cells. Halonen's interest in rabies virus led to the discovery of the hemagglutinin of that virus and the first descriptions of the physical characteristics of that hemagglutinin.

In the years after, at the University of Turku, Halonen and his colleagues developed assays for a remarkable diversity of viruses: adenoviruses, influenza viruses, parainfluenza viruses, respiratory syncytial virus, measles virus, Coxsackie B viruses and other enteroviruses, herpes simplex viruses, Epstein-Barr virus, varicella-zoster virus, rotaviruses, Pogosta disease virus (caused by a Sindbis virus subtype known as Ockelbo virus in Finland and as Karelian fever virus in Russia), LaCrosse virus, vesicular stomatitis viruses, and many others. His research on enzyme-linked immunosorbent assays for the detection of viral antigens and IgM antibodies was important in the development of many practical diagnostic tests. He was a pioneer both in the incorporation of monoclonal antibodies for increased specificity and in the development of radioimmmunoassays, time-resolved fluoro-immunoassays, and the polymerase chain reaction assay. These were incorporated at one time or another into the extensive range of tests that could be used for laboratory diagnosis.

Halonen appreciated the importance of understanding the host immune response as a key to developing better diagnostic methodology. In 1979 he spent three months in the Department of Medical Virology at the University of Uppsala working on IgA-based assays. Halonen was also fascinated with the possible viral etiology of central nervous system diseases, including multiple sclerosis, Parkinsonism, and, ironically, amyotrophic lateral sclerosis, the disease from which he suffered during his last years and which robbed him of his life and us of his extraordinary personality and the many more diagnostic innovations he surely would have made.

In 1993, with the encouragement of Walter P. Dowdle, at the time the Director of CDC, and of Frederick A. Murphy, long-time friend, mentor and colleague at CDC, my family and I left for a period of training for me in Halonen's laboratory in Turku. I had met Pekka at CDC years before, when he had been working on diagnosis of rubella virus infections and successfully producing a diagnostically-useful hemagglutinin of that virus in my laboratory. Charming, energetic, enthusiastic and innovative as he was, I had jumped at the opportunity to spend time with Halonen in Finland.

As soon as we arrived in Turku, we placed our children in a Finnish language school, an experiment that lasted about a day, after which they attended a Swedish language school. I also had some difficulty with Finnish. Once trying to purchase a small amount of hamburger meat, I actually requested 500 kilos instead; henceforth I let my wife or the children do the shopping.

Finland is a marvelous country with a terrible history of either one neighbor or the other attacking it for the worst of reasons. Finns, however, are tough and have built a marvelous and well-functioning society under the watchful eyes of its former enemies. The Finnish medical system is efficient and appropriately attentive and Halonen's group was well funded. My task was to learn as much as I could about rapid clinical diagnostic methods; I could not possibly have gone to a better place to do this. By the time our nearly one year visit ended and we were to return home to baseball and other familiar sights. I had learned how to "build" an IgM-capture and an IgG enzyme immunoassay, which is to say that I amplified virus in large volumes, concentrated and purified the virus, determined the protein content for determination of the immunizing dose, immunized guinea pigs and rabbits with virus according to a meticulous schedule, pre-tested and then exsanguinated the animals, cross-tested in checkerboard fashion (antigen dilutions vs. antibody dilutions) the rabbit and guinea pig antibodies and then either moved on to diagnosis or started over. I learned valuable lessons from the master. When I returned to CDC, I was prepared to revise our procedures and to improve our ability to make rapid and more specific serodiagnoses and to better understand the dynamics of antibody responses.

Contributions of Scientists from Sweden:

Ralf F. Pettersson: Born and receiving his early education in Finland, Petterson spent time with Nobelist David Baltimore at the Massachusetts Institute of Technology and then in the Department of Virology, University of Helsinki, then became Professor of Molecular Biology at the Ludwig Institute for Cancer Research, Karolinska Institute, Stockholm. His and his co-workers' efforts to investigate the fundamentals of virus receptor sites and actions, of virus entrance into cells, of the effect of inflammatory cytokines on cell surface receptors of viruses, and of multiple other aspects of virus characteristics have provided us with basic information necessary to begin to understand the complex steps of virus replication. Although not a traditional arbovirologist, Pettersson used arboviruses as models in his research and he was quite knowledgeable about arboviruses.

Others in Sweden who have contributed to our knowledge of arboviruses and rodent-borne viruses, particularly hantaviruses, are Bo S. Niklasson and Åke Lundkvist (Swedish Institute for Infectious

Disease Control, Stockholm). Their discoveries regarding Puumala virus (family *Bunyaviridae*, genus *Hantavirus*) and about Ljungan virus (family *Picornaviridae*, genus *Parechovirus*) have been not only intriguing but applicable world-wide, as they have shown similarities and differences between the natural histories of these viruses and related viruses in other countries. Working first at the Department of Virology of the National Biological Laboratory, Stockholm and then at the Department of Medical Cell Biology, Uppsala University as well as at Apodemus AB in Stockholm, Niklasson isolated Ljungan virus from bank voles (*Myodes glareolus*) and yellow-necked mice (*Apodemus flavicollis*) and has hypothesized that it is responsible for sudden infant death syndrome of humans and perhaps for other maladies. The end of this story has yet to be told.

Contributions of Scientists from Norway:

Terje Traavik, Reider Mehl and Richard Wiger: Traavik, at the Institute of Medical Biology, University of Tromsø, and Mehl and Wiger, at the National Institute of Public Health, Oslo, are among the few investigators in Norway who have specialized in studies of tick-borne viruses. Apparently, Norway and other Scandinavian countries are at or near the boundaries of extended-season viability of arthropods that are vectors of disease-causing viruses. Nonetheless, diagnostic studies at Sørlandet Hospital, Kristiansand, and at Haukeland University Hospital, Bergen, have revealed the scant few infections with tick-borne encephalitis flaviviruses and with Uukuniemi uukuvirus.

Contributions of Scientists from Austria:

Austrian virologists have been at the leading edge of virus discovery and characterization for many decades. In Vienna, W. Frisch-Niggemayer, Franz X. Heinz, Hanns Hofmann, Christian Kunz, and Christian W. Mandl at the Institute of Virology, University of Vienna, have been principal participants in providing knowledge of the molecular biology of flaviviruses, particularly of tick-borne encephalitis viruses. It was their work that eventually led to the development of a vaccine useful for preventing infections with these viruses.

Horst Aspöck: An entomologist, also of the University of Vienna, Aspöck did both field and laboratory research, including experimental infections of wild and domestic vertebrates with Tahyna and Čalovo (Batai) viruses, investigations of the role of birds as hosts of arboviruses, and studies of other Austria-related issues. More recently, Herbert Weissenbock, Norbert Nowotny and their co-workers recognized the emergence of Usutu flavivirus in Austria. That virus now is found widely distributed in Europe; its medical significance has yet to be determined.

Contributions of Scientists from Other European Countries:

Italy: Marco Balducci, Paola Verani, M.C. Lopes, Loredana Nicoletti and Maria Grazia Ciufolini have been involved in epidemiologic and ecologic studies of arboviruses since the 1960s. Working at the Istituto Superiore di Sanita in Rome, these investigators and others conducted studies of virus isolation from arthropods, humans and other vertebrates. They discovered the phleboviruses Arbia and Toscana, elucidated a portion of the ecologies of other arboviruses, and detected human infections with a tick-borne encephalitis virus as well as Tahyna and Tribec viruses. More recently, the first incursions of West Nile virus and chikungunya virus and their roles in human and equid diseases in Italy have elicited a resurgence of interest in arboviruses, with appropriate support for such studies forthcoming; the recognition of Usutu flavivirus in Italy also has contributed in this regard. Led by Michele Dottori, investigators Paolo Bonilauri, Mattia Calzolari, Davide Lelli, and others of the Istituto Zooprofilattico Sperimentale della Lombardia e dell'Emilia-Romagna, Brescia, with the support of the multiply accomplished Loredana Nicoletti in Rome, have done excellent work in sorting out all this.

Portugal: For many years, Armindo R. Filipe, National Institute of Health, Águas de Moura, and National School of Public Health, Lisbon, Portugal, studied and surveyed the arbovirological landscape. His work revealed the presence of West Nile virus (mosquitoes), Thogoto and Dhori viruses (ticks), a hantavirus (probably Seoul virus) in rats, and Bhanja virus (ticks), as well as serologic evidence for the presence of Crimean-Congo hemorrhagic fever in Portugal. Additional studies in Angola, a former Portugese colony, during the 1971 epidemic of yellow fever there were responsive and useful. Otherwise on the Iberian Peninsula, information is scanty and few studies have been done.

Spain: Despite its proximity to Africa, there is limited but significant evidence of the endemic presence of arboviruses in Spain. West Nile virus and mosquito-associated flaviviruses, bluetongue viruses and Toscana virus (family *Bunyaviridae*, genus *Phlebovirus*), are known to occur there. Some of this work was done in conjunction with Filipe from Portugal. More recently, arbovirus surveillance programs for both Iberian Peninsula countries have been improved. The presence in the Iberian Peninsula of African swine fever asfarvirus, which is transmitted by ticks of the genus *Ornithodoros*, and incursions of African horse sickness viruses, which are transmitted by culicoid midges, have provided useful impetus for additional studies.

Greece: Antony Antoniadis (now retired) and Anna Papa at the Department of Microbiology of the Medical School of Aristotle University in Thessaloniki, along with their colleagues within Greece and in nearby countries, have developed and improved laboratory methods to detect and to study infections with Crimean-Congo hemorrhagic fever, Dobrava, West Nile, Toscana, and other viruses, and the viruses themselves. Their studies of the natural histories of these viruses have included determinations of cytokine levels in hantavirus infections, collection of ticks associated with human infections of tick-borne pathogens and epidemiology of arboviruses.

Other: Studies of arboviruses in Switzerland as well as Romania, Hungary, Bulgaria, and other central and eastern European countries have been conducted by one or two or otherwise a small number of exceptional investigators. Most of this work at one time was done simply to determine the presence and prevalence of tick-borne encephalitis and other human or livestock pathogens. Now, sophisticated molecular studies are being done and epidemiologic peculiarities delineated.

Contributions of Scientists from Central and South America:

The rapid economic growth in Central and South Americas has been paralleled by an increased recognition of the need to improve diagnostic capacity and infrastructure there. National and university laboratories throughout that continent have been established or have superseded laboratories of the former Rockefeller Foundation system. Many have built modern competency and now can rapidly and accurately diagnose most illnesses caused by exotic or emerging viruses.

Panama: Many early, detailed, and expert studies of arboviruses and of their arthropod hosts and vectors were conducted at the Gorgas Memorial Laboratory by Bedsey E. Dutary, Carl M. Johnson (not Karl M. Johnson), Pedro Galindo, Gustavo Justines, Enid de Rodaniche, Sunthorn Srihongse, Margaret A. Grayson, Gladys Oro, Pauline H. Peralta, and Harold Trapido. Trapido later moved to the Rockefeller Foundation where he became involved in the discovery of Kyasanur Forest disease in India and in entomologic studies of arbovirus diseases in Colombia. Galindo became Director of the Gorgas Memorial Laboratory and led studies of the relationships of arbovirus transmission and arthropod systematics. His wide interests in ornithology, parasitology, and various viruses never distracted him from the importance of yellow fever in the Americas.

Alexis Shelokov: Alexis Shelokov had been another critical cog in the global wheel of arbovirology. Born of medical missionary parents (as were a seemingly inordinate number of other arbovirologists) and raised in China, Shelokov obtained an M.D. degree at Stanford University in Palo Alto, California, and then did a residency in Boston, working with one of Hans Zinsser's former students, John Enders who, with Thomas Weller and Frederick Robbins, later won a Nobel Prize. Weller and Robbins took the time to teach Shelokov the art of amplifying polioviruses in human embryonic cell cultures. When he later moved to the United States National Institutes of Health, Shelokov amplified polioviruses in monkey kidney cell cultures. Both Jonas Salk and Albert Sabin later sent fellows to his laboratory to learn the technique. The rest, as they say, is history.

At the NIH, Shelokov directed the Laboratory of Tropical Viral Diseases and the Laboratory of Viral and Rickettsial Diseases. Over the years his medical, experimental, and linguistics expertise led to collaborative studies of urinary tract infections, poliomyelitis, encephalomyocarditis, influenzavirus B, and coxsackie B viruses, enteroviruses, Rous sarcoma virus, vesicular stomatitis Indiana virus, and Venezuelan equine encephalitis virus, and to the discovery of Chagres virus.

In 1958 Shelokov was assigned by NIH to establish the Middle America Research Unit in Panama, staying there until 1961. Before he left, he hired Karl M. Johnson to replace him as Head of the virus section of that unit. In his last month at the Middle America Research Unit, Shelokov sent researchers Johnson, Ron Mackenzie, Merle Kuns, Gustavo Justines and Angel Munoz and Conrad Yunker (Rocky Mountain Laboratories, NIH) to San Joaquin, Bolivia, to investigate a "black vomit disease" in Beni Province in the eastern part of that country. When Johnson, Mackenzie, and Munoz all acquired the disease (within 48 hours of each other), Shelokov arranged with the Panamanian government to allow a United States Air Force plane to evacuate them to the Canal Zone for treatment. The virus causing this disease was isolated and named Machupo virus (family *Arenaviridae*, genus *Arenavirus*) after a river in the disease zone, and the disease was named Bolivian hemorrhagic fever. All three survived, but just barely. Johnson later was appointed Director of MARU.

As a result of his many years of association with the great Russian virologist-epidemiologist-vaccinologist Mikhail P. Chumakov regarding research on poliomyelitis viruses, other enteroviruses, and vaccine development, as well as their common interest in hemorrhagic fevers, Shelokov became re-involved with hemorrhagic fevers, including simian hemorrhagic fever, in the Soviet Union and elsewhere.

In 1964 a deadly outbreak at NIH killed all the freshly delivered Indian macaques (*Macaca mulatta*), that had been placed in quarantine. Shelokov learned that cages with a large shipment of monkeys from India had been exposed to cages holding African green (vervet) monkeys (formerly *Cercopithecus aethiops sabaeus,* now *Chlorocebus aethiops sabaeus*) at a European airport. The African green monkeys had excreted a virus deadly for the Indian macaques. The large Indian shipment was divided into three parts to satisfy orders from the United States, U.S.S.R., and West Germany. Three simultaneous epizootics resulted, at NIH/Bethesda, at Sukhumi in the Crimea, and at Marburg, Germany. Chumakov and his colleagues investigated the Sukhumi outbreak. Shelokov and colleagues Amos E. Palmer, Anton M. Allen, and Nicola M. Tauraso isolated a virus from a stump-tailed macaque (*Macaca arctoides*) and named it simian hemorrhagic fever virus, now recognized as a member of the order *Nidovirales*, family *Arteriviridae*, genus *Arterivirus*.

Shelokov's later efforts at developing vaccines included work on Junin (Argentine hemorrhagic fever) virus, yellow fever virus, and other hemorrhagic fever viruses. That work, done at the Salk Institute in Swiftwater, Pennsylvania, was supported by the United States Army. Because of his knowledge and many skills, his medical background and his charm, this virologic Renaissance man became engaged in the important task of helping to evaluate the potential for bioterrorism by various governments. With others, he assessed the disastrous 1979 outbreak of anthrax in Sverdlovsk, Russia. With Jordi Casals, Harry Hoogstraal, Karl Johnson, Ned Wiebenga, and Telford Work, he had participated in the first Cold War collaborative study of arboviruses and other viruses with Russian scientists (Figure 112). In 1978 Shelo-

Figure 112. Field survey for tick-borne encephalitis viruses, Astrakhan, 1965 (standing, l. to r.) Alexander Butenko and Alexis Shelokov; (seated, back row, l. to r.): Jordi Casals, Elena Leshchinskaya, and Mikhail P. Chumakov; (seated, front row, l. to r.): Ned Wiebenga, Bela Isaakovna Kaplan, Harry Hoogstraal (image courtesy of Telford H. Work)

kov moved to San Antonio, Texas, where he headed the Department of Microbiology at the University of Texas Science Center. In addition to his years of productive research, his nearly encyclopedic knowledge of historic events in virology, his analytical abilities, and his affection for and continuing support of the American Committee on Arthropod-borne Viruses solidified his position as an icon in virology as a whole and arbovirology in particular.

Colombia:

Jorge Boshell-Manrique: In Colombia, the noted physician-biologist Jorge Boshell-Manrique, Chief of the International Group for Malaria Evaluation of the Pan American Sanitary Bureau, with assistance from Richard M. Taylor, then at the Rockefeller Foundation office in Rio de Janiero, and others, including Fred L. Soper, Raymond C. Shannon, Loring Whitman and others from the Rockefeller Foundation, conducted field studies of mosquitoes in an attempt to determine which could serve as vectors of yellow fever virus and which could not. They implicated for the first time *Haemagogus* species mosquitoes and the monkeys on which they feed in the jungle cycle, investigated epidemic sites, and combined all this basic knowledge to formulate a hypothesis about the origin, persistence, emergence, and control of yellow fever. Boshell-Manrique and Soper were the first to use the term "jungle yellow fever". The family tradition continues with Jorge Boshell Samper, an accomplished arbovirologist and the former Director of the Colombian National Institutes of Health.

Hernando Groot: After obtaining his medical degree at Colombia's National University and a Master of Public Health at Harvard University and then returning to Colombia in 1943, Hernando Groot joined Boshell-Manrique in continuing work on yellow fever and began investigations of other tropical diseases as well, studying Venezuelan equine encephalitis and other things arbovirological. Groot also studied trypanosomes and helped to establish the University of the Andes in Bogota. Multiply and deservedly honored by national, international, and other organizations, Groot now is Permanent Secretary and Honorary Member of the Colombian Academy of Medicine.

A tour of the Salt Cathedral of Zipaquira: In 1972, while visiting Bogota on behalf of the Pan-American Health Organization, I was invited by Groot, at the time the Director of the National Institute of Health laboratory I had been asked to evaluate, to drive with him and a retired friend of his, Jorge Boshell-Manrique, to Zipaquira. I was young and inexperienced, not adequately grounded in the history of arbovirology, and had no idea who either of these gentlemen were or what they represented but I knew right away that I liked them and it was clear that they knew what they were talking about. The Salt Cathedral of Zipaquira is a Roman Catholic church built underground within tunnels of a mine in a mountain of salt. My first surprise was in seeing this remarkable devotional site. My second surprise came when I found who Groot and Boshell-Manrique really were.

In collaboration with Carlos Sanmartin Barberi (1929-1996) and Ronald B. Mackenzie, University del Valle, Cali, and with additional collaboration by Vernon H. Lee and others of the Rockefeller Foundation, in Colombia, these resolute investigators worked out the epidemiology of viruses, identified many new viruses, and improved both laboratory techniques and understanding of virus cycles. Sanmartin, an intellectual and physician-scientist began his career as an arbovirologist as Chief of the laboratory at the Carlos Finlay Institute in Bogota. Then he moved to Cali as Head of the Virus Section of the Faculty of Medicine and then Chief of Preventive Medicine at the University del Valle. Sharing his knowledge and insights, Sanmartin became Head of the Virology Unit at the Pan American Zoonoses Center, Pan American Health Organization, Buenos Aires, Argentina, having by then been awarded many honors.

Ecuador:

Ernesto Gutierrez: For most of the past more than 40 years, albeit with intermittent pauses, Gutierrez led Ecuadorian studies of arboviruses from the Ecuadorian National Institute of Health in Guayaquil. When Venezuelan equine encephalitis struck Ecuador in 1969, Gutierrez concerned himself with attempts to diagnose and control that disease of humans and horses. After a year of collaborative training at CDC in Atlanta in 1971, he organized cooperative studies with Aracely Alava of his institute and Thomas Monath, Bruce Francy, and others at CDC. When these were published it became clear that arboviruses in Ecuador were widespread and varied and included both human and livestock pathogens. Gutierrez went on to become his country's Secretary of Health but he eventually returned to the diagnostic laboratory, his original scientific love.

> Ernesto and his splendid family and I and my family have remained in contact for all these years. In 2010, we were once again united as we prepared for a rodent-trapping and mosquito-collecting trip to the Amazon region of eastern Ecuador. When

that ended, I visited the Galapagos National Park. That place, more than any, complemented my visit to Downe House, Charles Darwin's home in England, many years previously. These were remarkable experiences for me, as they would be for almost anyone, and I am grateful for those opportunities.

Peru:

Jose Madalengoitia and Maria Rosario Mendez-Lopez: Working at the University of San Marcos in Lima, Peru, along with William Scherer of Cornell University, they conducted ecologic studies of Venezuelan equine encephalitis virus and isolated not only that virus but also St. Louis encephalitis, eastern equine encephalitis, and Group C and Guama group orthoviruses, extending the known geographic distribution of these viruses into the western Amazon region of South America. Rosario Mendez, in continuing this work, has made not only the first isolations of yellow fever virus in Peru but also identified an orbivirus called Peruvian horse sickness virus, the details of which are fascinating.

In 1997 an epizootic occurred in the Department of San Martin, Peru, and Mendez isolated two newly recognized viruses. One, named Peruvian horse sickness virus, was isolated from horses with encephalitis or meningoencephalitis. Characterization of the genome identified it as a new virus within the genus *Orbivirus* (family *Reoviridae*). This was the first isolation of an orbivirus responsible for equine encephalitis in the Americas. Peruvian horse sickness virus also was isolated in Australia during 1997 (named Elsey virus at the time) from diseased horses in the Northern Territory. Peruvian and Australian Peruvian horse sickness virus isolates were shown to be identical. Serological and molecular studies demonstrated that Peruvian horse sickness virus is associated with encephalitis in horses. Characterization of the genome of the second virus, designated Rioja virus, showed that it is closely related to a virus called Yunnan orbivirus, which was initially isolated from wild-caught mosquitoes in China and then from cattle in Australia. Chinese and Peruvian Yunnan orbiviruses belong to the same serotype, but the Australian isolate belongs to a distinct serotype. Rioja virus is involved in illnesses in donkeys, cattle, sheep, and dogs. Sorting out the complex epidemiologies of these viruses, describing the clinical symptoms, determining how they can occur in such apparently disparate areas, and determining their importance for livestock is a task yet to be undertaken.

Figure 113. Julio Isidro Maiztegui (1931 - 1993)
(image courtesy of the National Institute of Human Viral Illnesses, Buenos Aires, Argentina)

Mexico to Argentina: Other investigators were associated with other national and university laboratories from Mexico (Caesar Wong-Chia, Maria Luisa Zarate, and Julio de Mucha-Macias) to Argentina (Marta S. Sabattini, Julio I. Maiztegui (Figure 113). Julio Barrera Oro produced a Junin virus vaccine while he was a visiting scientist at the United States Army Medical Research Institute of Infectious Diseases. Norma E. Mettler, collaborated on studies of Argentine hemorrhagic fever (Junin arenavirus) and its reservoir host rodent and propagated that virus with Mercedes Weissenbacher). Working with Sonja Buckley and Jordi Casals at the Rockefeller Foundation laboratories, Mettler was first to propagate Junin virus in cell cultures. These investigators and their colleagues did fundamental field and laboratory work on yellow fever virus and on many newly recognized viruses.

Contributions of Scientists from the former Soviet Union and other former Eastern Bloc Countries:

It is interesting to note that during the so-called "Cold War" (which, while not a peaceful period, obviously was much better than a "Hot War") both sides made efforts (1) to determine exactly what the other side was doing, (2) to appear to be medically helpful to strategically placed but ostensibly neutral countries in an effort to curry political favor with them, and (3) to prepare for possible biological warfare initiated by "the other side" (of course). Russian and Czechoslovak virologists and epidemiologists did collaborative field work in Cuba, Africa, and elsewhere, isolating and identifying viruses, conducting serosurveys, and collecting material that they took with them to institutes in Moscow for further analyses. At least some of the results of their discoveries were published and are of historic and epidemiologic importance. Unfortunately, as many of those publications were not in English, they were overlooked or ignored by most. The United States went so far as to produce vaccines against certain viruses and published those results only because it wanted the Soviets to read them, consider the possibilities, and divert efforts from their own agenda. More like something from Mad Magazine than based on reality, *in toto* these costly studies were valuable to both sides and to humankind, but it might have been more useful to collaborate ("Cool War") than to build expensive infrastructures. On balance, as it turned out, all this was of no particular advantage to anyone.

In spite of regulations, scientists of both "sides" exchanged viruses, reagents and information and personal regards. Both invited scientists from the other side of the Iron Curtain to participate in symposia, conferences, and meetings of one sort or another. While all this was in the best interests of science, medicine, and human and livestock health, it certainly did not have the approval of the respective countries.

Contributions of Scientists from the United Kingdom:

The impact on arbovirology of scientists from Great Britain and elsewhere in the United Kingdom has been considerable and heroic. They have supported countless programs, investigators, and discoveries, and contributed not only to arbovirology but to the improvement of human health, at home and in their former colonies.

Francis N. Macnamara: A physician-virologist, Macnamara was a medical officer in the colonial service in Nigeria, serving as Acting Director of the Virus Research Institute in Yaba, Lagos, Nigeria. From 1958 to 1962, he was Director of Laboratories, West African Council for Medical Research, Yaba-Lagos. He investigated disease outbreaks in eastern Nigeria and the Jos Plateau, described the frequency of the occurrence of encephalitis following administration of the French neurotropic yellow fever vaccine, studied the serologic reactions of people who had been vaccinated with yellow fever virus vaccine or who had acquired natural infections with yellow fever and related viruses, and organized long-term studies of the epidemiology of yellow fever and of vector biology.

James S. Porterfield: In 1953 Porterfield, also a physician-virologist, of the National Institute for Medical Research at Mill Hill, was assigned to Macnamara's group in Lagos. At the West African Council for Medical Research, he became fascinated with the serological cross-relationships between yellow fever and other "Group B" arboviruses, the flaviviruses, an interest shared with Macnamara.

From 1977 to 1989 Porterfield taught at the Sir William Dunn School of Pathology, a department within the University of Oxford Medical Sciences Division. Porterfield participated in many arbovirus meetings, wrote book chapters, edited books on arbovirology, and provided his insights to all. In addition he improved techniques, determined the immunology of flaviviruses and other viruses, and provided an acceptable virus taxonomy, particularly for viruses of the *Flaviviridae* and *Bunyaviridae.*

C.E. Gordon Smith, Colin Leake, Mary Pudney, M.G. Varma, Mary Jane Cardosa and Ana Teresa de Madrid: British training programs have provided foundational scientist-administrators throughout the world. C.E. Gordon Smith and others at the Microbiological Research Establishment, Porton Down, and Colin Leake, Mary Pudney and M.G. Varma at the London School of Hygiene and Tropical Medicine were at the cutting edge of arbovirological research for decades.

Along with Malik Peiris, who demonstrated antibody-mediated enhancement of viruses, Cardosa and de Madrid were with Porterfield at the Sir William Dunn School of Pathology at Oxford University. Cardosa went on to study enteroviruses and coxsackieviruses in Sarawak, Malaysia. de Madrid and Porterfield demonstrated the utility of porcine kidney cells for arbovirus amplification and developed microculturing as a method for use in plaque assays for many viruses, principally alphaviruses and flaviviruses.

David I.H. Simpson: A skillful, imaginative and observant physician-virologist, David I.H. Simpson worked at the East Africa Virus Research Institute, Entebbe, Uganda, then at the Arbovirus Epidemiology Unit of the Microbiological Research Establishment at Porton, England. He headed the Arbovirus Unit of the London School of Tropical Medicine and Hygiene, then became Head of the Department of Microbiology and Immunobiology, Queen's University of Belfast, Northern Ireland. Simpson, along with Ernest T.W. Bowen and scores of other colleagues world-wide, investigated the properties of viruses, their pathologies, and their epidemiologies. At essentially the same time they conducted experimental infections in monkeys as well as studies of imported, exotic, and indigenous arboviruses and hemorrhagic fever viruses, including Marburg virus and ebolaviruses. Simpson's knack for assembling teams of local and international experts in these studies proved helpful in using a team approach for the study of infections new to science or new to a particular area. In Africa he studied yellow fever with Andrew Haddow, Miles C. Williams, John P. Woodall, and others.

Figure 114. Ernest Andrew Gould (1942 -)
(image courtesy of Ernest Gould)

Ernest Andrew Gould: As an example of the close relationship between British academic and field virology, I use here Ernest Gould (Figure 114), who obtained a Ph.D. degree in Virology from the University of Liverpool in 1968. After a research fellowship at Birmingham University, a nine-year lectureship at Queen's University in Belfast, another nine-year lectureship at the London University School of Hygiene and Tropical Medicine, and 23 years as Assistant Director, Institute of Virology and Environmental Microbiology (now the Centre for Ecology and Hydrology) at Oxford University, he was appointed Director of that Center and, after a few more years managing other university posts, retired from there and is now Visiting Professor, Emerging Virus Unit, Université de la Mediterranée, Marseille, France.

Beginning with studies of influenzaviruses, rabbit hemorrhagic disease viruses (family *Caliciviridae*, genus *Lagovirus*), and human herpesvirus 2 (family *Herpesviridae*, genus *Simplexvirus*), Gould developed useful monoclonal antibodies as diagnostics, and published hundreds of papers on research completed by him and scores of graduate students and visiting scientists. However, in the most recent three decades his research has focused on arboviruses. Using self-developed infectious clones and diagnostic reagents, Gould and associates have intensely investigated tick-borne encephalitis flaviviruses, studying the mechanisms of the transmission of these viruses (with Tamara Gritsun), as well as their evolution, epidemiology and geographic dispersal (with Edward Holmes and Paola Zanotto). These studies have provided impetus for generation of further hypotheses, many of which now have been shown to be correct. Gould's predictions that arboviruses are being introduced to Europe by migrating birds have been confirmed and extended to the sources of chikungunya virus in Indian Ocean islands and Asia. Gould's contributions to our knowledge and perspectives regarding bluetongue viruses have been significant.

Through collaborative studies with investigators in Asia and Latin America, we now have more useful information regarding the epidemiology, pathogenesis and evolution of dengue viruses. Gould has coordinated diverse studies bringing together various disciplines, i.e., classical virology, immunology, molecular biology, viral pathogenesis, molecular epidemiology and diagnostic virology. Recent findings about dengue virus immunopathogenesis may lead to novel approaches to understanding the basis of pathogenesis of many of the flaviviruses. Gould has led or been involved with fundamental studies of Japanese encephalitis virus, yellow fever virus, West Nile virus, Usutu virus and several alphaviruses and bunyaviruses, some or all of which may lead to prevention or control of the diseases they cause. As with all devoted teachers, his principal legacy one day may be the work of the numerous students he has taught. Charming, polite and enthusiastic, Gould is a prime example of an involved and productive arbovirologist. Fortunately, he is among the many who have no idea how to retire.

Patricia Anne Nuttall: After obtaining her undergraduate degree in microbiology at the University of Bristol, Nuttall (Figure 115) attended the University of Reading for a Ph.D. in virology and the University of Oxford for a Master's degree. Although now the director of The Centre for Ecology and Hydrology at Oxford, she retains her interest and expertise in the biology of ticks, in particular the molecular biology of tick-borne pathogens and their interactions with tick vectors and vertebrate hosts. Nuttall's efforts to resolve these interactions at the parasite-host interface led to a series of classical studies in which she and her colleagues demonstrated saliva-activated transmission of the tick-borne Thogoto virus (family *Orthomyxoviridae*, genus *Thogotovirus*) whereby tick saliva (or salivary gland extract) potentiates the transmission of that virus to uninfected ticks feed-

Figure 115. Patricia Anne Nuttall (1953 -)
(image courtesy of Patricia Nuttall)

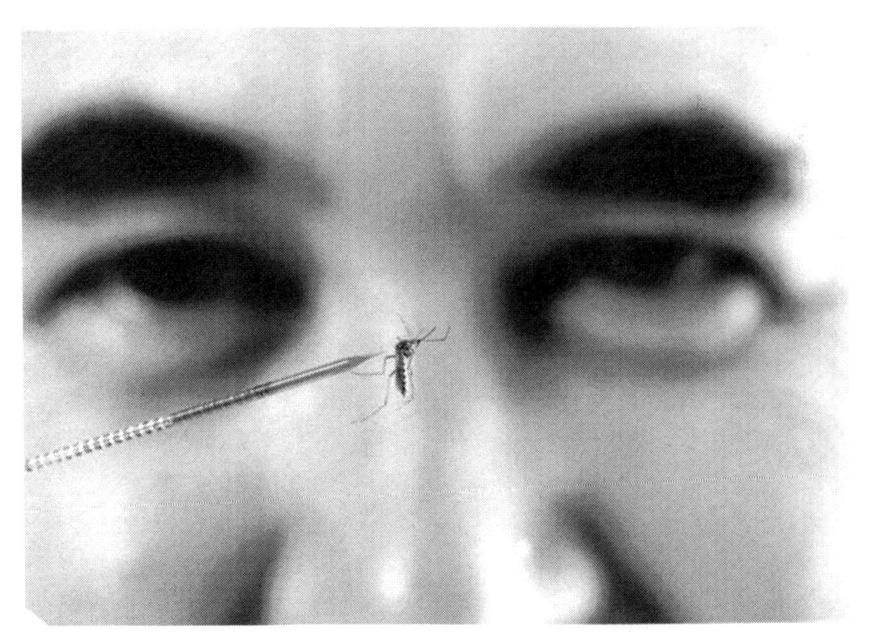

Figure 116. Stephen Higgs (1958 -) (University of Texas Medical Branch at Galveston) demonstrating the intrathoracic inoculation of an *Aedes aegypti* mosquito.
(image courtesy of John Glowczwski, University of Texas Medical Branch, Galveston)

ing on a non-viraemic guinea-pig. Her other fastidious investigations have provided informative insights regarding the biology of arthropod vectors.

Stephen Higgs: Higgs (Figure 116) obtained a B.Sc. degree in Zoology with Honors at King's College, London University, and then a Ph.D. in Parasitology at Reading University. An enthusiastic, persistent and innovative researcher, Higgs is also widely recognized as an excellent teacher. After a productive post-doctoral period with Ernest Gould at Oxford University, Higgs obtained another post-doctoral appointment, this one with Barry Beaty, Carol Blair and Kenneth Olson at Colorado State University in Fort Collins. There he began working on the identification of molecular mechanisms that could be used to reduce the efficiency of pathogen transmission. Furthermore, he developed novel strategies to reduce the impact of vector-borne diseases. Higgs and colleagues identified gene sequences that prevent transmission of several viruses, evaluated a scorpion neurotoxin that might be used for biological control of mosquitoes, and pioneered studies of the expression of green fluorescent protein in mosquitoes, which has since become a standard marker of mosquito transgenesis and which yet may be used to identify and track genetically engineered arthropods.

Moving to the University of Texas Medical Branch at Galveston, Higgs rose to full professor in the W.H.O. Collaborating Center for Tropical Diseases, the Center for Biodefense and Emerging Infectious Diseases and the Sealy Center for Vaccine Development and became the Director of the BSL-3 insectary there. He has evaluated the use of transgenic mosquitoes for the control of dengue; studied mosquito-virus-vertebrate interactions; used wild type and genetically engineered chikungunya, Sindbis, o'nyong nyong, West Nile, and yellow fever viruses to understand various aspects of virus-vector interactions; and identified the molecules and mechanisms involved in these phenomena. He and his colleagues demonstrated direct transmission of West Nile virus from infected to uninfected mosquitoes while the infected mosquitoes were feeding on an uninfected host. This discovery showed the possibility of an accelerated transmission cycle and suggests that many more vertebrates may be involved in transmission than originally thought. Their finding that virus lineage-specific epistatic interactions between substitutions at amino acid positions 226 and 98 of the E1 envelope glycoprotein of chikungunya virus has served to explain a basic epidemiologic phenomenon: the restriction of the ability of endemic Asian chikungunya virus strains to adapt to *Aedes albopictus* mosquitoes. Perhaps their seminal finding in regard to chikungunya virus epidemiology is that a single mutation in this virus affects its vector specificity and epidemic potential. Higgs has moved to Kansas State University, Manhattan, to become Director of the Biosecurity Research Institute.

David Bishop: From the moment that David Hugh Langler Bishop walked into his first meeting of the Subcommittee on InterRelationships Among Catalogued Arboviruses nearly 40 years ago, the study of arboviruses changed conceptually, shifting from one generation to another. Bishop already had had an extensive series of experiences: Liverpool University (Ph.D.), post-doctoral appointments and research associateships in France, Scotland and the United States, and faculty appointments at Columbia University, Rutgers University, and the University of Alabama. After serving as a Visiting Fellow at Oxford University, he became Director of the Natural Environment Research Council Institute of Virology at Oxford. Eventually, although still young, Bishop retired from those duties but continued to conduct laboratory and field research in Europe and Africa.

The shift alluded to above was due to Bishop's knowledge, confidence and perceptions as to where arbovirology should be headed. A very few arbovirologists at the time participated in molecular biological studies of arboviruses, mainly investigators at the United States Army Medical Research Institute of Infectious Diseases working with the dengue viruses. Bishop introduced an entirely new set of standards and goals and, with Hiroomi Akashi, Barry Beaty, Walter Brandt, Corrie Clerx-van Haaster, C.-Yong Kang, John Clewley, Richard Compans, Joel Dalrymple, John Gentsch, Richard Klimas, Frederick Murphy, John Obijeski, Polly Roy, Robert Shope, Dennis Trent and literally scores of others on many continents, defined the molecular basis of viral structure and function. Collaborating with many investigators of disparate virologic interests, Bishop led or played a major role in studies by Jack Obijeski (later of Genentech and other commercial organizations) and Frederick Murphy that showed, for example, that the genome of La Crosse orthobunyavirus comprised three circular RNA segments of different sizes – a huge contribution. These segments were later shown to be the large (L) RNA that encodes an RNA-dependent RNA polymerase, the medium (M) RNA that encodes a polyprotein precursor that is post-translationally cleaved to yield two envelope glycoproteins located on the virion surface, G1 and G2, and a third polypeptide, NSm, of unknown function, and a small (S) RNA. The three segments are encapsidated by a major nucleocapsid (N) protein encoded by the S segment, which also encodes an NSs protein in an overlapping reading frame. As it does in Bunyamwera virus, the prototype orthobunyavirus, the NSs protein may decrease RNA synthesis to act as an interferon antagonist and to play a role in viral pathogenesis. Further studies determined their molecular weights and determined the diameter of the La Crosse virion. They further found that the virion is enveloped and has irregular surface projections 10 nm in length. From these and other studies of the molecular characteristics of arboviruses a necessary sea change resulted. Casals and others before him had worked with crude but useful antigenic studies of arboviruses. But the advent of the detailed characterizations of viral genomes and proteins, the increasingly recognized relationships between structure and function, and the even more recent application of polymerase chain reaction assays led to the birth of molecular epidemiology. Investigators could now trace viruses to their geographic sources, document mutations and determine their effects. Gene therapy became a distinct possibility; baculoviruses became candidate insecticides; and viral taxonomy could have a genetic foundation. Non-infectious vaccines could be produced, safer diagnostic tests developed and the only limitation to further expansive inquiries would be imagination. Inevitably, other methods will continue in development but molecular biological specialization now acts as the tail that wags the dog, and justifiably so.

On one visit to Oxford to visit Bishop, Nuttall and Gould, I had the opportunity to visit Charles Darwin's home in Downe, just a few miles from the center of London. I was directed there by a former Editor of Transactions of the Royal Society of Tropical Medicine and Hygiene, with whom I had become acquainted because of a letter I had written to, and which was published by, that journal. Here is the letter –

"It was with guffaws and levity that I read the note by P. Baciewicz (1989; Transactions, 82, 944) regarding possible diagnostic usefulness of observing that in developing countries severely ill patients may be brought to clinic in wheelbarrows. From time to time on this side of the Atlantic we have made much the same determination but did not think, until now, to mention it.

Veterinarians have long recognized the potential diagnostic significance of seeing deer brought to the office strapped to the hood of an automobile, not to speak of having a child bring in his pet squirrel in a pizza box.

Whereas it has long been recognized that carrying an individual in on his shield correlates well with negative outcome (see Hamlet, Act V), when growing up in New York I always heard that it is a bad sign when someone is brought in on a door. In fact, one Friday when my father was brought home on a door my mother said that she immediately knew he had had a bad day at the office."

Richard Michael Elliott: One of the brightest and most productive investigators in arbovirology (and other fields of virology), Elliott is a molecular and structural virologist at the University of St. Andrews in Fife, Scotland. His work helps us understand the basics and practical applications of our knowledge of emerging RNA viruses, immunity to

Figure 117. Kenneth Lam Sai Kit (left) and John S. Mackenzie, discussing the epidemiology of various viruses in Asia and Australia, as well as enjoying each other's company.
(image courtesy of John Mackenzie)

viruses and vaccine design, and the isolation of novel anti-viral drugs. His fundamental studies have contributed to our knowledge of the mechanisms of arbovirus replication and to our understanding of the molecular mechanisms by which these viruses cause disease.

Contributions of Scientists from Asia:

It was not only Europeans and North Americans who moved arbovirology along.

Kenneth Lam Sai Kit, Malaysia: Professor Emeritus (University of Malaya, Kuala Lumpur) Kenneth Lam Sai Kit (Figure 117) arguably is the most influential virologist in southeast Asia. A portion of his work included not only studies of bacterial infections but Japanese encephalitis and dengue diagnosis and he and his colleagues showed that enterovirus 71 was and is a cause of a fatal hand, foot and mouth

Figure 118. Chan Yow Cheung (left) and Tissa Vitarana
(image courtesy of John Mackenzie)

disease in children in Sarawak. Lam and his colleague Kaw Bing Chua made the first identification of Nipah virus and, although retired, he continues to make himself available to advise virologists world-wide.

Chan Yow Cheung, Singapore: A dengue researcher at the University of Singapore, Chan (Figure 118) helped lay the groundwork for the continuing, intense studies of this disease and for the methods used to prevent it, first isolating dengue viruses in 1963 and then going on to study the epidemiology and molecular characteristics of these viruses and the diseases they cause.

Tissa Vitarana, Sri Lanka: As Director of the National Institute of Virology in Columbo, Sri Lanka (formerly Ceylon), Vitarana (Figure 118) began publishing studies of arboviral and other infections in 1969 (with Jelka Vesenjak-Hirjan). He followed this work with surveys for or studies of hantaviral infections (with Ho-Wang Lee), viral hepatitis, the epidemiology of dengue hemorrhagic fever, the occurrence of elevated tumor necrosis factor in dengue fever and dengue hemorrhagic fever, acquired immunodeficiency syndrome, bovine spongi-

Figure 119. (l. to r.) Bo Quan Chen (1933 -), Charles H. Calisher, Barry J. Beaty (image courtesy of Barry J. Beaty)

form encephalopathy, and varicella-zoster virus infections. He went on to become the Sri Lankan Minister of Science and Technology.

Because of the efforts of these and other exceptional scientists, Asian virology in general functions at a high level and is involved in important regional discoveries as well as investigations of viral epidemics. Still, for political and economic reasons, many Asian countries have little or no competence in diagnosis or in disease recognition. Many of these countries comprise natural areas that surely are arbovirus habitats.

China:

Bo Quan Chen: Although scientists in China have been involved for decades in studies of arboviruses, not much of the derived information has been available to Western colleagues. Bo Quan Chen (Figure 119) of the Institute of Virology, Chinese Academy of Medical Sciences, Beijing, a gentleman, inspiring teacher, superb scientist, and experienced arbovirologist, visited the laboratories at Yale University in the late 1970s in order to collaborate directly with staff there. With Sonja Buckley, he published studies of Japanese encephalitis virus vaccine strains in C6/36 cells, and with Barry Beaty he published on the replication and transmission of the same viruses in *Culex tritaeniorhynchus* mosquitoes. Upon his return to China, he produced, tested and applied monoclonal antibodies against Japanese encephalitis virus and dengue virus 4, conducted human surveys for antibody to various arboviruses in China, studied the immune responses of humans to Japanese encephalitis virus vaccine, determined the virulence of strains of that virus from China and Indonesia, and explored the use of various antibody assays in diagnosing and determining the prevalence of hemorrhagic fever with renal syndrome viruses (Hantaan hantavirus). Now retired, his students and other colleagues, vigorously led by Guodong Liang, continue and extend this work: to study tick-borne encephalitis, Crimean-Congo hemorrhagic fever, and measles, severe acute respiratory syndrome and severe acute respiratory syndrome-like coronaviruses; to discover many viruses new to China or simply new to science; to analyze in detail the efficacy of Japanese encephalitis virus vaccine; to pursue molecular and epidemiologic characterizations of many viruses; and to investigate the disease burden caused by Japanese encephalitis virus.

With increasing openness about medical matters in China, seemingly a consequence of the severe acute respiratory syndrome coronavirus epidemic there in 2003, Chinese virologists are either involved in more investigations or are publishing more of their results for the first time in Western journals. As might be expected of a country with the fourth largest land mass, China comprises widely diverse ecosystems and habitats conducive to the presence of a variety of arboviruses. In addition to the long-recognized presence of Japanese encephalitis and dengue viruses, recent studies have shown the presence of Crimean-Congo hemorrhagic fever, tick-borne encephalitis, Sindbis, Getah, chikungunya, Ross River, Tahyna, Batai, Banna, Kadipiro, Liaoning, Yunnan, and Chaoyang viruses and a densovirus from *Culex pipiens*. We can expect that many more viruses will be found in the great expanse of China, including pathogens of humans, livestock, and wildlife.

The global scientific community welcomes this increased transparency because it brings Chinese scientists into cooperative settings in which scientific information can be exchanged and, perhaps, trust built. Throughout Asia there is growing recognition of the need for all countries to be aware of emerging and spreading diseases. Laboratories that once depended on the Rockefeller Foundation and United States military medical interests have taken on responsibilities for disease diagnosis on their own and have become both knowledgeable and competent.

Joseph Sriyal Malik Peiris: In China's Hong Kong Special Administrative Region, at the Department of Microbiology and Pathology, Queen Mary Hospital, University of Hong Kong, Malik Peiris has been studying viruses for many years, beginning with studies of arboviruses with James Porterfield at Oxford University. Since arriving in Hong Kong from Sri Lanka, where he studied the epidemiology of Japanese encephalitis and other arboviruses, Peiris has been involved in investigations of influenzavirus A H1N1 (1997-2002) and other influenzaviruses and was part of the expert group that discovered and investigated the epidemiology of the severe acute respiratory syndrome coronavirus.

Influenzaviruses are classic causes of a repeatedly emerging disease. Influenza, which emerges (or re-emerges, depending on how one views it) annually, is caused by one or more of the influenzaviruses in one configuration or another. Severe acute respiratory syndrome coronavirus is caused by a virus that took the world by surprise twice, once when it first appeared in 2003 and began to spread globally and then a second time when bats were shown to be its natural hosts. The epidemiologies of these diseases involve (influenza) birds and other wildlife, farmed pigs, humans, and perhaps other vertebrates and bats (severe acute respiratory syndrome coronavirus), live street market vertebrates, and humans. Natural movements of wildlife, travel by infected humans, species-jumping, infection control or lack thereof, and other concatenations allow unusual interactions leading to virus amplification and spread. Thus it has always been, even though we have not recognized these natural complexities of host-virus interfaces and exchanges. All this makes for job security for virologists, however.

Contributions of Scientists from Australia:

A remarkable land with a remarkable ecosystem, Australia has its own history of arbovirology. With its outstanding universities and faculties (the *sine qua non* of outstanding universities) and a continuing interest in improving and protecting the health of humans, livestock, wildlife and plants, Australia has long supported virological research, including that of arbovirology. The Commonwealth Scientific and Research Organization, the Australian national science agency charged with providing solutions for such problems as may already be recognized or which may emerge, has many branches. The intellectual ferment inherent at Australia's universities and the various institutes distributed around that continent (Australia National University, University of Melbourne, University of Queensland, University of Sydney, Walter and Eliza Hall Institute of Medical Research, University of Western Australia; Elizabeth MacArthur Agricultural Institute, The Queensland Institute of Medical Research, Berrimah Veterinary Laboratories, and so on) produce rapid responses to dangers to human and animal health and to the economy of Australia and surrounding areas. Serosurveys and virus surveys conducted for many decades have yielded a plethora of newly discovered viruses from insects and vertebrates. Human disease may be highest on the Australian priorities list but agricultural studies of livestock and plants and of hosts of interest and importance have also been deemed essential. Australian scientists are well aware of the potential significance of viruses detected in insects, sentinel animals, and wild vertebrates. Over the decades, arbovirologists in Australia have shown just how many arboviruses can be found if one simply looks for them.

Figure 120. John Gregory Aaskov (1949 -)
(image courtesy of John Aaskov)

The Walter and Eliza Hall Institute of Medical Research in Parkville, near Melbourne, is nicely placed close to the University of Melbourne and The Royal Melbourne Hospital. It was the first medical research institute established in Australia, founded in 1915 with funds from a trust established by Eliza Hall following the death of her husband Walter, a pioneering transport, livestock, and mining entrepreneur.

When so many viruses are isolated in one context, a single geographic area as large as Australia, the aim must be to search for "important" viruses; other viruses have to be stored until such time as people, reagents and funding are available to study them. The arboviruses of livestock-relevance in Australia have been those that affect sheep and cattle, which are of significant commercial importance. These include bluetongue viruses, Akabane virus and bovine ephemeral fever virus. Studies of these viruses and the diseases they cause were done not only by investigators with the Commonwealth Scientific and Research Organization but also by university and more locally situated investigators. Australian collaboration with investigators in Asian countries has been close and effective in detecting and controlling diseases caused by these viruses. The list of knowledgeable, insightful, and well-trained Australian veterinarians, physicians, entomologists, and other specialists is long and includes John G. Aaskov (Figure 120), Annette K. Broom, Daisy H. Cybinski, Lynn Dalgarno, Anthony J. Della-Porta, Ralph L. Doherty, Geoffery P. Gard, Adrian J. Gibbs, Eric L. French, Barry M. Gorman, Roy A. Hall, Royle A. Hawkes, Ian H. Holmes, Linda Hueston, Cheryl Johansen, Peter D. Kirkland, John S. Mackenzie, Ian D. Marshall, Lorna F. Melville, Ian M. Parsonson, Scott A. Ritchie, Richard C. Russell (Figure 105), David W. Smith, Harry A. Standfast, Toby D. St. George, Peter J. Walker, Ron C. Weir, Edward G. Westaway, Peter I. Whelan, Paul R. Young, and many others. These conscientious investigators have discovered new viruses; described new and important diseases (not all of them caused by arboviruses); experimentally demonstrated differences, relationships and mechanisms of virus-cell attachments and pathogenetic processes; and showed the effects of the El Niño Southern Oscillation and general climate changes on arthropod biology. They produced and shared useful tools, all the while maintaining their humor and excellent scientific acumen.

Frank J. Fenner: No review of Australian arbovirology would be complete without mention of the singular Frank John (Johannes) Fenner (1914–2010), considered the father of Australian virology. Although not an arbovirologist, Fenner was interested in all viruses. Born in Ballarat, Victoria, he earned degrees in medicine and surgery from the University of Adelaide and a degree in tropical medicine from the University of Sydney. He served in the Royal Australian Army Medical Corps and, during World War II, served in the Middle East, New Guinea and Borneo. In New Guinea, he developed methods to control malaria and the other tropical diseases that were devastating Australian troops. At the end of his military service he was recruited by the eminent virologist Frank Macfarlane Burnet, co-recipient with Peter Medawar of the Nobel Prize in Physiology or Medicine for demonstrating acquired immune tolerance, to join the Walter and Eliza Hall Institute of Medical Research in Melbourne. There, Fenner studied the genetics of poxviruses and the effect of those genetics on the immune systems of experimental vertebrates and discovered that mousepox provided a useful model for investigating the incubation period of infectious viral diseases. After a year studying tropical diseases at the Rockefeller Institute for Medical Research (now the Rockefeller University) in New York City, he began studies of myxoma virus at the John Curtin School of Medical Research at the Australian National

University, Canberra, where he was the Chairman of the Department of Microbiology and, later, director of the school.

Fenner became a national hero in the early 1950s when he directed a program to control the 600 million-strong feral European rabbit (*Oryctolagus cuniculus*) population which was eating its way through Australia's pasturelands and threatening the life blood of the country. He and his colleagues conducted a pilot study in which myxoma virus (family *Poxviridae*, genus *Leporipoxvirus*) was shown to kill more than 99% of susceptible rabbits. A succeeding and expanded campaign to spread myxomatosis reduced the rabbit population to 100 million. Their findings, including those of resistance to the virus, served as a model for subsequent research on poxviruses, including variola virus (genus *Orthopoxvirus*), the cause of smallpox in humans. Fenner began advising the World Health Organization on a campaign to eradicate smallpox, and he was appointed Chair of the Global Commission for the Certification of Smallpox Eradication in 1977. The last known case of naturally transmitted smallpox was recorded in Somalia in 1977. Fenner had the honor of announcing that seminal moment in Geneva on May 8, 1980, removing from human concern a disease that had been causing 20 million cases and 2 million deaths annually. With Donald A. Henderson, the principal guiding force of the CDC smallpox eradication efforts, and others Fenner wrote the definitive history of the campaign, "Smallpox and Its Eradication" (available on line through the W.H.O. web site). Fenner's interest in epidemiology and population dynamics inspired him to establish the Center for Resource and Environmental Studies at the Australian National University in Canberra (now known as the Fenner School of Environment and Society), which he directed until he retired in 1979. He continued working at the University until nearly his last days.

A charming, insightful, intellectually muscular, elegant, reserved but gregarious soul, a prolific writer, a marvelous administrator and outstanding teacher, Frank Fenner trained a generation of Australian virologists – another legacy he left to us. Based on his pessimistic assessments of the environmental damage already done and the size of the growing human population, in one of his final public statements he darkly predicted that humans and many other vertebrates will become extinct within the next hundred years.

Ian David Marshall: One of Fenner's students, Marshall received a Bachelor's degree in Agricultural Sciences and became Fenner's research assistant at the John Curtin School of Medical Research. For the next 10 years, he conducted detailed studies of the epidemiology, pathogenesis, virulence, attenuation, innate resistance, immunity, control, mechanical mosquito transmission and other aspects of myxoma virus and myxomatosis in rabbits. A key finding by Marshall was that high environmental temperatures moderated the severity of myxomatosis and low temperatures greatly exacerbated its severity. Marshall obtained his Ph.D. from Australian National University in 1955 and then became a post-doctoral fellow in the Department of Epidemiology of the School of Public Health, University of California, Berkeley, with William Reeves. After that he returned to Canberra and established a W.H.O. center for arbovirus research, producing diagnostic materials for use in-house and by other laboratories. He also introduced insectaries and animal containment laboratories at a time when those were ground-breaking ideas.

After holding a Visiting Scientist position at the London School of Hygiene and Tropical Medicine and an Honorary Senior Research Fellowship in the Department of Microbiology, University of Birmingham, England, Marshall eventually became a Senior Fellow in the Department of Microbiology, John Curtin School of Medical Research. Along the way he characterized myxomatosis in brush rabbits (*Sylvilagus bachmani*) in California with David Regnery (Stanford University) and described the mechanical transmission of this virus by mosquitoes, elucidated the effects of dual arbovirus infections of mosquitoes with Ken S. Lam, described the pathogenesis of arboviruses with Telford Work, and, with his student, Geoff Gard, described the annual reoccurrence of human epidemic polyarthritis and its association with Ross River virus activity in mosquitoes in coastal New South

Figure 121. Sentinel chicken arrangement, California)
(image courtesy of William Reisen, University of California at Davis)

Wales. Conducting surveillance for arboviruses in Australia and New Guinea, Marshall and his many Australian colleagues, including Lynn Dalgarno and Ronald C. Weir, detected and partially characterized the presence, pathogenesis, and molecular properties not only of Ross River virus but also of Murray Valley encephalitis, Kunjin, Edge Hill, Sindbis, Koongol, Wongal and Kowanyama viruses, and of many previously undescribed arboviruses, including Barmah Forest virus, which he had helped discover. Marshall was a pioneer of studies of Murray Valley encephalitis and the virus that causes it. Nearly 40 years ago, he put into place a sentinel chicken program, learned from Reeves at the University of California (Figure 121), a program still in place, still functioning, and still valuable in helping to predict epidemics and outbreaks. An articulate writer, Marshall should have written novels as well as scientific papers but he was far too modest for that.

Marshall's first graduate student was Royle Hawkes, who was first to observe antibody-dependent virus enhancement, later more fully studied by Scott Halstead, James Porterfield, and their co-workers. Hawkes described his finding thusly:

"In 1961 I came to do a Ph.D. in the Department of Microbiology at the John Curtin School. My supervisor, Ian Marshall, suggested that I develop the agar gel precipitin method for arboviruses, using Getah virus, an alphavirus, and Murray Valley encephalitis virus, a flavivirus. I used domestic fowls, immunized with viruses grown in mouse brain, as the source of antisera, and infective mouse brain as antigen. With hindsight, it would have been better to have used mice as the source of the antiserum, to avoid the subsequent need to absorb out the anti-mouse antibodies from the fowl antisera.

"One of the recognized properties of antiviral antibodies is their ability to neutralize viral infectivity. The time came to carry out neutralization tests on the antisera, to compare the levels of precipitating and neutralizing antibodies. For convenience, I used chick embryo fibroblasts as the assay system, employing a method in which serial dilutions of antisera are mixed with standard amounts of virus. The usual finding with potent antibody was that neutralization of the virus occurred at high concentrations of antiserum, the degree waning with progressive antiserum dilution until eventually, if dilution proceeds far enough, the residual virus in the mix became the same as that in the standard virus mixed with normal serum. Embarrassingly, my results showed that the apparent virus level increased, rather than decreased, when mixed with diluted antibody. I concluded that I had set up the experiment wrongly, being unable, like so many others, to envisage a situation where antibody acted contrary to reason and all previous experience. Assuming that I had botched it, I put the whole thing away and went on to have an enjoyable two years doing arbovirus epidemiology in New Guinea.

"However, later I repeated the experiment on the avian sera, just tidying up for my thesis, and got exactly the same results as I had two years earlier. I thought that I was not likely to make exactly the same mistake twice, and that the phenomenon was probably real. A flurry of experiments followed. The magnitude of the enhancement was considerable, it occurred with many viruses, it was virus-specific, and it occurred only when avian antisera were assayed on avian cells. Avian antisera assayed on mammalian cells, and mammalian antisera assayed on avian cells, always produced neutralization. Later work by others showed that mammalian antisera demonstrated the effect on mammalian cells. Kevin Lafferty lent his considerable expertise to purifying the active immunoglobulins and elucidating the kinetics of the reaction. We speculated that somehow the attachment of antibody to virus particles increased the proportion of the viral population that could attach to and penetrate cells. It was a busy and exhilarating time.

"It took about ten years for the phenomenon to be accepted and for other workers to begin to fill in the gaps. It is now well established that antibody- dependent enhancement occurs in many viral families, and that it is clinically important in certain situations, the most striking of which is dengue haemorrhagic fever. As so often happens, there was a lot of luck in the discovery; I happened to produce the antisera in chickens, I assayed the virus-antibody mixture on chicken cells, I had a supervisor (Ian Marshall) who displayed benevolent skepticism until the phenomenon was beyond doubt and strong support thereafter, and another established scientist (Kevin Lafferty) who was willing to collaborate but careful not to dominate. Perhaps the best of all was the opportunity to visit the matter twice, at an interval of two years. Dogma is a difficult thing for the novice to surmount. I needed a second try before I could challenge it."

Geoffrey P. Gard: Another of Marshall's graduate students, Gard obtained a veterinary degree at the University of Sydney and worked as a Veterinary Officer in the New South Wales Department of Agriculture. Gard was with Marshall at the John Curtin School of Medical Research, studying the epidemiology of Ross River virus, which Marshall had discovered. A post-doctoral Research Fellowship at the University of Alabama, Birmingham, followed, during which time he studied the molecular biology of arenaviruses. After that it was a post-doctoral research opportunity at the Animal Virus Research Institute,

Pirbright, England, where he investigated the pathogenesis and virulence of bluetongue viruses. When he returned to Australia, Gard took the position of senior virologist at the Animal Health Laboratory, Northern Territory Department of Primary Production in Darwin, staying for eight years. He served in many posts, but from 1988-2002 he was the Principal and then Senior Research Scientist with the Animal Health Science Office of the Chief Veterinary Officer, Department of Agriculture, Fisheries, Forestry, Canberra. Armed with this wide range of experiences and expertise in so many areas of veterinary medicine, infectious diseases, and virology, Gard eventually retired but continues to serve as a very active consultant to various organizations within the Australian Government, teaching and demonstrating on a wide variety of virus problems not only in Australia but in Indonesia, India, Malaysia, the Philippines, New Zealand, Ethiopia and South Africa. Equally at home abroad as in Australia, remarkably knowledgeable about important veterinary infectious disease problems, a passionate sports participant, and a cheerful, fun-loving and energetic colleague, Gard represents the best of Australian veterinary medicine; Marshall certainly was proud of his students.

Kenneth Lam Sai Kit: Now Professor Emeritus of the Department of Microbiology at the University Malaya, Lam also obtained his Ph.D. with Marshall. His thesis work involved dual infections of *Aedes* species mosquitoes, through which he demonstrated that there was no interference when two closely related flaviviruses infected the same individual mosquito. He also studied the epidemiology of arboviruses from Papua New Guinea. Lam has spent nearly his entire career looking for viral etiologies of diseases, focusing a great deal of his interest on dengue and the viruses that cause it. He received the Prince Mahidol Award of Thailand ("the Nobel Prize of the East") and France's second highest award, the Knight of the National Order of Merit. Like many retirees, he remains available to provide whatever help he can to younger scientists.

Figure 122. Ralph Leonard Doherty (1927 -)
(image courtesy of John S. Mackenzie)

Linda Hueston: Marshall's last Ph.D. student, Hueston now serves the Sydney area as the diagnostician for arbovirus and other virus infections and as the de facto expert reference resource for many other areas of Australia. Stationed at Westmead Hospital, Sydney, New South Wales, she heads the Arbovirus and Emerging Disease Unit, which is a division of the New South Wales Department of Health. Hueston not only provides diagnostic assistance for people scattered over huge geographic areas but in differing ecologic areas as well and provides them with reference reagents.

Ralph L. Doherty: Another of the outstanding Australian arbovirologists, Doherty (Figure 122), a physician and Ph.D., is an older cousin of Peter C. Doherty, the Nobel Prize laureate. He has said that innovations suggested by William Reeves, who had traveled to Australia in 1952 to take part in field studies of Murray Valley encephalitis, resulted not only in various useful hypotheses but also in ideas that essentially "directed arbovirus research in Australia for a generation". Doherty indicated that Reeves had been a major figure in the development of Australian arbovirus research because of the people he had influenced while there. Likely so, as Reeves was influential everywhere he went. Still, it was Doherty who invited Reeves to Austrailia. They knew each other well because Reeves had served on Doherty's doctoral thesis committee (as well as the doctoral thesis committees for Ian Marshall and Brian H. Kay).

Doherty became Director of the Queensland Institute for Medical Research in Brisbane (1966-1978), then the Dean of the Medical

School, and finally the Pro-Vice Chancellor for Health Sciences at the University of Queensland. Beginning his career with studies of leptospirosis, typhus, coxsackieviruses, Q fever, enteroviruses, adenoviruses and Epstein-Barr virus, he recognized additional opportunities in what at the time was a poorly investigated northern Australia. Doherty's arboviral reputation was built in great part during the 1950s-1980s by his studies of aboriginal health and arboviruses in northern Queensland, particularly near the Gulf of Carpentaria at the Mitchell River Mission, Cape York Peninsula, and in the Northern Territory. He and his colleagues, who included Alan L. Dyce, Barry M. Gorman, Ian Holmes, Harry A. Standfast, and Toby D. St. George, isolated viruses and conducted serosurveys and, of course, disease surveys, which revealed the presence of scores of arboviruses and arboviral diseases. First to isolate Ross River virus (from *Aedes vigilax* mosquitoes collected near Townsville in 1963), he and his collaborators, particularly Toby St. George, were first to identify viruses or first to find recognized viruses in many areas: Alfuy, Barmah Forest, CSIRO Village, Belmont, bluetongues, bovine ephemeral fever, Bunyip Creek, Corriparta, dengues, Edge Hill, Eubenangee, Facey's Paddock, Humpty Doo, Gadget's Gully, Kokobera, Kowanyama, Kunjin, Leanyer, Mapputta, Marrakai, Murray Valley encephalitis, Nugget, Precarious Point, Saumarez Reef, Sindbis, Stratford, Taggert, Thimiri, Wallal, Warrego, Wongorr, and more. In addition, they obtained the first isolations of Murray Valley encephalitis virus from mosquitoes. A few of these viruses were isolated on islands in the far south Pacific, what the Australians call the "South Ocean", from birds and bird ticks, while others were isolated from mosquitoes or culicoids, other birds and other vertebrates. Once one begins looking for viruses, one finds them: new viruses, new subtypes, new disease associations, and new insights into the natural cycles of viruses and virus evolution.

An instructive example of virus and disease associations and how little we know about Australian (or other) arboviruses is the recognition by Hooper et al. of Wallal virus as a cause of blindness in macropods, mostly western gray kangaroos (*Macropus fuliginosis*) but also red kangaroos (*M. rufa*), eastern gray kangaroos (*M. giganteus*), and euros (*M. robustus*), during an outbreak of chorioretinitis between 1994 and 1996. The epizootic spread from the east to the west coast. Isolated by Ralph Doherty and colleagues in 1970 from *Culicoides dycei* in Queensland, Wallal virus has also been isolated from culicoids in the Northern Territory. The illness was attributed to Wallal virus (family *Reoviridae*, genus *Orbivirus*) by testing affected macropods and by experimental infections. Wallal virus RNA was also detected by PCR in a paraffin-embedded retina taken from a blind kangaroo in 1975, so this virus was causing disease long before it was first isolated. This, of course, supports the distinct possibility that arboviruses not associated with diseases may simply be understudied, as is the case with all viruses.

Just as Chinese virologists have now joined the rest of the world's virologists in looking for and finding viruses, so will the virologists of any under-studied area. One wonders what lies ahead for unstudied rain forests (or for the rain forests themselves), deserts, and islands where unrecognized arboviruses lurk. Taken together, the virologic results of Australian surveys helped fill the International Catalogue of Arboviruses.

Because of the great expanse of Australia and its variety of ecosystems and habitat types, arboviruses there are equally varied, so that those studying arboviruses in Eastern and Western Australia may have responsibilities and goals that are very different from each other. Nonetheless, the human population of Australia is relatively low, and these folks seem to know each other and to communicate regularly, so that knowledge about the arboviruses of this gigantic land mass is shared readily.

Contributions of Scientists from New Zealand:

New Zealand is a lovely island nation (more accurately two main islands) in the same general geographic area as Australia, but comprising a distinct ecosystem. More than 50 years ago, Frank J. Austin, Terry Maguire, John Arthur Reginald Miles and their associates at the University of Otago, Dunedin, found evidence of arbovirus infections in New Zealand and isolated Whataroa virus, an alphavirus closely related to Sindbis virus. Note that the initial arbovirological studies in New Zealand were done with support from the Rockefeller Foundation.

Although endemic arboviruses may cause human infections in New Zealand, there is no evidence that these viruses cause human illnesses there. Investigators at the University of Otago, however, conducted studies of arboviruses in Fiji and elsewhere in the south Pacific area, including detailed studies of epidemic polyarthritis caused by Ross River virus.

One might ask how arbovirologists in all these very different countries could fit together in any semblance of "organization". The answer is a simple one: Because of the initial idea funded by the Rockefeller Foundation, the American Committee on Arthropod-borne Viruses continues to meet annually, maintains the efforts of the subcommittees, sponsors symposia, sponsors "white papers" in an advisory capacity for governmental and international health organizations and administrators, and otherwise maintains the tradition and the good works. It can honestly be said that the work of this committee functions at the highest of levels. Membership in the American Committee on Arthropod-borne Viruses has not grown in recent years because younger people do not look upon themselves as strictly arbovirologists and because specialization has narrowed their focus. Nonetheless, many new members have joined that group, and many have dropped out due to retirements and deaths. Still, the roots put down years ago by the founders have nourished work done world wide and international collaboration between arbovirologists continues and is useful. The early leaders may all be gone, but it is obvious that the informal organization they demanded of the American Committee on Arthropod-borne Viruses has led to and maintained global influence. Furthermore, those who work in the field have received and passed on a sense of identity and unity and, as I suspect was also a primary intent, a basis for having great fun.

The International Catalogue of Arboviruses and Certain Other Viruses, which at one time provided an essential reference source for finding published and unpublished information, has not been published on paper since 1985. Data in that invaluable book have been transferred to a web site http://wwwn.cdc.gov/arbocat/index.asp. Errors are corrected, data are added, and inquiries are possible through the CDC/Fort Collins, where the web site is maintained.

CHAPTER 9

Entomologists, field work, and virus discovery

What would a book on arboviruses be without an extended mention of the entomologists who did sweaty and dangerous but essential labors far from home? Historically, diseases were investigated based on the extent and seriousness of the medical problem and then treated with whatever was available. Little thought was given to searching for legitimate causes and prevention until the Hungarian obstetrician Ignaz Semmelweis, working at the Vienna General Hospital, recognized a relationship between puerperal ("childbed") fever (principally caused by streptococci) and the lack of hand washing by physicians examining women delivering babies. The suggestion by Semmelweis in 1847 that the incidence of puerperal fever could be reduced if physicians rinsed their hands in chlorinated lime water (calcium hypochlorite) was soon adopted. Wherever that procedure was included in hospital routines, mortality rates from puerperal fever decreased rapidly, by more than 98% in the hospital where Semmelweis worked. John Snow's study of cholera in London found the source of the disease-causing organisms and so founded what we call epidemiology. Later hypotheses and studies by Louis Pasteur (1860s), Joseph Lister

(1870s), Robert Koch (1880s), and others added some new controversies but more useful information. Nonetheless, for arboviruses as for other viruses, a more complete understanding of disease processes was impossible until infectious agents and their sources were identified. For arboviruses, the arthropod vectors and their vertebrate hosts were yet to be determined and the natural cycle of the viruses delineated.

Given that there are perhaps five or more million species of arthropods, that they may be widespread geographically or found only in certain areas, that they feed on numerous or few vertebrate hosts, that they can be exceedingly difficult to identify, and that they are captured only with great effort and usually only with certain arcane methods, entomology is not a field for the faint of heart. How entomologists kept all this straight in pre-computer days is astonishing, but they did have "keys", drawings of individuals of various species and, eventually, photographs. There are more than 22,000 recognized species of ants (family Formicidae) alone, which indicates what entomologists are up against. Nevertheless, when a virus is isolated from an arthropod or a "pool" of many arthropods, one at least knows a possible mode of transmission. Not all possible modes of transmission, however, are obvious. One novel example was shown by an Oxford University group led by Patricia Nuttall, with visiting scientist Milan Labuda, Director of the Institute of Zoology, Slovak Academy of Sciences, Bratislava. They found that uninfected brown ear ticks (*Rhipicephalus appendiculatus*) acquired Thogoto virus (family *Orthomyxoviridae*, genus *Thogotovirus*) when co-feeding with infected *Rhipicephalus appendiculatus* ticks on the same guinea pig host even though the guinea pigs on which they fed did not develop detectable levels of virus in their bloods. They thereby demonstrated that a vertebrate apparently refractory to infection by an arbovirus can play an important role in the epidemiology of the virus. Although additional odd mechanisms may be discovered from time to time, it seems likely that direct arthropod-to-vertebrate transmission, the most commonly observed mechanism, is the principal mechanism of virus transmission.

Nuttall's continuing studies of tick-borne viruses have led to the discovery of many new ones. Isolations of orbiviruses from ticks collected from seabirds and from their nests have allowed a better understanding of the geographic distribution, host ranges, and vectors of these viruses. Analyses of the double stranded RNA of these viruses showed a high frequency of reassortment in dually-infected cells, extending the earlier findings of Barry M. Gorman of the Queensland Institute of Medical Research in Brisbane, who led the way to our present understanding of orbivirus evolution.

Interestingly, some of these orbivirus antigenic groups appear to constitute a single gene pool. Given that these viruses have been isolated from ticks parasitizing birds from Iceland in the northern hemisphere to Macquarie Island in the southern Pacific Ocean, the observations provide a rationale for the hypothesis of a wide geographic range not only of the bird hosts and bird ticks but of the genetic assemblage.

Entomologists interested in arboviruses worked from the Rockefeller Foundation; at the United States Centers for Disease Control; the United States Army and Navy; and various state, local government, and university laboratories in the United States, the Pasteur Institute system laboratories and the Office de la Recherche Scientifique et Technique d'Outre-Mer (ORSTOM) of France; the Commonwealth Scientific & Industrial Research Organization and university laboratories of Australia; the Ivanovsky Research Institute of Virology at the Russian Academy of Medical Sciences and the M.P. Chumakov Institute of Poliomyelitis and Viral Encephalitides of the Russian Academy of Medical Sciences in Russia and predecessor organizations; the Institute Evandro Chagas and associated organizations in Brazil; and many individual national and university laboratories around the world. Here are a few examples of the work of these remarkable people.

William C. Reeves: William (Bill) Carlisle Reeves, was perhaps the world's foremost authority on the spread and control of arthropod-borne virus diseases. For many decades requests for consultations came to him from every conceivable part of the world and from some inconceivable ones. In the early 1940s, he was working in the Yakima Valley of Washington State for the University of California-San Francisco Hooper Foundation for Medical Research. With William McD. Hammon, he accumulated evidence that *Culex tarsalis* mosquitoes were the vectors of both western equine encephalitis and St. Louis encephalitis viruses. These mosquitoes were numerous and were known to feed on chickens (determined using primitive but effective precipitin tests, in which antibody reacts with a specific antigen to form a precipitate) of blood from mosquitoes and antibodies to bloods of various types of vertebrates), domestic mammals, and humans. "The feeding habits of this species alone could result in the incidence of encephalitis antibodies demonstrated in domestic animals and man in the Yakima Valley.", they concluded. Thus, this team developed an epidemiological view of these diseases and highlighted the importance of including entomological information in the study of all arboviral diseases.

It was Reeves who coined the term "arbovirus" and suggested the use of "sentinel chickens" for determining the presence, incidence, and seasonality of certain arboviruses, thus establishing a means of local and state surveillance for arboviruses.

George Brownlee Craig, Jr.: When I was in graduate school at the University of Notre Dame in South Bend, Indiana, a more advanced student suggested to me that I at least sit in on a class taught by a young George Craig (Figure 123). It was an undergraduate class in parasitology but, I was told, any class he taught would do. I did not register for the course but I attended the class; I never considered that decision anything but a great one. George was exceptionally enthusiastic about his work and about teaching. The joy he obtained from both was obvious. His splendid lectures, with unforgettable examples, remain with me, more than 50 years later.

When Craig began his painstaking studies of mosquito genetics few papers on the subject had been published, with only a scant few focused on *Aedes aegypti.* However, by 1967 Craig and others had described 87 mutations and 28 loci assigned to the three linkage groups and were on their way to focusing on genetic control of insects of public health importance.

Figure 123. George Brownlee Craig, Jr. (1930 - 1995)
(image courtesy of University of Notre Dame Archives)

With Paul Robert Grimstad, a former student of Craig's and then one of his colleagues, he published on vector competence of *Aedes triseriatus* and its sibling species *Aedes hendersoni* in transmitting La Crosse virus; midgut and salivary gland barriers to La Crosse virus dissemination in *Aedes triseriatus* mosquitoes; vector competence of *Aedes hendersoni;* and evidence of a salivary-gland escape barrier for that virus. Grimstad and Craig observed a modification of feeding behavior of *Aedes triseriatus* mosquitoes due to La Crosse virus infection. Grimstad also published with his own students at the University of Notre Dame. Their further studies of La Crosse virus and other orthobunyaviruses in mosquitoes, small mammals, and in deer (*Odocoileus virginianus*); serologic evidence for infection of humans and wildlife with the underrecognized Jamestown Canyon virus; and many other aspects of orthobunyavirus biology in the Upper Midwestern United States.

Craig never would have claimed to have been an arbovirologist. He was a recognized international expert in entomology, with emphasis on the genetics and characteristics of mosquitoes, particularly those of the genus *Aedes*, including *Aedes aegypti* and *Aedes albopictus*. Nonetheless, he was a faithful member of the American Society of Tropical Medicine and Hygiene and of the American Committee on Arthropod-borne Viruses. At annual meetings he always had useful and stimulating comments, made in his good-humored way. That Society awarded him the prestigious Walter Reed Medal and the Hoogstraal Medal was bestowed upon him by the American Committee for Medical Entomology, a subgroup of the Society. He was a member of the United States National Academy of Sciences.

Craig's interests included studies of genetic variability of *Aedes* species mosquitoes, identification of mutations, preparation of chromosome maps linking specific locations to a wide variety of genetic traits, host feeding patterns, insecticide susceptibility of larvae, sexual behavior, midgut and salivary gland barriers to virus dissemination, vector competency for yellow fever virus and more – all leading to his quest for methods to genetically control mosquitoes. At the same time, he was drawn to studies of arboviruses by the presence of La Crosse orthobunyavirus in *Aedes triseriatus* and by the serious illnesses it was causing in children in Indiana and throughout the Upper Midwest. He analyzed many aspects of the genetics of diapause, an important trait in this instance because La Crosse virus is transovarially transmitted.

He played a role in using genetic information to determine the geographic origin of *Aedes albopictus* mosquitoes which had invaded the United States in used tires from Asia in 1987 and which were breeding in huge dumps of discarded used tires (Figure 124). He participated in the identification and description of the ecologic characteristics of the area of Florida where the first United States isolate of any virus, in this case eastern equine encephalitis virus, was detected in *Aedes albopictus* mosquitoes. He also collaborated on the isolation of a newly recognized orthobunyavirus (Potosi virus) from mosquitoes of this species.

Craig spoke loudly, often critically, and publicly about the lack of emphasis the United States Government had put on studying this invasive mosquito and warned of its potential importance in disease transmission. Interestingly, it now appears that the spread of *Aedes albopictus* in southern North America has corresponded with a decline or even an extinction of the previous invader *Aedes aegypti;*

Figure 124. Discarded used tires, a potential breeding site for mosquitoes. (image courtesy of Barry J. Beaty)

that this is consistent with interspecific competition. Only time will tell whether Craig's prognostications will come true, but it already is clear that *Aedes albopictus* mosquitoes have played an enormous role in the world-wide spread of chikungunya virus. Perhaps Craig's suggestion that *Aedes albopictus* may be "the ultimate vector" may yet be proven correct.

Thomas H.G. Aitken: Working at the Yale Arbovirus Research Unit, Aitken continued the laboratory work he had begun decades before and published important papers on the vector capacities of various geographic strains of *Stegomyia* species mosquitoes for yellow fever virus and on the transovarial transmission of yellow fever virus in these mosquitoes. That work explained the long-standing puzzle of the inter-epidemic survival of the virus and provided evidence that Asian *Aedes* species mosquitoes were incompetent vectors of that virus. Aitken was recognized worldwide for his important contributions to tropical public health and was considered a valued colleague and mentor by the faculty and graduate students at the Yale University School of Medicine. The American Society of Tropical Medicine and Hygiene presented him with the Richard M. Taylor Award for outstanding contributions to arbovirology and the Hoogstraal Medal for outstanding achievements in medical entomology. Aitken was also known for his great good humor as well as for his attention to details.

I once published a paper describing a new arbovirus in Colombia. A month or so after the paper appeared in the journal I received a call from Aitken. "Charles", he said, "you have the degrees correct but the minutes incorrect for the location of the site at which the mosquitoes were collected."

In 1999, many years after he retired from Yale University, Aitken honored me by attending a seminar I was presenting there on West Nile virus; he was 86 years old at the time and in failing health. Someone asked me whether this virus replicated in ticks; I knew nothing about this. However, in 1960 Aitken and Loring Whitman had published results of their studies of the possibility that *Ornithodoros moubata* ticks might serve as reservoirs of West Nile virus and so I asked Aitken whether he might help me out by commenting. Rising slowly from his chair with some difficulty and straightening his jacket and necktie, Aitken explained his involvement in prior studies while in military service during World War II, presented a summary of what was known about the replication of this virus in ticks and provided us with the minutiae of their results. It was a remarkable performance, recognized by all in attendance as an example of the immense knowledge he possessed and why he was known as one of the greatest of medical entomologists – to the end of his accomplished life.

The American Committee on Medical Entomology: This active group was founded in 1987 by an outstanding group of entomologists who wanted to focus on more specialized areas of medical entomologic research than could be provided by membership in the American Committee on Arthropod-borne Viruses. Many of those people were and are active members of both groups. During the organizational period of the first few years, members included Ralph Barr, William Reisen, William Romoser, Kenneth Linthicum, Bruce Harrison, Robert Gwadz, Joseph Piesman, Ronald Ward, Charles Bailey, Eddie Cupp, Ron Rosenberg, Jerome Vandenberg, Carl Mitchell, Robert Washino, Larry Lacey, Edward Houk, Abdu Farhang Azad, Charles Beard, and Andrew Spielman. There have been the inevitable retirements and deaths, but this group continues to recruit many of the most outstanding medical entomologists of our time. Given the influx of young entomologists, this group will likely continue to function at a high level for many years to come. In addition to annual symposia and suggestions regarding public health, this is the group that presents the Harry Hoogstraal Medal for Outstanding Achievement in Medical Entomology. The awardees, since the first medal was presented in 1987, have been: William C. Reeves, Lloyd E. Rozeboom, Robert Traub, William R. Horsfall, William L. Jellison, James H. Oliver, Thomas H.G. Aitken, A. Ralph Barr, Gene DeFoliart, Chris Curtis, Michael Service, Andrew Spielman, John D. Edman, Robert Washino, Mario Coluzzi, Bruce Eldridge, Daniel Sonenshine, William E. Collins, Willy Burgdorfer, and, in 2012, William Reisen. Quite the list of experts!

Harry Hoogstraal: An American entomologist and parasitologist, Hoogstrall perhaps was the greatest authority on ticks and tick-borne diseases who ever lived, Hoogstraal obtained undergraduate and Master's degrees from the University of Illinois and served as an entomologist in the United States Army during World War II, after which he earned Ph.D. and D.Sc. degrees from the London School of Hygiene and Tropical Medicine. His multiple field expeditions in Mexico (1938-1940) had provided massive and valuable collections of animals and plants. During World War II he was assigned to an Army laboratory in what was called Dutch New Guinea, now Irian Jaya, Indonesia. There he made enormous collections of mosquitoes and studied them taxonomically. His studies, with Willard V. King provided new information regarding the culicid fauna of the southwest Pacific region. Their collections were placed in what became the Smithsonian Museum in Washington, D.C., and provided resources for other investigators. Rather than returning home after the war, Hoogstraal was discharged in Manila and, with the support of Chicago's Field Museum, spent the next two years collecting samples on the islands of Mindanao and Palawan. Returning from the Philippines in 1948, he found employment with the United States Navy and joined a University of California expedition to Africa. When the expedition ended, he stayed on in Madagascar and then moved to Cairo, Egypt, where he organized and became Head of the Department of Medical Zoology, United States Naval Medical Research Unit No. 3 (NAMRU-3), a position he held until his death in Cairo in 1986.

At NAMRU-3 he collected specimens and collections of specimens from understudied areas of the world and collaborated, often in writing, with investigators throughout the world. Anyone who wrote to Hoogstraal received an answer, often a lengthy one, replete with original references, whether in English, Russian, or any other language (he spoke many languages himself and hired translators to assist him). His letters were typed, probably in the middle of the night, as was his habit, and he maintained copies of everything. Insomnia allowed Hoogstraal to accomplish an enormous amount of work, authoring or co-authoring more than 500 publications, editing at least that many, joining and being active in scores of professional societies and editorial positions, lecturing widely, and training graduate students. Honors conferred upon him came from many countries and the American Society for Tropical Medicine and Hygiene's Harry Hoogstraal Medal for Outstanding Achievement in Medical Entomology honors his contributions to science and now honors investigators of entomologic aspects of arbovirology. Significantly, more than 200 species are named for Hoogstraal, no doubt the world's pre-eminent medical entomologist of his time. Thanks to Lt. Col. Terry Carpenter, Dr. Rich Robbins and Dr. Stanton E. Cope, the Harry Hoogstraal room in the Armed Forces Pest Management Board offices of the United States

Department of Defense recently was dedicated to his life work and memory.

Roy W. Chamberlain and W. Daniel Sudia: When the (now) United States Centers for Disease Control and Prevention was established (*vide supra*) by the United States Public Health Service as the Communicable Disease Center in Montgomery, Alabama, the new organization wisely hired Roy Chamberlain and Dan Sudia as entomologists. Chamberlain came from the Department of Parasitology, School of Hygiene and Public Health, Johns Hopkins University, Baltimore, Maryland and Sudia came directly from his graduate work at Ohio State University.

Chamberlain studied composition when he was in college and it showed. His writing skills were of great help when he placed his observations into the scientific record, results of his experimental studies and his views of epidemics and the roles played by arthropod vectors of viruses. A clear thinker, Chamberlain's entomologic contributions were enormous. He was able to combine scholarly work on mosquitoes with studies of mosquitoes that were relevant to public health. He recognized that both were needed and that academic knowledge of mosquito behavior and life cycles is necessary to an understanding of the epidemiology of the viruses they transmit. Merging these interests, Chamberlain and Sudia, in collaboration

Figure 125. CDC (Sudia-Chamberlain) light trap with an insulated paper bag containing dry ice as a source of carbon dioxide to attract questing mosquitoes.
(image courtesy of U.S. Centers for Disease Control and Prevention)

with other public health workers at CDC and entomologists and virologists elsewhere, conducted experimental infections with colonized mosquitoes, combined their laboratory results with results of their field work and produced fundamental information. Notably, Sudia and Chamberlain developed the CDC light trap (Figure 125), now and for many years used world-wide for collecting mosquitoes and other arthropods of medical significance.

Thomas W. Scott: Scott (Figure 98) attended Bowling Green State University, obtaining the unusual combination of a B.S. in business administration and an M.S. in Biology. He received a Ph.D. in ecology from Pennsylvania State University and pursued post-doctoral research in epidemiology with Barry Beaty at Yale University. Following a faculty position in the Department of Entomology, University of Maryland, he became Professor and Director of the Mosquito Research Laboratory, Department of Entomology, University of California at Davis.

Scott's scientific career began when he used Turlock virus (family *Bunyaviridae*, genus *Orthobunyavirus*) to conducted experimental infections of birds, then transmit the virus by mosquitoes. Working with a variety of top-notch entomologists, virologists, and others at CDC and elsewhere in the United States and abroad, Scott produced a remarkable series of publications detailing the replication of eastern equine encephalitis, West Nile, and other viruses in mosquitoes; reproductive effects of Fort Morgan virus (maintained and transmitted by nest bugs, *Oeciacus vicarius*) on birds; virus evolution; pathology in virus-infected mosquitoes; and patterns and effects of blood-feeding by mosquitoes. Only then did he begin what could be considered his most important work: studying the multiple facets of infections of mosquitoes and of humans with dengue viruses. These studies comprised both academic and applied aspects of dengue virus studies in Latin America and Thailand: transmission patterns, virulence, host characterizations, adaptation, evolution, genetics, and multiple other aspects of the epidemiology of these important and widely prevalent viruses. Taken together, Scott's studies not only contributed to our understanding of virus replication and transmission but have provided practical applications of this information.

CDC Field Stations: At one time, CDC had laboratories in Kansas City, Kansas; San Francisco, California; Phoenix, Arizona; Savannah, Georgia; Anchorage, Alaska; San Juan, Puerto Rico; and Greeley, Colorado and a Water Projects Section in Logan, Utah that conducted metaanalyses of biology and control data in several western states. There also was a laboratory in Texas located in the "panhandle", the High Plains of Hale County. That laboratory was actually a branch of the Greeley, Colorado, laboratory, and the Greeley laboratory was a branch of the Kansas laboratory. When established, each laboratory had one or two specific responsibilities: rabies, arbovirus ecology, respiratory viruses, plague, tuberculosis, histoplasmosis, and more. The Kansas City Field Station was established in 1950 to conduct epidemiologic studies of tuberculosis, then histoplasmosis, a fungal infection; it closed in 1973 due to budgetary restraints.

Thomas D.Y. Chin became Director of that facility in 1954, with the virus research laboratory later headed by Jack D. Poland in collaboration with Herbert A. Wenner of the University of Kansas. In 1954 Chin and others investigated an extensive outbreak of central nervous system disease in Hidalgo County, south Texas. That outbreak was soon shown to have been caused by St. Louis encephalitis virus, the largest since the first recognized epidemic of that disease in St. Louis, Missouri in 1933; 70% of human infections were shown to have been inapparent, i.e., asymptomatic. *Culex quinquefasciatus* mosquitoes were shown for the first time to be the mosquito vector under natural conditions.

The San Francisco laboratory, which focused on plague, moved to Greeley in 1968 under the directorship of Archie D. Hess (Figure 68). In 1966 David Sencer, CDC's Director, reorganized and upgraded the operations of the field stations and, except for the Savannah laboratory, placed them all under a new Ecological Investigations Program, headed by Chin.

Poland was transferred to Greeley, taking responsibility for plague investigations. In 1971 that laboratory was moved to improved facilities in Fort Collins, on the grounds of Colorado State University, where it remains, with arboviruses now a central focus. Many excellent epidemiologic studies of western equine encephalitis and St. Louis encephalitis viruses in Hale County had been done by George W. Sciple, Preston Holden, Louis C. LaMotte, Jr., and Richard O. Hayes, with technical assistance by Ronald B. Shriner and Lawrence J. Kirk. Those studies, both longitudinal and detailed (seroconversions [no antibody in the first sample collected, antibody in a subsequently collected sample] in sentinel rabbits and horses, serosurveys in wild birds, principally house sparrows, *Passer domesticus,* and sentinel chickens, human and horse case surveillance, air temperature measurements, and so on), provided us with data showing that year-to-year fluctuations in virus prevalence depend on ecologic changes and habitat peculiarities and that fluctuating ecologic parameters may or may not be directly related to virus prevalence. Some studies done by personnel of the CDC Colorado laboratories were by assignment. For example, LaMotte had been invited by William Hammon to join a team comprising an epidemiologist, entomologist, mammalogist, ornithologist, clinician, and others in looking for evidence of Japanese encephalitis virus in birds migrating through the Philippines from Japan. No evidence of Japanese encephalitis virus was found, but an epidemic of dengue hemorrhagic fever occurred during their stay and the group shifted their focus and isolated dengue viruses from both humans and mosquitoes. It was common for field workers of many organizations to travel far and wide to collect samples of all sorts so that they could be studied in the home or in a local laboratory.

The Fort Collins laboratory continues to focus on arboviruses, although it also is responsible for studies of plague, Lyme disease, and other vector-borne diseases. Its first Director, Archie Hess, was succeeded by Thomas Monath, then by Duane Gubler and now by Lyle

Petersen. Under the direction of Hess, a field station was established in Hale County, Texas, with the intent of conducting longitudinal studies of western equine encephalitis and St. Louis encephalitis viruses. Through many years the Hale County field station made excellent and complex analyses of mosquito population densities, virus prevalence, seroconversions in rabbits and horses, weather data, and other factors in the complex epidemiologies of these viruses. When the arbovirologic competence of CDC/Atlanta was transferred to Fort Collins in 1973, Hess retired and Monath became the Director.

Under Monath's direction research assumed a wider world view and greater scientific reach. Scientists in the Fort Collins laboratories studied yellow fever in Africa, details of transmissions of hemorrhagic fever agents, encephalitis in Latin America, and pathophysiology of well-known but understudied diseases. They also developed diagnostic tools for numerous virus diseases.

John T. Roehrig and his co-workers developed useful monoclonal antibodies not only for the detection of viruses and for use in ELISA tests but also to probe the virus polypeptides themselves, providing tools to help understand the structure and function of arboviral proteins and to identify and map viral epitopes (the parts of antigens that are recognized by the immune system). D. Bruce Francy, Richard O. Hayes, Carl J. Mitchell, Chester G. Moore, Gordon C. Smith, Werner L. Jakob, assisted by their field and laboratory staff collected and identified mosquitoes and other arthropods throughout the United States and elsewhere. By doing so, they were constructing bases for epidemiologic evaluations of various epidemics and outbreaks: eastern equine encephalitis in Michigan and Massachusetts, St. Louis encephalitis in Colorado and Tennessee, vesicular stomatitis New Jersey virus in Colorado, and yellow fever in the Republic of the Gambia. They conducted arbovirus surveys and investigated a Rocio virus disease epidemic in Argentina, conducted detailed studies of the ecology and epidemiology of Colorado tick fever virus in Rocky Mountain National Park (Colorado), discovered hitherto unrecognized viruses in Brazil, Ecuador and in the United States (Weldona orthobunyavirus; Bahia Grande, Reed Ranch and Muir Springs rhabdoviruses; Tonate and Fort Morgan alphaviruses). They conducted surveys in various parts of the United States to map the distribution of the then newly invasive mosquito *Aedes albopictus,* which had arrived in North America from Asia in used automobile tires. Later, they isolated the previously unrecognized Potosi orthobunyavirus from these mosquitoes. In addition, they conducted valuable experimental infections of various arboviruses in mosquitoes and in vertebrates. Many of these field and laboratory studies were done in collaboration with Robert G. McLean, a mammalogist, ornithologist, and all-around field person. McLean's knowledge and experience led more than one field and laboratory study down the right path.

Monath's insistence on combining basic and field research guided the Fort Collins laboratory for many years, setting it on a firm scientific base and establishing a tradition of excellence for that laboratory, one that has served it well through difficult times. His emphasis on overseas work underscored the philosophy that arboviral threats to the United States cannot be anticipated and that international research can be equated with United States biodefense.

Led by Dennis W. Trent, John T. Roehrig, A. Vance Vorndam, and Richard M. Kinney, they as well as some hard-working graduate students began to investigate the molecular and immunologic properties of various viruses, particularly the alphaviruses and flaviviruses. First using oligonucleotide fingerprint mapping, then using the more sensitive and specific methods that were developed, they provided insight into the structural and non-structural proteins and the glycoproteins of many arboviruses. Among other findings, their research provided evidence that the 45 S RNA of St. Louis encephalitis flavivirus serves as the messenger during virus replication, which stands in contrast to the 26S RNA, which functions as the predominant messenger during alphavirus replication. The latter discovery was fundamental to the taxonomic separation of the flaviviruses from the togaviruses, with which they had been grouped.

Many exceptional entomologists and others labored long and hard to understand the life cycles and behaviors of various arthropods and how this might affect their abilities to participate in virus-vector transmission cycles. Not only did people such as Bruce Eldridge, Bob Washino, John Edman, Bill Reisen, and Thomas Scott conduct sophisticated laboratory work in the United States and elsewhere, they also conducted field work to help us further comprehend these natural cycles.

Individuals such as Professor of Medical Entomology Richard Charles Russell, Director of the Department of Medical Entomology, Institute for Clinical Pathology and Medical Research, Westmead Hospital, University of Sydney Medical School, Australia, and Dennis LeRoy Knudson, who was Professor of Entomology at the College of Agricultural Sciences with a joint appointment in the Department of Microbiology of the College of Veterinary Medicine and Biomedical Sciences, Colorado State University, Fort Collins, are among the many who understood the impact of local conditions on arthropods and the viruses they harbor, discovered viruses new to science, and delineated the molecular differences and epidemiologies of arboviruses.

VIRUS DISCOVERY

Briefly mentioned earlier in this book were some of the works by Walter Reed and his colleagues studying yellow fever; Eustace Montgomery and Nairobi sheep disease; Meyer, Haring and Howitt and western equine encephalitis; Webster and Wright and eastern equine encephalitis; Kubes and Rios and Venezuelan equine encephalomyelitis; Muckenfuss et al. and St. Louis encephalitis; Daubney, Hudson and Garnham and Rift Valley fever; Hayashi and Japanese encephalitis; Smithburn et al. and West Nile fever; multiple investigators in Australia working on what came to be known as Murray Valley encephalitis; and others. These might be considered simply as notes on a list, but the individual accomplishments and significances should not be considered trivial or routine, nor should those involved in these seminal studies be thought of as anything but exceptional. How can so many people be exceptional, you ask? Perhaps the challenges of the field attracted certain types of eclectic people. Whatever the fortunate reason, it is so, and that is why this book was written. Here are a few useful illustrations, with personal details included for perspective.

Mikhail Petrovich Chumakov: After his 1931 graduation from medical school, Chumakov joined a 1937 scientific expedition to the Khabarovsk region of the Soviet Far East, which was led by Professor Lev Aleksandrovich Zilber. Together with his colleagues, he discovered the etiology of a new transmissible neurological disease, which they called tick-borne encephalitis, and isolated the virus that causes it.

Unfortunately, Chumakov was accidentally infected with that virus, which resulted in encephalitis, and led to permanent loss of hearing, partial blindness, and paralysis of one arm, a condition which worsened over the years but which did not prevent him from continuing his work. For this discovery he was awarded the Stalin Prize of First Degree in Science and Technology in 1941. In 1948 Chumakov became a corresponding member and in 1960 a full member of the Academy of Medical Sciences of the U.S.S.R. In the 1940s he organized multiple medical expeditions to Siberia and other regions of the Soviet Union to investigate outbreaks caused by new viruses. What is not well known is that Chumakov had heroically refused to obey a command from Josef Stalin to dismiss all Jews from his staff in Moscow. As he was already recognized as an outstanding scientist, rather than being imprisoned in Siberia or elsewhere for this refusal, Chumakov was assigned to study diseases in eastern Russia.

Among the viruses he, Zilber, Seitlenok, Levkovich, and others eventually discovered was the tick-borne virus that caused human encephalitis ("tick-borne encephalitis"), which they named Russian Spring-Summer encephalitis virus. They described the clinical course and pathology of this disease, outlining its epidemiology, and isolating the virus from *Ixodes persulcatus* ticks. That virus was shown to be distantly related to Japanese encephalitis virus, St. Louis encephalitis, yellow fever virus, and certain other viruses, soon to be known as the "Group B arboviruses".

Over many years, beginning in 1939, a superb hypothesis regarding the circulation of tick-borne encephalitis virus in nature had been put forth by Eugenyi Pavlovsky. That hypothesis had an impact on Chumakov's subsequent work. Although Pavlovsky published, in all, more than 800 papers, book chapters, and textbooks on the subjects of parasitology, zoology and related fields, his book *Natural Nidality of Transmissible Diseases* was his classic. In this book he proposed that there is a close relationship between maintenance of zoonotic agents and the characteristics of the landscape in which they are found. No work since has provided as much information and insights on the basic qualities and relationships of ecosystems and infectious disease epidemiology. However, it should be recognized that the work of T.S. Detinova of the Marcinovskij Institute of Medical Parasitology and Tropical Medicine of the USSR Ministry of Health, Moscow, delineated the importance of age- and reproductive-grading methods for mosquitoes in understanding vector transmission.

In addition to the discovery of tick-borne encephalitis virus, Chumakov and other Russian investigators isolated for the first time Omsk hemorrhagic fever and Kemerovo fever viruses, hemorrhagic fever with renal syndrome virus (now called Hantaan virus), Crimean-Congo hemorrhagic fever virus, and many other viruses.

Omsk hemorrhagic fever: The natural history of the virus causing this disease is a fascinating one that has been well summarized by Ninel N. Kharitonova and Yuri A. Leonov. Now recognized as a member of the tick-borne encephalitis complex of flaviviruses, this virus causes a hemorrhagic disease and therefore is handled according to Biosafety level 4 conditions. Omsk hemorrhagic fever virus is most commonly transmitted by hard ticks *Dermacentor reticulatus* ticks, although it has been isolated from Ixodes species ticks. Vertebrate hosts of the virus are rodents, particularly muskrats (*Ondatra zibethicus*) and voles, which are mammals (both are classified in the family Arvicolidae), and handling them is the most common source of acquisition of this virus. The virus has been found only in western Siberia and only within a large area surrounding Omsk, never in nearby Khazakhstan, China or Mongolia. Laboratory infections with this virus have been associated with aerosols. Surprisingly, Omsk hemorrhagic fever virus infections of humans have been traced to water, quite likely the result of its contamination with urine from infected muskrats, which are native to North America but have been introduced to parts of Europe, Asia, and South America. Because there is no evidence of the presence of Omsk hemorrhagic fever virus anywhere except near Omsk, it may be that the virus was endemic to, but unnoticed in, that area until the introduction of muskrats. Indeed, muskrats are not only susceptible to infection with this virus, they often become fatally infected with it, suggesting that they are not the natural host of Omsk hemorrhagic fever virus. An arthropod-borne virus that also is water-borne? Makes arbovirology even more interesting, doesn't it?

Crimean-Congo hemorrhagic fever virus: Originally named "Crimean hemorrhagic fever virus" by the Russian workers who discovered it and who described the disease in 1944, this virus was isolated in 1967 from humans, later from ticks of a variety of species, and from other vertebrates on which ticks feed. However, in 1956 Ghislaine Courtois, head of the Provincial Medical Laboratory in Stanleyville (Kisangani), Belgian Congo (Zaire) had seen in his clinic a 13-year-old boy who had fever, headache, nausea, vomiting, backache, generalized joint pains, and photophobia. He took a blood specimen by venipuncture and inoculated the blood into 3-day-old mice by both the intracerebral and intraperitoneal routes. One mouse became sick 12 days after inoculation and, after two more passages in suckling mice, the strain was mouse-adapted.

Papers describing all this were published by David I. Simpson and Ernest T. Bowen aand others and by John P. Woodall and colleagues, who named it Congo virus. However, in 1968 Jordi Casals showed it to be essentially identical to Crimean hemorrhagic fever virus. The names were merged to Crimean-Congo hemorrhagic fever virus to take into consideration the importance and widespread nature of the disease and the fact that the human disease had been recognized first in the Crimean peninsula on the Black Sea in 1944 (and to keep peace in the arbovirology community, sometimes the naming of viruses has a political bent). This zoonotic virus, transmitted by ticks, is now recognized to cause single cases, clusters, or outbreaks of hemorrhagic fever and deaths (10% to 40% case-fatality ratio) from eastern Europe, to Asia and Africa, wherever the migratory bird hosts of virus-infected ticks transport them. Crimean-Congo hemorrhagic fever virus is transmitted to humans either by infected ticks that feed on them or through contact with viremic animal tissues during or soon after slaughter. The virus is not pathogenic for ruminants, which can serve as its amplifying hosts. Crimean-Congo hemorrhagic fever outbreaks constitute a continuing threat to public health because of their epidemic potential, high case fatality ratios, potential for nosocomial (hospital) outbreaks, and the difficulties in treatment and prevention. Crimean-Congo hemorrhagic fever virus is endemic in all of Africa, the Balkans, the Middle East, and in Asia south of the 50° parallel north, the geographic limit of ticks of the genus *Hyalomma*, the principal tick vector of the virus that causes this disease.

Beginning in 1950, Chumakov became the Director of the Ivanovsky Institute of Virology in Moscow, but in 1955 he organized a new research institute near Moscow, with his wife and co-investigator Marina M.K. Vorošilova at his side. The intent was to work on vaccines against poliomyelitis and other viruses. In spite of the charged political atmosphere at the time, his work on poliomyelitis vaccines was done in close collaboration with American scientists Jonas Salk and Albert Sabin. During 1958-1959 he organized the first mass production and clinical trials of Oral Poliovirus Vaccine made with the live-attenuated strains developed by Sabin. This made the Soviet Union the first country to develop, produce, license, and use this highly effective vaccine. Within the first few years of its use, poliomyelitis was practically eliminated from the country. The vaccine produced by Chumakov's Institute was exported to more than 60 countries and was instrumental in stopping outbreaks of poliomyelitis in eastern Europe and Japan. The success of the Russian clinical trials was critical to Oral Poliovirus Vaccine licensure in the United States in 1962, and that vaccine became the main tool used in the global poliomyelitis eradication campaign. Chumakov and his colleagues also created other human and veterinary vaccines, including inactivated vaccines against tick-borne encephalitis, measles, and influenza, and against canine distemper virus, which is widely used to protect farmed fur animals. In all, Chumakov published more than 960 research papers, scholarly articles, and books. He was awarded many honorary degrees, memberships, and titles in several countries outside the Soviet Union. After his death, the institute he founded was renamed in his honor, the M.P. Chumakov Institute of Poliomyelitis and Viral Encephalitides of the Russian Academy of Medical Sciences.

Orchestrated and led by Dmitri K. Lvov, researchers in that institute continued to conduct serologic and virologic arboviral surveys of enormous areas of the Soviet Union and participated in similar work in Guinea, Somalia, and elsewhere. For many years, Alexander M. Butenko (Figure 69), Sophia Gaidamovich, Elena A. Vladimirtseva (Figure 70), and scores of other Russian scientists and their colleagues worked to develop laboratory methods, conducted virologic and serologic studies of samples collected in widely disparate ecologic zones, and completed other studies somewhat in isolation from the rest of the world's community of arbovirologists. An important exception to this isolation was their continued contact with members of the American Committee on Arthropod-borne Viruses and its subcommittees.

DECADES OF AMERICAN ARBOVIRAL DISCOVERY

In the United States western equine encephalitis virus is found principally west of the Mississippi River; the closely related, but relatively non-pathogenic Highlands J virus, supplants it in the eastern United States. Although these viruses have different evolutionary origins, both are descendants of an ancient recombination event and therefore are related to other arboviruses, including eastern equine encephalitis virus, forming what was known as the Group A arboviruses, now called the alphaviruses (family *Togaviridae*, genus *Alphavirus*). Exceedingly challenging and comprehensive field work and laboratory experimental studies of this and other arboviruses in California were conducted over a multi-decade period by a group at the University of California at Berkeley School of Public Health led by William C. Reeves, the *de facto* leader of arbovirology for decades. Studying the principal mosquito vector of western equine encephalitis virus, *Culex tarsalis,* Reeves and colleagues improved mosquito trapping methods; devised vector control programs; developed fluorescent dusts to mark mosquitoes for population density studies, life tables and movements. They accumulated knowledge of vector-virus associations and used that information to influence state legislatures to provide funding for vector control.

Along with workers at the Rockefeller Foundation laboratories and many Latin American scientists, working in collaboration and independently, and with the American Committee on Arthropod-borne Viruses as the glue that held all this together, western equine encephalitis virus was shown to occur in many areas of South and Central Americas. The slight genetic differences detected between North and South American western equine encephalitis viruses probably account for the lower pathogenicity of South American strains. The geographic distribution of the mosquito vectors likely explains differences in vertebrate hosts and transmissibility of these viruses. In North America western equine encephalitis virus is associated with illness, sometimes leading to death (case-fatality rate about 4%) or with serious sequelae in infants and children and serious illness and death in equids. A dramatic decline in cases of western equine encephalitis in California and throughout North America has been associated with modern conveniences, such as television and computer use (inclining people to stay indoors, rather than sitting on porches in the evening, when mosquitoes are questing for blood meals). The recognition that use of air conditioning and window screening and additional behavioral changes had taken place solved epidemiological problems. No commercially-available vaccine against western equine encephalitis virus is available and, as with so many other virus infections, no therapeutic drugs are available to treat the infection.

Shortly after the discovery of western equine encephalitis in the western United States, a similar disease, eastern equine encephalitis, was recognized in horses in New England. In 1933 a virus was isolated from horses and then from humans, affected with what was then called "horse sleeping sickness". The disease was shown to be caused by eastern equine encephalitis (or eastern equine encephalomyelitis) virus. Because cases had occurred in the late summer and fall and because cases were found in greatest numbers near salt marshes (intertidal zones between land and salty or brackish water), it was hypothesized that insects, perhaps mosquitoes, played a role in transmitting this virus between vertebrate hosts. The virus was demonstrable in the blood of horses for only a brief period of time, leading Carl Ten Broeck, E. Weston Hurst and Erich Traub of the Rockefeller Institute for Medical Research in Princeton, New Jersey, to hypothesize that it had been transmitted to them from another host by mosquitoes. In 1938 the virus was isolated from the brain of a human encephalitis patient and also shown to replicate in mosquitoes. LeRoy D. Fothergill, John H. Dingle, Sidney Farber, and M.L. Connerly, and Leslie Webster and F. Howell Wright isolated the virus and, using serologic tests, Ten Broeck and Malcolm H. Merrill showed that western equine encephalitis virus and eastern equine encephalitis viruses were different from each other. This has been summarized nicely by Roy F. Feemster.

According to the CDC, between 1964 and 2009 a mean of 6 cases (range = 0-22) of neuroinvasive human eastern equine encephalitis infections are detected each year, with most cases occurring in the southeastern United States but a few cases in the Upper Midwest and rare cases in eastern Canada as far north as Nova Scotia. The case-fatality rate for eastern equine encephalitis is 33%; most survivors are left with significant brain damage.

The number of confirmed cases of human western equine encephalitis in the United States between 1964 and 2005 was 639 (15 cases per year). Sequelae, such as mild to severe neurologic deficits, occur in survivors and individual case costs range from $21,000 for transiently infected individuals to $3 million for severely affected individuals.

In California, William Reeves and William McD. Hammon established surveillance systems not only for western equine encephalitis virus but for other viruses, both recognized and unrecognized as well. Their surveillance system included not only the capturing and testing of mosquitoes, but also sentinel chickens and horses, wild birds, and humans with febrile illnesses.

Because of the continuing search for yellow fever virus and other viruses, the Rockefeller Foundation was busy identifying the viruses collected and sent to its New York City laboratories. The need for more rapid, simpler, and less expensive methods was becoming urgent. With many score of long-term and short-term visitors, each bringing with them viruses to be identified at what was by then serving as a world reference center (later formalized to exactly that by the World Health Organization), with many unidentified viruses sent to the Rockefeller Laboratories, and with Rockefeller Foundation staff members themselves periodically traveling to the New York headquarters from remote sites bringing viruses they could not identify, it was clear that the flood of viruses soon would inundate the laboratory and overwhelm its facilities and personnel. The efforts of staff members Sonja Buckley, Jordi Casals, Delphine Clarke, Wilbur Downs, Nick Karabatsos, Peter Olitsky, Robert Shope, Max Theiler, Gregory Tignor, Leslie Webster and Loring Whitman made virus identification much easier and improved our knowledge of the epidemiology and geographic distribution of arboviruses and the clinical pictures of arbovirus diseases

Those who were interested in clinical aspects of human and wildlife disease and of epidemiology , relationships between viruses, entomologic aspects of arbovirus transmission and persistence, virus epidemiology, and virus diagnosis, included staff members Thomas H.G. Aitken, Charles R. Anderson, Sonja M. Buckley, Ottis R. and Calista E. Causey, Norma E. Mettler, Leslie Spence, Telford H. Work, and scores of others who developed or collaborated in the development of diagnostic techniques and wrote classic papers describing hundreds of viruses.

Commencing with his recognition that some viruses were closely or distantly related to each other but were not identical or were not at all related to other clusters of viruses related to each other, Casals soon became interested in distinguishing these "groups" of viruses. His findings were based on serologic tests: hemagglutination-inhibition, complement-fixation, and neutralization; these were crude in some ways, but nonetheless exceedingly useful assays. "Group A arboviruses", now known as the alphaviruses (family *Togaviridae*, genus *Alphavirus*), comprised eastern equine encephalitis, western equine encephalitis, Venezuelan equine encephalitis, Sindbis, and many other viruses. The "Group B arboviruses", now known as the flaviviruses (family *Flaviviridae*, genus *Flavivirus*), comprised yellow fever, Japanese encephalitis, Russian Spring-Summer encephalitis, St. Louis encephalitis and many other viruses. The "Group C arboviruses" (family *Bunyaviridae*, genus *Orthobunyavirus*), comprised Caraparu, Apeu, Marituba, Murutucu, Nepuyo, and other viruses. Numerous groups of related viruses (the *sine qua non* of "antigenic group") were established by this strategy and named for the first virus in the group to be distinguished, i.e., the Bunyamwera group was named for Bunyamwera virus.

As more and more viruses were discovered and identified, the question of nomenclature arose and Casals' dicta were viewed with suspicion. What does one do with viruses of two antigenic groups when a single virus member of one group reacts with one or two viruses in another group, perhaps only by use of a single test, complement-fixation but not by hemagglutination-inhibition or neutralization, for example? Casals and others found many such reactions and, because they were repeatable with multiple reagent preparations, considered them valid and convincing. He therefore established what he called "Supergroups" – groups of viruses that were, somehow, even if tenuously, related to viruses of other groups. One such "Supergroup" was the Bunyamwera Supergroup (the orthobunyaviruses), another was the Nairobi sheep disease Supergroup (the nairoviruses). Today we know that the family *Bunyaviridae* comprises five genera: *Orthobunyavirus, Nairovirus, Phlebovirus, Hantavirus,* and *Tospovirus*, distinguished from other viruses based on their tripartite genome organizations and by their physicochemical and physical properties, as they have four structural proteins, replicate in the cytoplasm, and have other characteristics in common. The biological features of these viruses are distinct in many ways. For example, most orthobunyaviruses are transmitted by mosquitoes; most nairoviruses by ticks; most phleboviruses by phlebotomines, mosquitoes, ceratopogonids, or ticks; all hantaviruses by vertebrates (mainly rodents); and, remarkably, all tospoviruses (from the words "tomato spotted wilt viruses") by plant-feeding insects, thrips, of the genera *Frankliniella* and *Thrips*. Obviously, tospoviruses and hantaviruses are not arboviruses because they are not transmitted by hematophagous insects, but their genetic (genomic) characteristics and some other attributes are similar to those of viruses of the other bunyavirus genera. This may be an evolutionary clue that has yet to be delineated. Rather than nomenclature, this is taxonomy, expression of genetic and other properties that are used to place viruses in taxa. Indeed, Casals' fastidious efforts over many decades, certainly in partnership with multiple collaborators and contributors, laid the groundwork for and made major contributions to modern taxonomy of arboviruses, the latter becoming less of a group of viruses than a biological category of viruses. Nonetheless, it is emphasized here that almost all of these antigenically-based groups have survived the tests of time and molecular genetics in that viruses placed into antigenic groups are molecularly similar.

Studies of the physical and biological properties of many arboviruses, notably the dengue flaviviruses, were being characterized at the

Walter Reed Army Institute of Research by a group including Walter E. Brandt, Edward L. Buescher, Philip K. Russell, Joel M. Dalrymple, Erik A. Henschal, Patricia M. Repik, Jack M. McCown, and Robert M. Scott. They found that by using differential centrifugation with sucrose gradients and other increasingly advanced methods, they could separate many virus components. They also found that the infectious virus exhibited hemagglutinating and complement-fixing activities and that electron microscopy of the infectious virions showed they were about 50 nm in diameter and had 7 nm spherical structures on their surfaces. They determined the buoyant density of the virions, found that a small noninfectious component with a lower buoyant density had both hemagglutinating and complement-fixing activities, and observed "doughnut" forms (incomplete virus).

Later, the use of antigen-specific monoclonal antibodies improved the capacity to determine not only which dengue viral antigens were in cells but where they were located during viral replication. Dennis Trent et al. at CDC and Rico-Hesse at Yale University and the Southwest Foundation for Biomedical Research, using more advanced techniques, demonstrated the occurrence of many genotypes of each of the four dengue viruses. This opened the way to studies of the molecular epidemiology and molecular evolution of these and other viruses and provided a basis for understanding the geographic distributions and limitations of these viruses.

Painstaking electron microscopic studies by Murphy and others of the cellular and tissue pathologies caused by these viruses showed that viruses that were related antigenically were also similar morphologically and that the mechanisms by which antigenically-related viruses replicate and the sites at which they replicate support the conclusions Casals had deduced using serology. That is, Group A arboviruses (alphaviruses) appeared to be round, similar in size (about 70 nm in diameter), and have a single-stranded RNA genome about 9.7-11.8 kilobases [kb] in length, whereas Group B arboviruses (flaviviruses) are round, similar in size (about 50 nm in diameter), and have a single-stranded RNA genome about 11 kb. Bunyamwera group viruses of the genus *Orthobunyavirus* are also round but are 80-120 nm in diameter and have three unique molecules of single-stranded RNA, named S (small), M (medium), and L (large), each with a different size and function; the total nucleotide content is slightly more than 12 kb. The consensus terminal nucleotide sequences of the three genome segments of all orthobunyaviruses are UCAUCACAUGA... at the 3′ end of each molecule and AGUAGUGUGCU ... at the 5′ end, so that any virus with these terminal sequences can be identified as an orthobunyavirus. Consensus sequences at the 3′ and 5′ ends of viruses in each bunyavirus genus differ from those of viruses in other bunyavirus genera.

Differences in size, nucleic acid genome composition, and other properties have been shown for arboviruses in all antigenic groups and for viruses in groups of viruses that are not arthropod-borne. In other words, the antigenic studies of Casals and others, while not encompassing all viruses and certainly not the first evidence that some viruses are related and others are not, demonstrated biological and antigenic similarities and laid the groundwork for more practical applications, including vaccine formulation, studies of genomic structure and functions, virus evolution, and so on. In some instances, peculiarities of antigenic reactions provided impetus for further understanding of virus protein functions.

The viral genome, the nucleic acid sequence, is the entity that specifies production of proteins (sequences of amino acids). It is this genome that controls cellular metabolism and, in virus-infected cells, specifies virus structure (and function). More specifically, subviral particles, such as antigens, are produced under command of the viral genome. As an example, I will use the interrelationships of the Group C viruses.

In initial studies of the Group C viruses, newly discovered members were added to the recognized group as they were isolated and identified. In a classic study by Shope and Causey, published in 1962, the viruses Oriboca, Itaqui, Caraparu, Apeu, Marituba, and Murutucu were shown to be variously related to each other: Oriboca and Itaqui

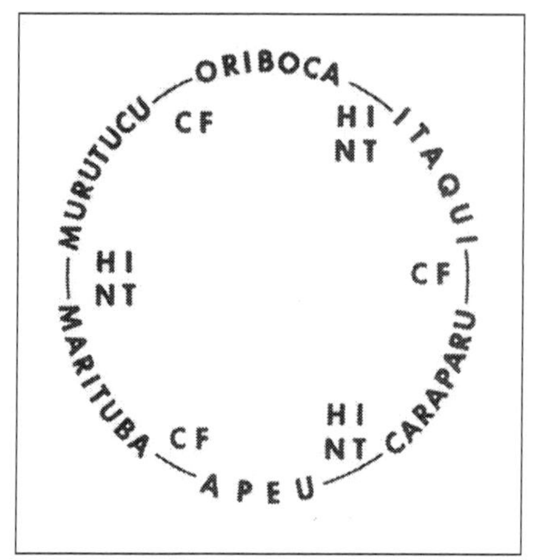

Figure 126. Antigenic reactivity of six Group C orthobunyaviruses as determined by hemagglutination-inhibition, neutralization and complement-fixation. (figure courtesy of the American Journal of Tropical Medicine and Hygiene)

by hemagglutination-inhibition and neutralization, Itaqui and Caraparu by complement-fixation, Caraparu and Apeu by hemagglutination-inhibition and neutralization, Apeu and Marituba by complement-fixation, Marituba and Murutucu by hemagglutination and neutralization, and Murutucu and Oriboca by complement-fixation, as shown in Figure 126.

It seemed reasonable that viruses shown to be related by one or another test would cross-react to varying extents, but how could they react by one test and not react by another test and still be related? Indeed, not only did some not cross-react with certain relatives, others cross-reacted completely by one test and not at all by another. In 2005, Marcio R.T. Nunes, Amelia P.A. Travassos da Rosa, Scott Weaver, Robert Tesh and Pedro F.C. Vasconcelos published a study of the 13 Group C viruses recognized at that time. Sequencing the entire S RNAs and part of the M RNAs (705 nt) of each of these viruses, these investigators found that the S RNA of Caraparu virus was nearly identical to the S RNA of Oriboca virus, and concluded that Caraparu virus is a (segment) reassortant virus. These and other data indicated that the Group C viruses include many natural reassortants. These authors also corroborated the earlier serologic (antigenic) studies of Shope, Casals, Karabatsos, and others and suggested that in order to more fully understand the epidemiology of these and other arboviruses, a combination of methods is necessary. Once again, incrementally accumulating pieces of information were used to build the structure of our present knowledge. One never knows where a finding, a fortuitous observation, or a series of coincidences might lead.

Because the genomes of viruses of certain families are segmented, reassortment of those genes may occur, for influenzaviruses (family *Orthomyxoviridae*) and Group C viruses (family *Bunyaviridae*) but also for other viruses in these and other families of viruses with segmented genomes (*Reoviridae, Arenaviridae*). When two similar, closely related, viruses infect the same cell at the same time, their unique genomes may be variously incorporated into the progeny viruses. For example, should two bunyaviruses, A and B, each with three genomic segments, co-infect a cell, progeny virus may comprise a mixture of the L RNAs, M RNAs and S RNAs of the two viruses, such that the progeny could be any combination of the three, including progeny identical to the infecting parental viruses. Obviously, the possibilities are numerous but the important point is that such reassortment of multiple genomes can introduce radical phenotypic changes caused by such combinations. For instance, a virus that is highly infectious but not highly pathogenic could recombine with a virus that is not highly infectious but is highly pathogenic, resulting in recombinants that not only have low infectivity and low pathogenicity but recombinants that are highly infectious and highly pathogenic. For viruses with more than three RNA segments, the potential recombinants are essentially endless, which is the reason we are vaccinated against the latest reassortant influenzavirus (8 segments) each year. That orbiviruses have 10 double-stranded RNA segments and rotaviruses have 11, demonstrates the complexity of reassortment and the phenotypic possibilities of reassortment among these viruses.

For decades, the outstanding viral pathogeneticist Neal Nathanson led a series of studies of California serogroup orthobunyaviruses. In a brilliant series of papers, Nathanson and his collaborators, including Francisco Gonzalez-Scarano, Robert Shope, Barry Beaty, Laura Chandler, Daniel Sundin, Michael Endres, David Jacoby, and Robert Janssen, meticulously dissected the molecular basis of replication of La Crosse, Tahyna, and other California serogroup orthobunyaviruses and determined the structure-function relationships of the virus genome. They first produced monoclonal antibodies to these viruses and were able to show that those specific for the G1 glycoprotein were either neutralizing or non-neutralizing but that there was a concordance between hemagglutination inhibiting and neutralizing activities. They further demonstrated that anti-nucleocapsid proteins were all cross-reactive and concluded that all this provided a molecular basis for antigenic relationships.

Janssen, Gonzalez-Scarano, and Nathanson then analyzed mechanisms of virulence of California serogroup orthobunyaviruses by comparing a virulent strain of La Crosse virus with an avirulent strain of Tahyna virus, demonstrating that, whereas both viruses were pathogenic in intracranially-inoculated suckling mice, they differed markedly in their neuroinvasiveness and sites of replication. It was then shown that the large viral RNA segment encodes the large viral protein, the viral polymerase.

Pursuing their hypothesis that the virulence of La Crosse virus is under polygenic control, they turned to the structure-function relationships of the virus as they impacted infection of *Aedes triseriatus* mosquitoes, the principal vector of that virus. In studies suggesting that viral attachment proteins may be the basis for virus-vector interactions, and that these interactions may serve as the basis for the limited vector host specificity observed with mosquito-borne viruses, it was observed that La Crosse virus-vector interactions are markedly influenced by the efficiency of the fusion function of the G1 glycoprotein operating in the midgut of the arthropod. The reassortants for those studies were obtained using reassortant viruses isolated from cell cultures infected with two viruses. Subsequent efforts to determine whether these viruses also reassort in *Aedes triseriatus* mosquitoes showed that they do. Ultimately it was shown that the M RNA segment is the major determinant of virulence but that the other two gene segments might modulate the virulence of a nonneuroinvasive California serogroup virus. It is now clear that neuroinvasiveness and neurovirulence are quite distinct features of these and other viruses.

Many other observations have shown that natural reassortment events also may confound diagnostic efforts. For instance, a virus with high pathogenicity and low transmissibility may reassort with a virus having low pathogenicity and high transmissibility, yielding not only progeny with low pathogenicity and low transmissibility but also progeny with high pathogenicity and high transmissibility. The former is not much of a problem in diagnosis but the latter is. Many viruses originally thought to be completely new to science are now known to be reassortants of two recognized viruses or one recognized virus and an undefined other virus.

Ngari virus (also known as Garissa virus) may be used as an illustration of this complexity in arboviral diagnosis. In 1997-1998 an outbreak of a hemorrhagic fever was recognized in Kenya and Somalia and investigated by CDC workers and others. Whereas 23% of 115 hemorrhagic fever patients had evidence of acute infection with Rift Valley fever virus, samples from two hemorrhagic fever patients, one from Kenya and one from Somalia, yielded virus isolates that were not Rift Valley fever virus. When electron microscopy indicated that these two isolates were bunyaviruses (i.e., members of the family *Bunyaviridae*), regions of the S and L segments were amplified by polymerase chain reaction and the amplified sequences were shown to be essentially identical to the same regions of the S and L segments of Bunyamwera virus, which had not been shown to cause severe clinical illness in humans. Surprisingly, the M segment of each virus was about 32% different from that of Bunyamwera virus; the corresponding M segment amino acid difference from that of Bunyamwera virus was 28%. The reassortant virus was named Garissa virus. The RNA of this virus was detected in 12 other hemorrhagic fever patients in the epidemic zone.

The source of the M segment of Ngari/Garissa virus appears to be Batai virus. Thus, Garissa virus is an isolate of Ngari virus, and both are reassortants of Bunyamwera L and S segments and the M segment of Batai virus. Obviously, reassortment among viruses with segmented genomes is a diagnostic issue because assays to detect certain virus antigens or antibodies to them may fail even when otherwise sensitive reagents are available.

Other examples of bunyavirus reassortment may be given: Iquitos virus contains the S and L segments of Oropouche virus and the M segment of a novel Simbu group virus; Jatobal virus is a reassortant containing the S RNA of Oropouche virus; RNA segment reassortment of La Crosse virus and of Akabane virus have been demonstrated; the European Schmallenberg virus is a reassortant, containing the M RNA segment from Sathuperi virus and the S and L RNA segments from Shamonda virus, both known only from Africa; certain Patois group and Simbu group orthobunyaviruses are reassortants; Cholul virus, recently detected in the Yucatan Peninsula of Mexico, is a novel reassortant of Potosi and Cache Valley viruses, known only from the United States; reassortants between RNA segments of groundnut ringspot and tomato chlorotic spot tospoviruses have been demonstrated, etc. It appears that most recognized reassortants of orthobunyaviruses possess the L and S RNAs of one virus and the M RNA of another virus. Why? Are reassortants in actuality reassortants of reassortants? Where is Square One? No matter these conundrums, it is clear that natural genome reassortment is a driving force in the evolution of bunyaviruses, influenzaviruses, and many other viruses.

Knowledge of the relationships among arboviruses; of the biological and genetic characteristics of arboviruses; and of the transmission, geographic distribution, and vectors of arboviruses all are important, but none of these directly prevents disease or saves lives. What is needed to prevent disease spread are comprehensive studies of the pathology and pathogenesis of the virus infections themselves. Use of laboratory hosts, such as cell cultures or mice, rats, rabbits, guinea pigs and other non-primate vertebrates may provide clues, often very useful clues, but without the occurrence of either extremely fortuitous and unusual circumstances or direct experimental infections to study in detail, one can never be certain that the natural disease is being reproduced. Monkeys and other primates used as experimental hosts are difficult to obtain, expensive to house and examine, dangerous, and too limited in quantity to meet the statistical demands of such studies. The ethics of using primates is debatable; humans, of course, are not used by members of any ethical institution as experimental hosts for pathogenic viruses.

Thomas P. Monath: One might assume that all or most of the important studies of yellow fever and the virus that causes it would have been done by now. In addition, an excellent, if not perfect, vaccine divised by Max Theiler and others is available. However, there are no definitive and complete studies of anything at all, particularly not of viruses or diseases. The physician-epidemiologist-virologist Thomas P. Monath, who has studied Lassa fever in Africa, as well as other hazardous virus diseases, has been revisiting yellow fever for the past four decades, evaluating current yellow fever vaccines and their adverse effects, and devising new yellow fever vaccines using modern molecular tools. He investigated yellow fever epidemics in Africa and experimentally-infected monkeys and studied their responses to infection. He elucidated the pathogenetic processes by which the virus infects and causes the physiologic effects leading to death. Monath determined the antibody responses in the major immunoglobulin classes after vaccination with the classical "17D" live attenuated vaccine of Theiler. He demonstrated the limitations of certain laboratory diagnostic tests in areas of Africa where many flaviviruses occur simultaneously and devised more sensitive, specific and rapid laboratory diagnostic tests. His work included analyzing the genetic differences among yellow fever viruses from different sources and locations, tracking the persistence of antibody to vaccine virus decades after vaccination of humans, determining the effects of vaccination on pregnant women and their offspring, calling for inclusion of yellow fever in vaccination programs in Africa, and generally educating the scientific community and people in national and international positions of responsibility, suggesting that an expanded effort is cost-effective in endemic areas. Monath's presentation to the American Society for Tropical Medicine and Hygiene annual meeting in New Orleans in 1990, *Yellow fever: Victor, Victoria? Conqueror, conquest? Epidemics and research in the last forty years and prospects for the future.* was a *tour de force,* an in-depth summary of what was known and what still needs to be done with respect to this disease. The published version of that presentation is a must read for anyone interested in yellow fever, in arbovirology, or in how to make a presentation. An earlier paper by James Porterfield, Oxford arbovirologist and long-time Africa hand, complements Monath's overview. In it Porterfield reviews the history of yellow fever research, the situation at the time he wrote the paper, and some historical photographs – in all, a notable contribution and significant retrospective.

As an undergraduate, Monath was a photographer for the National Geographic Society in French Guiana and worked in Mexico, British Honduras (now Belize), and Ethiopia while at Harvard University, working at the university's Museum of Comparative Zoology with a focus on amphibians and snakes. He then attended Harvard Medical School, where he became a favorite of Thomas Weller, the Nobel Laureate. In 1968, Monath joined CDC in Atlanta as a medical officer in the Public Health Service, trained in laboratory techniques, developed laboratory techniques, and eventually was assigned to Africa, where he investigated yellow fever outbreaks as well as infections with other arboviruses. Notably, his interest in hemorrhagic fevers carried over from yellow fever to Lassa fever, which was then occurring sporadically in Nigeria. Monath explored many critical aspects of this disease and the arenavirus that causes it. He isolated Lassa virus from the Natal multimammate rat (*Mastomys natalensis*), documented hospital outbreaks, improved diagnosis, described in detail the clinical symptoms, and improved case-patient management, documented hospital outbreaks and demonstrated methods to bring them to an end or prevent them. His efforts were not done in isolation, however. He had the laboratory, field and intellectual support of Carlos Campbell, Jordi Casals (who had nearly died of Lassa fever), James C. Demartini, Akinyele Fabiyi, David W. Fraser, Michael B. Gregg, Graham E. Kemp, Robert E. Kissling, Frederick Murphy, Vernon F. Newhouse,

Lily Pinneo (another recovered victim of Lassa fever), Sylvia G. Whitfield, Washington C. Winn, Jr., Herta Wulff, and others to investigate Lassa fever epidemics in Jos, Nigeria, Sierra Leone, and Zorzor, Liberia, showing that this is a relatively common disease in West Africa.

First recognized in Nigeria in 1969, Lassa fever was shown to be an acute viral hemorrhagic fever, with a case-fatality rate of >30%. Epidemics in that year and in the next few years affected patients and staff in hospitals and were the result of person-to-person spread, fomites, aerosol transmission, and reuse of contaminated needles. Although the etiologic agent of the disease and many fundamental facts about it were known, its natural history, transmission cycle, and reservoir hosts remained unclear.

In 1972, a large outbreak of Lassa fever occurred in eastern Sierra Leone. Since cases appeared to be occurring in villages and towns (in addition to spread within the hospital environment) a unique opportunity arose to uncover the source of human infections. Monath, who had experience working in West Africa on Lassa fever, yellow fever, and other hemorrhagic fevers, was assigned to investigate these variables and the sources of the virus.

He brought together an experienced team of physician-epidemiologists, including David W. Fraser, M.D. (a physician-epidemiologist at CDC who later led the investigation of the first outbreak of Legionnaire's disease and eventually became president of Swarthmore College and executive director of the International Clinical Epidemiology Network, created in 1980 as a project of the Rockefeller Foundation), Carlos C. 'Kent' Campbell, M.D., M.P.H. (later President of the American Society of Tropical Medicine and Hygiene), Jordi Casals, of the Rockefeller Foundation (immune to Lassa virus by virtue of his near-fatal laboratory infection acquired during the original work in 1969), Vernon F. Newhouse, Ph.D., a CDC virologist-zoologist and experienced field researcher, and Graham E. Kemp, D.V.M., M.P.H., a Rockefeller Foundation veterinary virologist with whom Monath had worked closely in Nigeria and who had been part of the original work on Lassa in Nigeria in 1969.

The team arrived at the epicenter, Panguma, Sierra Leone, in September 1972 to find a town replete with residents justifiably frightened of this fatal hemorrhagic disease. In order to interrupt nosocomial spread of the virus, they established an isolation ward for patients with suspect Lassa fever, mapped the town, traced cases to specific households, trapped and sampled potential rodent and bat vectors (because of their known associations with other arenaviruses), preserved vertebrate specimens for later definitive identification to species, and took other appropriate and necessary steps. Without the application of specific control measures, the outbreak ended, even though a few cases continued to be identified. It was in Panguma that Karl Johnson later established a CDC field station.

Returning to Atlanta, some of the team tested the material collected in Panguma and its environs and identified the rodent reservoir, the Natal multimammate rat. The expert Colorado State University veterinary pathologist James C. DeMartini and Monath later showed that the Lassa virus-infected Natal multimammate rats collected in Sierra Leone had subtle pathologic changes that could influence not only the rodents but also the natural cycle of the virus. It became clear from those and other studies that arenaviruses affect their rodent hosts even without outward signs of illness, effects such as disruption of reproduction and smaller litter sizes.

It is been estimated that 300,000 to 500,000 cases of Lassa fever and 5,000 deaths occur yearly across West Africa. The overall case-fatality rate is 1% but up to 15% in hospitalized patients. Paralleling some other arenavirus diseases, Lassa fever is particularly severe late in pregnancy, with maternal death or fetal loss occurring in more than 80% of cases during the third trimester.

After returning from his African expedition, Monath was appointed Chief of the Arbovirus Unit at CDC and supervised studies of Venezuelan equine encephalitis viruses, St. Louis encephalitis virus, and a host of other arboviruses. His concept of the difference between "important" and "possible", combined with his medical and virological knowledge guided that group, and his insistence on publishing data ensured that the information would neither be lost nor forgotten.

In 1973, when the unit was transferred to a newer and safer facility on the campus of Colorado State University in Fort Collins, Monath was a resident at Peter Bent Brigham Hospital in Boston, Massachusetts, leaving the experienced Patricia A. Webb in charge. When he returned to the Fort Collins facility he did so without missing a beat and those laboratories continued to produce important research regarding arboviral diseases. Given his tirelessness, his insight, and his imagination as the primary tools and motivations, those arguably were among the most productive days of that group.

Three outstanding studies by Monath and his colleagues are used here as examples of his foresight and intellect. As I worked for and with him for more than 20 years, I believe I can accurately say that if a young researcher were to follow him around and carry out experiments that Monath bypassed as interesting but not sufficiently significant, s/he could make a very nice career. The American Committee on Arthropod-borne Viruses and the American Society for Tropical Medicine and Hygiene recognized Monath's abilities and elected him Chair and President, respectively.

The first of his remarkable studies was an investigation of the pathophysiologic effects of yellow fever virus infections of monkeys, published in 1981. In this study Monath and co-workers documented the clinical course leading to death of the monkeys. Viremia first was detected 48 hours after inoculation and peaked 48 hours later. Abnormal liver function was not detected until about 24 hours before death, and hypoglycemia was not detected until eight or fewer hours before death. Numerous other pathophysiologic changes were monitored and liver and kidney pathologies were documented, as were metabolic aberrations. Many other comprehensive observations were made and certain of their findings suggested "that acute tubular necrosis may be the end result of prerenal hemodynamic alterations and azotemia, and thus be preventable." As always, further studies were suggested to answer heretofore unasked questions about yellow fever pathology.

A second pivotal study by Monath and colleagues focused on the mode of entry of St. Louis encephalitis flavivirus into the central nervous system of hamsters, which share with humans low or undetectable viremia and many clinical and pathoanatomical features of infection with this virus. Tissue infectivity studies of peripherally inoculated hamsters demonstrated increasing virus titer in the olfactory neuroepithelium four days after infection, in the olfactory bulbs the next day, and in the remainder of the brain the day after that. Taken together with other data from the same study, the team concluded that the olfactory pathway is the principal route of entry of St. Louis virus into the central nervous system. One could extrapolate this conclusion to include many flaviviruses in many vertebrate hosts and, in fact, this pathway has been determined for Venezuelan equine encephalitis virus. This is the kind of basic investigations that leads somewhere.

The third study was really a series of studies. When Monath left the CDC, in the face of increasing budgets for studies of AIDS and decreasing budgets for studies of arboviruses, he first went to USAMRIID Fort Detrick to become Chief of Virology Division, then to Acambis Company (acquired in 2008 by Sanofi Pasteur Biologics) in Cambridge, Massachusetts. There he directed the use of live yellow fever virus as a vector for genes of dengue, Japanese encephalitis, and West Nile viruses, creating new vaccines against these diseases by complex and highly innovative modern molecular techniques. As do all flaviviruses, yellow fever virus comprises a genome with the sequence 5′-C-prM-E-NS1-NS2A-NS2B-NS3-NS4A-NS4B-NS5-3′, with C indicating the gene specifying the capsid, prM being the premembrane gene, E the envelope gene, and the others being nonstructural genes that specify production of various enzymes or have immunological functions. Monath and colleagues replaced the prM and E genes of yellow fever 17D live attenuated vaccine virus with those of Japanese encephalitis virus, West Nile virus, and all four dengue viruses. These chimeric viruses replicated to high titer in Vero cell cultures and in monkeys were safe, immunogenic, and protective against the viruses whose prM and E genes had been used to replace the prM and E genes of yellow fever virus. In addition, these chimeras were not neurovirulent in adult ICR mice inoculated intracranially. The tetravalent dengue recombinant vaccine (on a yellow fever virus backbone) was successfully employed in immunizing both non-human primates and humans in early clinical trials, portending well for use of this chimeric scheme for production of safe and effective vaccines for other flaviviruses and, perhaps, other viruses. Monath brought the first of these "ChimeriVax" vaccines, against Japanese encephalitis, through pivotal clinical trials, and the vaccine is now licensed in various countries under the brand name Imojev®. The West Nile vaccine was taken through Phase 2 clinical trials and proved very satisfactory, with >95% of the subjects developing protective (neutralizing) antibodies. The dengue vaccine is currently in large Phase 3 trials conducted by Sanofi Pasteur.

The exceptional researchers described above were selected from numerous possible candidates. A reasonable conclusion to be drawn is that arbovirology, as are other fields of interest and importance in virology, was not founded, pursued, and published by a single genius but has been a collaborative effort of numerous energetic, industrious, productive, intelligent, and enthusiastic scientists working in accommodating environments and within teams of colleagues of similar professional worth.

As accomplishments were made, a structure took definitive form. However, funding for studies of arboviruses began to decline and leaders of laboratories that once were the most accomplished and the most influential in the field retired, as governmental mandates and changing public needs and perceptions allowed the dissemination of personnel to other, better funded fields. In addition, the growing use of molecular tools and the advances made possible by their adoption changed the view from biological to genomic. Now expert molecular viral geneticists discover details not dreamed possible in earlier days.

There still is an enormous need for field studies, but these are not being done as was common years ago. This is beyond unfortunate because viruses stored in freezers originated somewhere other than freezers. At this very moment, unrecognized viruses exist (quietly for now) or continue to arise other than where we have been looking. Some likely are never to be found, others surely will be recognized under the most unfortunate of circumstances, epidemics. Long-term (20-50 years or even longer) field studies obviously cannot be conducted everywhere and forever and there is simply not enough money to do this anyway, not to speak of the paucity of young scientists being trained to do field work these days. This is a huge deficit to overcome, but it must be overcome if we are to stay ahead of the recognition of these pathogens. At the least, very long-term studies could be conducted in a few relatively small sites in many of the more prosperous countries, likely providing predictive information and perhaps saving lives.

Nonetheless, the cutting edge of virology now diverges in two directions: (1) virus discovery, leading to diagnosis amd prevention of virus infections, and (2) comprehension of virus replication. These are mirrors of each other, of course, but with increasing frequency they are interreliant. Lipkin and Briese and their team at Columbia University's Mailman School of Public Health have demonstrated what is being done and what can be done. Although not strictly "arbovirologists" (Lipkin and Briese began their collaboration with studies of Borna disease virus (family *Bornaviridae*, genus *Bornavirus*), in 1999 they were the ones who first identified West Nile flavivirus in the brains of patients with encephalitis in New York. With rapid and specific virus identifications demonstrated, opportunities became available to study multiple aspects of the epidemiology of that continuing problem in the Americas. The methods they are using and developing are so novel and advanced that the Columbia University group is now considered by many as the final arbiter in numerous instances of diagnosis and virus identification. They have published on severe acute respiratory syndrome coronavirus, orthobunyaviruses, viral hemorrhagic fever agents, influenzaviruses, rhinoviruses, orbiviruses, rhabdoviruses, and scores of other viruses. This more general approach, always with a view toward clinical aspects, surely will move the field forward using deep sequencing, gene synthesis, and other useful techniques. Arbovirology has come a long way since Charles Anderson and Max Theiler inoculated their first mouse.

CHAPTER 10

Viral taxonomy

Taxonomy is the study, science, and practice of defining groups of biological organisms on the basis of shared characteristics. Taxonomy is perhaps but only perhaps, tangential to discussions of medicine, of the geographic distribution of viruses, and of their impact on human history and those who people it. Frederick Murphy, only half-jokingly (I think), said that "It is best that religion, politics, and taxonomy not be discussed in polite company." He likely was correct but it is as necessary to discuss virus taxonomy as it is to discuss other useful categorizations; people need to know where things belong.

The word "taxonomy" is rooted in the Greek *taxis* (meaning "order" or "arrangement") and *nomos* (meaning "law" or "science"). One can arrange biological entities in many ways but some are more logical and useful than are others. For example, we could arrange mammals by size, by habitat, or by diet, but none of those is useful to consider their relationships. The very existence of a biological taxonomy for viruses is controversial, given that there are questions as to whether viruses are living beings in the usual sense and, if they are not, why then are they classified within the generally accepted scheme of living beings? Still, virologists are no less compulsive than other biologists, and viral taxonomy does provide insights about the evolution of these entities, so a taxonomic system for viruses was devised, as all taxonomies are devised, rather than discovered.

There are many thousands of viruses of vertebrates, insects, plants, bacteria, fungi, and parasites. Each is so distinct that placing them in categories (taxa) is a necessity in order to teach about them and to keep them orderly in our minds. Viruses themselves are classified according to certain characteristics, including nucleic acid type (DNA, RNA, or both), morphology, mode of replication, hosts in which they replicate, and perhaps diseases they cause. Such classification is based on practical aspects regarding the concrete entity, the virus itself. Taxonomy, however, is based on more general characteristics, so that a particular taxon (a taxonomic unit) is based on an ideal for viruses placed in that taxon.

At the highest level of virus taxonomy are the orders, their names ending in *-virales*, i.e., *Mononegavirales*; family names ending in –*viridae*, i.e., *Rhabdoviridae*; subfamily names ending in –*virinae*, i.e., *Alphaherpesvirinae*; and genus names, ending in –*virus*, i.e., *Nairovirus*. Below that (within genera) are species, i.e., *Eastern equine encephalitis virus*. The names of viruses, the concrete entities, are not italicized because they are not taxa, not ideals; they are what they are.

A virus species has been defined by van Regenmortel as "a polythetic class of viruses that constitutes a replicating lineage and occupies a particular ecological niche." As used here, the phrase "polythetic class" is intended to indicate one whose members have several properties in common but do not necessarily all share a single common defining property. In other words, a species is a non-concrete entity, it does not exist. A person exists, but *Homo sapiens* does not exist in the physical world. A species is an artificial construct intended to provide a taxon in which viruses, concrete entities, can be collectively placed for our convenience. Accept or reject all this if you will, but that is the current accepted definition, and it is useful. Viral taxonomy is the official business of the International Committee on Taxonomy of Viruses, which is part of the Virology Division of the International Union of Microbiological Societies.

Today the basis of viral taxonomy principally is genetics, as it is in the taxonomic placement of other biologic forms. For many decades, beginning with the most primitive virus characterizations, phenotype (observable characteristics, such as shape), therefore was all that could be measured, therefore that was all that was considered. Studies of phenotypes are not as primitive as they might appear. Phenotypes actually are biological expressions of genotype. In addition, determining the phenotype is the only way to determine what a virus actually does; genotype is only speculative.

Slowly, techniques measuring other characters were developed and became generally available. With the invention of polymerase chain reaction assays, a technique by which one is able to amplify one or a few copies of a piece of nucleic acid by many orders of magnitude, thus generating thousands to millions of copies of a particular sequence, a paradigm shift occurred. For inventing this assay method and for taking us leapfrogging into the future, Kary B. Mullis received the Nobel Prize in Chemistry in 1993.

From an historical standpoint regarding the current taxonomy of arboviruses and, indeed, other viruses, the role of Jordi Casals is highlighted here. Casals was not by any means the founder of viral taxonomy. He was more focused on virus classification (phenotype) than on virus taxonomy (genotype) because he was responsible for identifying viruses and making sense of their interrelationships. However, his vast and intimate knowledge of the arboviruses, which include viruses of many families and genera, provided him an overview that allowed him to have a wider perspective, an overview that allowed him and us to speculate not only about viral relationships but also about evolutionary concepts. Using a combination of hemagglutination-inhibition, complement-fixation and neutralization tests, he accomplished a great deal at the level of phenotype and laid the groundwork for genetic studies using polymerase chain reaction, a method not available to Casals when he was at the height of his accomplishments. Little by little, he, Shope, and a few others, fascinated by what was related to what and how close or distant those relationships were, provided molecular biologists, electron microscopists, pathologists, and entomologists with a base for their investigations and leads as to what to study.

CHAPTER 11

New laws, administrators, and other roadblocks

"We trained hard, but it seemed that every time we were beginning to form up into teams, we would be reorganized. I was to learn later in life that we tend to meet any new situation by reorganizing; and a wonderful method it can be for creating the illusion of progress while producing confusion, inefficiency, and demoralization." – Charlton Ogburn, Jr.

"The Dodos have lost the race, and now we must watch the Bobos – those eternal managers that rise in the administration of science without contributing to it." – Marion C. Horzinek

Terrorist attacks plus paranoia have led us to take extraordinary care as to who is shipping what to whom and why. This may be appropriate under the present circumstances; however, the new national and international laws, as well as the concerns of shipping companies, have made it difficult for the innocent among us to go about our business. Shipping a virus or an organism from one scientist to another is no longer done as easily as it was not so many years ago. It might be shocking to younger researchers to know that colleagues in far-off lands, even those in countries whose relations with our own were hostile, could simply mail a virus or even hand-carry it, usually lyophilized, from their home laboratory to a collaborating laboratory half way around the world. I have no idea how many times a visitor from a virus laboratory outside the United States handed me a vial containing a newly discovered virus and asked me to identify it. In those days, we considered that "international collaboration"; now it might be considered akin to treason. Were such trusting, collaborative efforts dangerous? Obviously not, but we all were surely naïve regarding the possibilities for mischief. Even unwittingly, an exotic, perhaps somewhat dangerous or even highly pathogenic virus might have been in that vial. Virus identification was our job, however, and the best safety practices of the time were in place. National policies aside, virologists are no less decent people than anyone else. In addition, and perhaps more important, there is no piece of paper, no signature, no evidence of training, no rule or law that can absolutely guarantee the safety of a shipment or the law-abiding (or non-law-abiding) nature of the shipper.

To send an infectious virus today, one must jump through endless hoops, so that shipping companies will be willing to take on board their aircraft a package containing not only the infectious agent but the dry ice that preserves it during the journey. That package must be double or triple sealed, the contents certified, and the person shipping the package must have been trained according to the standards of the International Air Transport Association. It is the price we pay for living in the world as it is. Is all this justifiable? Surely; anything is justifiable to those who intend to justify it. However, a paper by Rambhia, Ribner and Gronvall points out that many of the so-called select agents that are subject to strict regulations are actually common and occur naturally. They suggest that a review of the entire policy might be a good idea. Those who have financial interests in any aspect of these policies likely have a different perspective.

Nonetheless, such hoop-jumping takes an inordinate amount of time and considerable expense and slows the necessary course of action. The enthusiasm and frequency with which arbovirologists and others exchange viruses and collaborate is lessened and work takes longer to initiate than it did even a decade ago, or might be impossible to conduct. To avoid such problems, viral nucleic acids are extracted from viruses; then the nucleic acids, being non-infectious, are shipped to the receiving laboratory for molecular analysis. The problem with this is that analysis of a viral nucleic acid is not the same as the analysis of an infectious virus, in much the same way as the analysis of a human brain is not the same as the analysis of the person from whom the brain was obtained. Phenotypic data can only be assumed, so the biological characteristics of the virus can only be implied, and we can only guess about dangers and other characters.

As always when new laws exist, some people who are overly enthusiastic in enforcing those laws (for self-protection or for more reasonable motives), read between the lines, and interpret them as they see fit. This may be understandable, but it creates administrative impediments. Every organization includes people who try to be helpful and some very few others who micromanage, are simply officious, or who are intentionally obstructive. Attempting to build one's own reputation by impeding the work of others never is successful. It has been my experience that, thankfully, obstruction has been exceedingly rare in the institutions where arbovirology is and has been done. That holds for institutions world-wide, no matter the nation or form of government. This may be one of the reasons behind the many accomplishments of arbovirologists as an international group.

According to my dictionary, an administrator is one who manages other employees, i.e., a bureaucrat, someone who is a functionary in the greater scheme of things, a person who sees to it that things run smoothly and according to the extant rules of the organization. The origin of the word "administrate" itself is from Middle English *administracio*, Latin for "service". Something seems to have been lost in translation. In their book, The Peter Principle, Laurence Peter and Raymond Hull stated, "In a hierarchy every employee tends to rise to his level of incompetence." That is, members of a hierarchy are promoted so long as they work competently but, after a while, they get promoted to one position higher than they can actually manage and therefore find themselves doing a job for which they are not competent. Peter and Hull's tenet was posed humorously, of course, but it was not far from the truth. According to a corollary of this principle, employees all end in dead-end jobs from which they cannot be promoted, and so the real work to be accomplished is left to those employees who have not yet been promoted to their own level of incompetence. Sound familiar? Reorganizations of well-functioning institutions have been tried but rarely have they succeeded in bringing about anything but chaos and reduced productivity.

In contrast, and for the most part, the scientist-administrators (or "scientist-leaders") I have observed, from up close or from a distance, have been more than competent. The leadership of Harvey Artsob, Barry Beaty, David Bishop, Roy Chamberlain, Bo Quan Chen, Wilbur Downs, Scott Halstead, Karl Johnson, Kenneth Lam Sai Kit, Thomas Ksiazek, Dmitri Lvov, Thomas Monath, C.J. Peters, James Porterfield, William Reeves, Roslyn Robinson, Philip Russell, Alexis Shelokov, Wayne Thompson, Telford Work, and scores of others was and remains of the highest order.

One of the reasons for the unquestioned success of the Rockefeller Foundation, of the CDC, the Pasteur Institute system, and of many other accomplished organizations was that a remarkably sensible and intelligent administrative staff was established early on, a group of people enthusiastic about the work and understanding its importance. Their job was to find ways to get things done, not to find ways to keep things from being done. Repeated and nonsensical reorganizations, well intended or simply for cosmetic purposes, often do less to improve communications within and the general efficiency of an organization than simply leaving things as they were.

As the world as a whole, and laws in particular, become more complex, it is the rare (and needed) administrator who does her or his best to see that the scientist is able to get his or her work done, whatever that may take. Indeed, that philosophy might serve as a motto for arbovirology or any other field of interest: "Whatever it takes".

CHAPTER 12

Biogeography

Biogeography deals with the geographical distribution of animals and plants. It would not take much to extend this to include viruses (why should ecologists have all this fun?) but the scientific community has not yet had discussions specifically addressing biogeography of viruses. The outstanding author David Quammen, has pulled together his own overviews, as well as those of others, in his exceptional book *The song of the dodo. Island biogeography in the age of extinctions.* Studies of area effect, distance effect, edge effect, habitat diversity, inter-species relationships, climate changes, and general biological dynamics could be applied to viruses as well as to rodents, bats and elephants. Certainly the geographic distribution of human-to-human transmitted and other easily transported viruses is not constrained because their hosts are not geographically constrained. It has been clear almost from the beginning of arbovirus discovery, however, that the geographic distributions of most arboviruses are at least somewhat limited or, for many, extremely limited. That is also the case for viruses that are strictly rodent-borne, the hantaviruses and arenaviruses, for instance, for which virus distribution coincides with host-rodent distribution; that is, if the host is not present, neither will the virus be present. Arbovirus vectors, which include mosquitoes, ticks, and culicoids, are less specific in their vectorial capacities; that is, arthropods other than the principal vector may also have the capacity to transmit viruses.

An example of the complexity of virus distribution is the apparent inverse relationship between the prevalence of Sin Nombre hantavirus and perhaps other hantaviruses, other rodent-borne viruses elsewhere, and the rodent species diversity in the area observed. At three sites in Colorado where we conducted long-term studies of rodents and Sin Nombre virus, we found that the prevalence of Sin Nombre virus infection was inversely proportional to the richness (the number of species) of the rodent assemblage. Metastudies showed this inverse relationship to be highly statistically significant for study sites throughout the southwestern United States. Many hypotheses have been proposed and many more likely can be proposed to explain this, but such a finding might be key to a greater understanding of virus-host dynamics and therefore to epidemiological predictive power. Such insights cannot be acquired sitting behind a desk.

The inverse relationship between prevalence and diversity was only clear after combining data collected over many years. What has always been necessary and likely will always be necessary is to conduct very long-term field studies, as a physician monitors a patient's temperature, leukocyte count, and enzyme levels to detect changes. It is apparent by now that as many parameters as can be measured should be measured: virus, vectors, host assemblage, climatologic characteristics and variations, presence of predators and of invasive species and human-made changes (e.g., dams, lakes, fences, ditches, irrigation, conversion to agriculture). Only in this way can whatever changes occur be attributed to particular events, natural and otherwise, the epidemiology of the virus(es) be determined and infection by the virus be prevented. In the absence of such information, we are left with studies of viruses obtained during and after epidemics or viruses removed from a freezer and compared with another virus removed from a freezer. The remarkable molecular tools that are now available are just that, tools. It is as true today as when Telford Work said, "The field is the patient". It is a good idea to recognize that knowing what viruses are is fascinating and useful but that what they do is important.

The geographic distribution of each arbovirus is dependent on the presence of competent virus vectors (e.g., mosquitoes, ticks, culicoids, etc.) and of susceptible vertebrate hosts (e.g., humans, equids, cattle, birds, rodents). If either of these components of the natural cycle of the virus is not present, then the virus cannot be present for the long term. For example, West Nile virus was known to occur in Africa, Europe, Asia and Australia but not in the Americas. In 1999 that changed when the virus was found first in New York City, then spread, principally by birds, throughout North and South Americas, where it is now well established. Adequate vectors and susceptible hosts had been here all along, but the virus had not been introduced. An example from another kingdom (parasites) is schistosomiasis, which occurs in Egypt but not in Israel.

Other viruses that can infect birds can move as far as the birds can move, either during limited local movements or during migrations, which can cover considerable distances, for example about 12,000 miles (19,000-plus km) during the pole-to-pole migration of the arctic tern (*Sterna paradisaea*). Whether virus-infected birds can remain viremic during the entire period it takes for them to fly great distances or whether virus-infected birds are even slightly disadvantaged by such an infection, and whether hematophagous arthropods are present at the terminus of the migratory route are important factors in movement of viruses. We do know such movement occurs, at least with some viruses, at least sometimes, but not much more than that.

The purpose of migration for the bird is to maximize food availability, find a safe haven for raising its young, and avoid weather extremes. Arboviruses might find new arthropod vectors and new vertebrate hosts. The scientific record contains numerous reports of "seeding" locations where a virus had not occurred previously. West Nile virus, St. Louis encephalitis virus, Japanese encephalitis virus, Sindbis virus, eastern equine encephalitis virus, western equine encephalitis virus, and many other arboviruses have been shown to be moved by infected birds. This is not a simple mechanism however. Many subtypes and varieties of Sindbis virus have been studied and compared by Dalrymple, Lundström and Pfeffer, Grešíková and others; variants have been named (Ockelbo virus, Karelian fever virus), adding to the confusion. Isolates of Sindbis virus have been obtained from a wild-caught black-bellied hamster (*Cricetus cricetus*) and from a marsh frog (*Pelophylax* [formerly *Rana*] *ridibunda*) in Slovakia and numerous isolates have been obtained from birds in India, Tajikistan, Azerbaijan, Finland, Estonia, Israel, Slovakia, Czech Republic, Australia and elsewhere. Results of sequencing the RNA genomes of many of these viruses support the hypothesis that their dispersal mechanisms include movement in infected migratory birds. From their molecular analyses, Weaver et al. concluded that Highlands J virus (found only in the eastern United States) is a recombinant of eastern equine encephalitis virus (not found in the western United States) and Sindbis virus (not found anywhere in the New World). In various forms, Sindbis virus gets around!

In addition, eastern equine encephalitis virus in North America, which causes occasional but severe to fatal disease in humans and horses in the eastern United States and eastern Canada, differs slightly but significantly from eastern equine encephalitis virus in South America, where it seldom has been shown to cause disease. Casals was the first to show antigenic differences between the North American and South American varieties of eastern equine encephalitis virus using a novel method, kinetic hemagglutination-inhibition, which depended on the avidity of a particular antibody to the antigen against which it was produced. Later studies by Scott Weaver, Patricia Repik and others confirmed and extended these findings, providing a molecular basis for the phenotypic characteristics and clarifying the epidemiologic features of this virus.

The North American variant is known to move southward in infected migratory birds in the fall each year. This may initiate the odd cluster of cases on islands of the Caribbean Sea but not much further south. Likewise, the South American variant is known to move northward into the United States with infected northbound migratory birds in the spring but has not been shown to cause disease in North America. Because of relatively brief viremias caused by these viruses and because they are avian pathogens, it is likely that infected birds either die en route or make landfall at sites in the United States along the Gulf of Mexico early in the spring, when mosquitoes are absent or rare.

Another example of probable movement of viruses by birds is Weldona virus. More than 20 years ago two isolates of this virus were obtained from ceratopogonid midges collected in northern Colorado. Electron microscopy suggested that Weldona virus was a bunyavirus; the isolates were further identified as hitherto unrecognized members of the Tete group of orthobunyaviruses. Prototype Tete virus had been isolated from a bird in South Africa and from birds in Nigeria. Others of that virus group had also been isolated from birds: Bahig virus from birds in Egypt, Cyprus and Italy and from ticks in Egypt and Italy; Batama virus from birds in the Central African Republic; Matruh virus from birds in Egypt, Cyprus and Italy and from ticks in Egypt; and Tsuruse virus from a bird in Japan. Antibodies to many of these viruses have been detected in migrating and resident birds; many of the isolates came from migrating birds. No human infections with any of these viruses are known to have occurred and the few surveys done have detected no antibody to these viruses in humans. The isolations of Weldona virus from Colorado midges and the presence of antibody to Weldona virus in both waterfowl and passerine birds in Colorado raises unanswered questions about what enabled the introduction and establishment in the Americas of Tete serogroup viruses. A lost African bird? An event before the break-up of the Pangaea supercontinent? It is likely that any question regarding the origin of Weldona virus will not be studied for lack of practical necessity and, therefore, of funding. Gaining knowledge for the sake of knowledge seems less popular these days, less well supported.

It is reasonable to consider birds as sporadic sources of arboviruses and as blood meal sources for certain female mosquitoes primed to lay eggs. Certainly this is a simplistic description because each virus has its own biogeographic constraints and its own natural cycle, including the need for competent blood-feeding arthropods unique to the area. Even though a virus might be carried hither and yon by birds, that virus might have many genotypes, each with biogeographic limits.

Viruses that use terrestrial mammals as part of their natural cycles have biogeographic constraints. If a particular virus is principally transmitted only by arthropods of a particular species and only to rodents or other vertebrates that are themselves geographically limited due to resource availability and other "fitness" requirements, then that virus will be limited in its range. That is probably one reason that certain mammal-requiring viruses have been found only in certain places: Group C, Anopheles B group, Capim group, and Patois group orthobunyaviruses are restricted to the Americas; Olifantsvlei group orthobunyaviruses to Africa; Changuinola group orbiviruses to the Americas; Palyam group orbiviruses to Australia and Asia; and so on. Still, these biogeographic limitations may be confounded by geologic peculiarities, such as continental movement and land bridges, or by viral evolutionary changes, local climate changes, introductions (usually of vertebrates, rather than viruses, though intentional and accidental introductions of viruses are always considerations).

Clearly, biogeographic restriction of arenaviruses and hantaviruses, which have as their principal hosts rodents of certain species, is due to geographic limitations of the host rodent. Thus Junin virus (Argentine hemorrhagic fever), Machupo virus (Bolivian hemorrhagic fever), Sin Nombre virus (hantavirus pulmonary syndrome), and others are unlikely to become medical problems anywhere but where they currently occur, unless environmental conditions change somewhat (small problem) or change considerably (large problem). Movement of viruses by infected migrating bats is also a possibility, as now has been shown for many bat-borne viruses.

Justifiably focused efforts to detect pathogens intentionally overlook many viruses. Some viruses that were isolated with considerable frequency in the past (e.g., in the United States, Tensaw, Flanders, Turlock, and Colorado tick fever viruses) are not being detected these days and may not have been detected for more than a decade; Colorado tick fever virus is a human pathogen. From examining the reported data, one would think these viruses no longer occur or are rare. The same can be said for some arboviruses that were formerly found with considerable frequency elsewhere. If one does not look, one does not find.

For decades Jack D. Poland a conscientious physician-diagnostician at CDC took responsibility for diagnosis of human infections with Colorado tick fever virus, which occurred with some regularity in the Rocky Mountain states. When human blood samples arrived at the laboratory, Poland separated the serum from the clot and inoculated each into a litter of suckling mice. Brains from mice that died or were symptomatic following inoculation were tested for the presence of a variety of commonly occurring arboviruses, including Colorado tick fever virus. When Poland retired, no one took this regional responsibility. Colorado tick fever is no longer a nationally reportable disease. That is, diagnosed cases are summarized but not reported, so that one could assume that this virus is no longer infecting people. State health departments have deemphasized diseases that are neither prominent (in the news) nor highly pathogenic or life-threatening (think funding). Thus, the overall decline in the reported incidence of Colorado tick fever could as well be attributed to Poland's retirement and political necessities as to an actual decline in occurrence. With the advent of almost universal application of polymerase chain reaction assays because of their remarkable sensitivities and ease of application, and of use of prepared kits for detecting certain antibodies and antigens, laboratory diagnoses and surveillance have properly focused on diseases of importance, however one defines that. However, without field surveys and specific efforts, the only viruses we might find are those we are looking for, and the days when virus surveys were done will hereafter be simply a historical note of interest. This limited approach to a "What is out there?" question does not serve well efforts to predict or to prepare for virus emergence incidents. To counter this deficit, the United States Agency for International Development's Bureau of Global Health has established and funded the "PREDICT" program to monitor and increase the local capacity in "geographic hot spots" to identify the emergence of new infectious diseases in high-risk wildlife such as bats, rodents, and non-human primates that could pose a major threat to human health. At present, the University of California at Davis leads a coalition of experts in wildlife surveillance, including the Wildlife Conservation Society, the Wildlife Trust, the Smithsonian Institute, and Global Viral Forecasting, Inc. http://www.usaid.gov/press/releases/2009/pr091103.html Using deep sequencing (multiply repeated sequencing of genome fragments), many other laboratories are engaged in detection of recognized and previously unrecognized viruses and virus discovery is a growth industry, and a useful one.

The expense and requirements (including experienced personnel) for conducting field work impede long-term planning at the local level. Even were such work to be funded beyond the perfunctory studies that are too common today, experienced and insightful field workers would be exceedingly difficult to find. Yet all the problems of the world cannot be solved by sitting in front of a computer.

Complicating what at first glance might appear to be a relatively simple array of natural "rules" is viral nucleic acid reassortment between viruses with segmented genomes and viral nucleic acid recombinant events between viruses with nonsegmented genomes. For example, it is now clear that many viruses of the western equine encephalitis virus complex of alphaviruses in North America (western equine encephalitis virus, Highlands J virus, Fort Morgan virus, and Buggy Creek virus) are descendants of an ancestral alphavirus that itself was the product of a recombination event, involving the E1 and E2 envelope protein genes from a Sindbis-like virus and the other genes from an eastern equine encephalitis virus-like ancestor. How the Sindbis-like virus arrived in North America, where there is no evidence for the presence of such a virus now, is unknown, although it is possible that a bird infected with a Sindbis-like virus was blown off course from Africa and made its way to the Americas. Many other scenarios are possible but no definitive answers have been provided.

Fort Morgan and Buggy Creek viruses also are interesting. While searching for arboviruses such as western equine encephalitis virus and St. Louis encephalitis virus in nesting birds in eastern Colorado, CDC scientists D. Bruce Francy, Gordon Smith and others isolated Fort Morgan virus from nestling cliff swallows (*Petrochelidon pyrrhonota*) and nestling house sparrows (*Passer domesticus*) and from swallow nest bugs (Cimicidae, *Oeciacus vicarius*) infesting those nests. Unpassaged field strains of that virus were non-pathogenic or of low pathogenicity for suckling mice but selected plaque variants of the virus were pathogenic for a variety of laboratory hosts. The virus was shown to be antigenically related to western equine encephalitis virus and its close alphavirus relatives but more closely related to the western equine encephalitis complex virus Highlands J from the eastern United States than to other western equine encephalitis complex viruses. Another virus in this antigenic complex, Buggy Creek virus, isolated from these swallow nest bugs in Colorado, Oklahoma and Nebraska, has been studied with considerable intensity, first by the noted entomologist Cluff E. Hopla at the University of Oklahoma and more recently by Charles R. Brown at the University of Tulsa in Oklahoma. Their studies showed that Buggy Creek virus overwinters in the bugs, is vertically transmitted in the bugs, and infects incoming birds in the spring. The virus was not brought to the sites by migrating birds. It affects the ecology of the birds and affects viral gene flow. In sum, mosquitoes, ticks, true bugs, birds, mammals, and a variety of other life forms make a fascinating stew in which all sorts of viral permutations and combinations can occur. The viruses themselves can recombine and evolve. This translates to job security for virologists and others.

The biogeography of arboviruses is a complex issue but one that might be studied profitably. Knowing the current distributions of hosts, vectors, and viruses and observing their range expansions or contractions through long-term surveillance may be the only way to understand and predict the effects of climate change on the distribution of these viruses and the changing risk for human populations so that we can prepare for potential events. Finally, the close genomic relationships of certain viruses, those that are found in relatively restricted geographic areas, may serve as reminders of what Alfred Russel Wallace seminally said about various life forms on Sarawak in 1855: "Every species has come into existence coincident both in space and time with a pre-existing closely allied species."; beat Charles Darwin to the punch, too.

CHAPTER 13

Viral hemorrhagic fevers, bat viruses, and rabies-related viruses

A hemorrhagic fever is one in which the patient bleeds, sometimes profusely, particularly from orifices. Internal bleeding may occur, leading to organ failure and death, often following seizures, central nervous system malfunction and coma. It isn't pretty. Many infectious causes of hemorrhagic fevers are known, including bacteria (*Leptospira* spp., *Ehrlichia* spp., *Escherichia* coli O157:H7, *Campylobacter* spp., *Orientia* spp.) and certain viruses. In this section only viral hemorrhagic fevers (VHF) will be discussed.

If you were a public health official who saw the need to put together a team of physicians and virologists to investigate a locally reported outbreak or epidemic of a VHF, would you want to gather experienced investigators or investigators who were much less experienced and likely to die because of their ignorance? With few exceptions, initial studies of VHFs were and are made first by local physicians, then reported to the regional responsible health officials, after which national and international authorities are notified and alerted. If the country affected has the capacity and experience to conduct its own investigations, it does so. However, many VHFs occur in isolated regions of third world countries without such capacity. In some places, medical infrastructure either is woefully inadequate or completely lacking, and often illnesses and deaths are so common that they are not reported, or at least not reported immediately. In such situations, national or international teams must be brought in to conduct the studies and carry out preventative measures under conditions as safe as can be brought to bear. Safety must be the first consideration when dealing with VHFs, as has been shown numerous times, when physicians, nurses, and others attending patients also became ill and died. To understand the hazardous nature of VHFs, it is necessary to provide a general description of them.

Though the illnesses may be similar, VHFs may be caused by viruses of several families. These viruses damage the vascular system, resulting in bleeding, which may be slight or considerable, possibly life-threatening. The course of the illness may be brief, with patients manifesting non-specific signs and symptoms but their condition deteriorating rapidly to become life-threatening.

Yellow fever was the first hemorrhagic fever shown to have a viral etiology. Whereas yellow fever ostensibly has been recognized for hundreds of years, many other mosquito-borne, tick-borne, and rodent-borne viruses now have been shown to cause hemorrhagic fevers. These include flaviviruses (family *Flaviviridae*) in addition to yellow fever virus (mosquito-borne), dengue viruses (mosquito-borne), Kyasanur Forest disease virus (tick-borne), and Omsk hemorrhagic fever virus (tick-borne and water-borne); bunyaviruses (family *Bunyaviridae*): Rift Valley fever (genus *Phlebovirus*) (mosquito-borne), Nairobi sheep disease (genus *Nairovirus*), and Crimean-Congo hemorrhagic fever nairovirus (tick-borne); certain of the European and Asian hantaviruses (rodent-borne) that cause hemorrhagic fever with renal syndrome; arenaviruses (family *Arenaviridae*): Junin virus (Argentine hemorrhagic fever), Machupo virus (Bolivian hemorrhagic fever), Sabiá virus (Brazilian hemorrhagic fever), Lassa virus (Lassa fever), and Guanarito virus (Venezuelan hemorrhagic fever); and filoviruses (family *Filoviridae*) Marburg virus (Marburg hemorrhagic fever) and an increasingly recognized number of ebolaviruses causing ebola hemorrhagic fevers). Most of these viruses are so highly pathogenic for humans, have such high case-fatality rates, and are so easily transmissible, that they have high potential for use as bioweapons and are of both biomedical and national security interest. None of the known viral hemorrhagic diseases are indigenous to the United States. Accordingly, a primary risk factor of VHFs includes travel to areas where a particular virus is endemic (e.g., portions of Africa, Asia, the Middle East, and South America).

Work with these viruses must be conducted only in high containment (BSL-4) laboratories. All personnel working in BSL-4 laboratories must work in negative pressure rooms and wear protective clothing, including double-gloves, biohazard suits, shoe coverings, face shields and respirators. Taking such precautions is difficult and expensive. BSL-4 laboratories are located in Australia, Belarus, Canada, China, Czech Republic, France, Gabon, Germany, India, Italy, Netherlands, Russia, Singapore, South Africa, Sweden, Switzerland, Taiwan, United Kingdom, and the United States. Slightly lower biosafety level laboratories (BSL-3) are located in many countries. Unfortunately, most countries have appreciably lower biosafety containment facilities.

Although ribavirin, an antiviral drug, has been shown to have some effectiveness against arenaviruses and at least some of the bunyaviruses and other viruses, there currently are no antiviral medications effective against filoviruses or flaviviruses. Although a vaccine is available for use against infection with yellow fever virus, the best way to avoid illness and death from these viruses is by taking adequate precautions to avoid infection.

Vaccines against a variety of arboviruses and other viruses have been devised, and more seem to be on the way. Vaccinology is a justifiably trendy field at this time, as it has been for many years. Nonetheless, there is a huge difference between devising an acceptable vaccine and applying such a vaccine to a wider population. Acceptable vaccines for use in humans against eastern equine encephalitis, western equine encephalitis, Venezuelan equine encephalitis, Rift Valley fever, and others have been used for many years to protect laboratory workers and military personnel. However, it is not usually under the purview of the military to produce and apply vaccines for non-military personnel. The legal ramifications of such use are unsettled. Pharmaceutical companies are reluctant to produce vaccines that are expensive to produce and which have limited profit potential. Therefore, such vaccines are, in effect, unavailable for general application. This situation once again demonstrates that availability does not translate to accessibility.

Abundant information regarding specifics of all VHFs and the viruses that cause them can be found elsewhere. Although the causes, natural histories, and control strategies of VHFs differ for each causative agent, their clinical manifestations and the histopathologic findings are similar enough that differentiating among them can be difficult. This is critical because early recognition and correct diagnosis are essential to initiate effective control measures.

Arenaviruses

The first recognized arenavirus was lymphocytic choriomeningitis virus, isolated in 1933 by Charles Armstrong and R.D. Lillie from autopsy material of a fatal case of what was thought to be St. Louis encephalitis. At about the same time, Thomas Rivers and T.F. McNair Scott of the Rockefeller Institute for Medical Research isolated the virus from patients diagnosed with aseptic meningitis, and Erich Traub isolated the virus from mice in a colony at the Rockefeller Institute in Princeton, New Jersey. This virus, which is not uncommon in wild and laboratory mice, can cause a human febrile illness that sometimes progresses to aseptic meningitis. As visualized by electron microscopy, arenaviruses have a grainy or sandy appearance because of the viral ribosomes acquired from the host cell during replication. The name of this family of viruses was derived from the Latin word "arenosus", meaning "sandy".

Many other arenaviruses have been discovered after the occurrence of single cases or multiple case outbreaks or epidemics. For instance, Junin virus, the etiologic agent of Argentine hemorrhagic fever, was recognized in 1958 after an outbreak of that disease in field workers and other humans living in agricultural areas of the Argentine pampas. Detailed investigations of this disease by Julio Maiztegui and others, including Marta Sabattini, Norma Mettler, and Julio Barrera Oro, included clinical and histopathologic findings: coagulation changes in case-patients and immune system responses to infection. They developed experimental infections in laboratory hosts and devised possible methods of treatment. In addition, they developed diagnostic assays, performed electron microscopic studies of the virus, and observed epidemiologic patterns. Their biogeographic observations included the prevalence of the virus in the host rodent, the drylands vesper mouse (*Calomys musculinus*), and rodent densities. Because of the severity of this illness and its widespread occurrence among crop workers, a vaccine was developed and applied to them and to others at risk. The disease can now be considered controlled in humans.

Safety precautions for working with Junin virus were developed and have been shown to be quite useful in subsequent studies of other viral hemorrhagic fevers. Maiztegui and others involved in those early studies served as expert consultants when other arenaviruses later appeared as disease agents. After a long period of observation, disease description, and accumulation of necessary information, a live-attenuated vaccine against Junin virus was developed in 1964 by Armando S. Parodi and Celia E. Coto. Development of the Junin virus human vaccine program was completed in 1965, with critical scientific and technical input by Shelokov at NIH, Julio Barrera Oro, Julio Maiztegui, C.J. Peters, Nicola Tauraso, Gerald A. Eddy, Kelly T. McKee, Jr., and others in Argentina and at the United States Army Medical Research Institute of Infectious Diseases.

In 1963, in the Beni River valley of Bolivia, another hemorrhagic fever was recognized, this one called Bolivian hemorrhagic fever. United States experts Karl M. Johnson, Patricia A. Webb, Ronald

B. Mackenzie, Merle L. Kuns, Ned H. Wiebenga and Panamanian national Gustavo Justines from the Middle America Research Unit in Panama went to the epidemic zone, which was in and near the town of San Joaquin, to see what they could do to put a stop to the spread of this terrible disease. With the collaborative efforts of Patricia Webb, Merle Kuns and others, and under extreme biohazard conditions, the team determined the viral cause of the epidemic, another arenavirus, which they named Machupo virus and its rodent host (the large vesper mouse, *Calomys callosus*). They resolved its epidemiology, determined that control of this rodent would control the occurrence of the disease, and implemented a plan of action to accomplish this. Several members of the team acquired the disease and nearly died, but eventually the epidemic ended, although Bolivian hemorrhagic fever continues to occur from time to time in and near San Joaquin. Collaboration by C. J. Peters, Conrad Yunker, Gustavo Justines, Frederick Murphy, and Wallace Rowe, demonstrated that persistent infections of the virus occurred in the large vesper mouse. This team also developed laboratory diagnostic tests for antibody to the virus and participated in establishing the taxonomy of the arenaviruses. Of course, these findings became the basis of even more studies, as is usual in virology and other scientific fields of importance.

Many other arenaviruses have been isolated or otherwise detected, as listed in Table 2. Thus far, Chapare, Junin, Guanarito, Machupo, Lassa, Lujo, lymphocytic choriomeningitis, and Sabiá viruses have been shown to be associated with human illnesses, and asymptomatic infections of humans with other arenaviruses have been documented in laboratory workers. Long-term effects of tolerant infection in rodents include mild runting, decreased survival time, and almost total sterility among females, largely caused by fatal virus infection of embryos.

The arenaviruses have been classified as "Old World" or "New World", depending on their geographic distribution. Lymphocytic choriomeningitis virus, although it also is found in the Americas, is considered an Old World virus. Another, more useful and contem-

Table 2. Recognized arenaviruses (family *Arenaviridae*, genus *Arenavirus*), listed alphabetically.

Virus	Original source[a]	Country of origin	Year first described
Allpahuayo	bicolored arboreal rice rat (*Oecomys bicolor*) and Brazilian arboreal rice rat (*Oecomys paricola*)	Peru	1997
Amaparí	Guiana bristly mouse (*Neacomys guianae*)	Brazil	1964
Bear Canyon	California mouse (*Peromyscus californicus*)	U.S.A.	2002
Big Brushy Tank	white-throated woodrat (*Neotoma albigula*)	U.S.A.	2008
Catarina	southern plains woodrat (*Neotoma micropus*)	U.S.A.	1999
Chaparé	human (natural host unknown)	Bolivia	2003
Cupixi	rice rat (*Oryzomys* sp.)	Brazil	1970
Flexal	rice rat (*Oryzomys* sp.)	Brazil	1975
Guanarito	(human) Known natural host: short-tailed cane mouse (*Zygodontomys brevicauda*)	Venezuela	1990
Ippy	African grass rat (*Arvicanthis niloticus*)	Central African Republic	1970
Junín	drylands vesper mouse (*Calomys musculinus*)	Argentina	1958
Lassa	Natal multimammate mouse (*Mastomys natalensis*)	Nigeria	1969
Latino	large vesper mouse (*Calomys callosus*)	Bolivia	1965
Lujo	human (natural host unknown)	South Africa	2008
Luna	Natal multimammate mouse (*Mastomys natalensis*)	Zambia	2009
lymphocytic choriomeningitis	house mouse (*Mus musculus*)	U.S.A.	1933
Machupo	large vesper mouse (*Calomys callosus*)	Bolivia	1963
Merino Walk	bush vlei rat (*Myotomys unisulcatus*)	South Africa	1985
Middle Pease River	southern plains woodrat (*Neotoma micropus*)	U.S.A.	2008
Mopeia	Natal multimammate mouse (*Mastomys natalensis*)	Mozambique	1977
Mobala	soft-furred mouse (*Mastomys natalensis*)	Central African Republic	1983
Ocozocoautla de Espinosa	Mexican deer mouse (*Peromyscus mexicanus*)	Mexico	2012
Oliveros	dark bolo mouse (*Bolomys obscurus*)	Argentina	1990
Paraná	Paraguayan rice rat (*Oryzomys buccinatus*)	Paraguay	1965
Pichindé	Tomes's rice rat (*Oryzomys albigularis*)	Colombia	1965
Pirital	Alston's cotton rat (*Sigmodon alstoni*)	Venezuela	1995
Real de Catorce	white-toothed woodrats (*Neotoma leucodon*)	Mexico	2010
Sabiá	human (natural host unknown)	Brazil	1990
Skinner Tank	Mexican woodrat (*Neotoma mexicana*)	U.S.A.	2008
Tacaribe	great fruit-eating bats (*Artibeus lituratus*) and a large pool of mosquitoes of various species	Trinidad	1956
Tamiami	hispid cotton rats (*Sigmodon hispidus*)	U.S.A.	1965
Tonto Creek	white-throated woodrat (*Neotoma albigula*)	U.S.A.	2008
Whitewater Arroyo	white-throated woodrat (*Neotoma albigula*)	U.S.A.	1996

[a] Except for Tacaribe virus, all arenaviruses detected thus far have been from rodents (order Rodentia); other exceptions include Lujo and Chaparé viruses, for which the natural hosts are unknown. The Old World arenaviruses are restricted to rodents of the family Muridae, subfamily Murinae, and the New World arenaviruses are restricted to rodents of the family Cricetidae, subfamilies Sigmodontinae and Neotominae.

Thanks to Charles Fulhorst for assistance with this table.

porary, classification has been accomplished using molecular comparisons of arenaviral genomes to place these viruses in three clades. The accomplishments of Michael J. Buchmeier, Michael B. Oldstone, William E. Rawls, Charles F. Fulhorst, Mary Louise Milazzo, Stuart T. Nichol, Paula M. Cannon, Christina F. Spiropoulou, Scott C. Weaver, Hilda Guzman, Robert B. Tesh, Douglas M. Watts, Amelia P. Travassos da Rosa, Michael D. Bowen, and a host of others, from mammalogists working in the field to collect samples, to molecular biologists skilled at the use of polymerase chain reaction, to protein chemists searching for receptor usage and entry pathways, as well as those developing hypothetical models to simulate pathogenic mechanisms have moved forward this important field of study. Without such efforts and accomplishments, all that could be done is to develop better diagnostic tools (to determine what has already happened) and other methods of post-facto documentation. Understanding pathogenic mechanisms holds out at least a hope for prevention and treatment.

The first arenaviruses to be discovered included some that are formidable and others that have not yet been shown to be hazardous for humans. Additional investigations undoubtedly will reveal the existence of more arenaviruses, some of them human pathogens. In 1969, Lassa virus emerged, causing an acute febrile illness in humans in West Africa and challenging researchers because they had no clue about the causative agent of the illness, despite considerable experience in and knowledge of the region. Initially, two missionary nurses died after treating very ill patients from a small village, Lassa, Nigeria. A third nurse, Lily Pinneo, was airlifted to New York City along with blood samples from her dead colleagues. The samples from Nurse Pinneo and the two fatal cases were sent to the Yale Arbovirus Research Unit in New Haven. The staff still retained many of the world's most eminent virologists, epidemiologists, and laboratorians in the world. The Yale researchers, including Wilbur Downs, Sonja Buckley, and Jordi Casals, with the collaboration of John Frame of Columbia University's School of Public Health, soon showed this to be a newly recognized arenavirus.

Sonja M. Buckley: The career of this researcher is illustrative of how far we had to go, how far we have come and, perhaps, how far we still have to go. Born in Switzerland, Buckley obtained a degree in medicine at the University of Zurich, trained by William Loeffler (pulmonary eosinophilia) and Herman Mooser (murine typhus). Married to an American classmate, she and her husband moved to Johns Hopkins University in 1947. Her husband became a Chief resident while Sonja had only a poorly paid research position in the Department of Bacteriology, School of Public Health. She was assigned to study the epidemiology of polioviruses and, under the guidance of George E. Gey, learned cell culture techniques, which Gey and others were then developing. In 1948 she moved to the Sloan-Kettering Institute of Cancer Research in New York City to supervise studies of the effects of various compounds on sarcoma-180 tumors. These cells were later used by Tikasingh, Spence, and Downs to produce huge volumes of antibody to arboviruses in mice, making distribution of these reagents easier for everyone (except the mice). Buckley became Associate Medical Bacteriologist in the New York State Department of Health under Gilbert Dalldorf, where she expanded her experience and knowledge of cell cultures but also applied immunofluorescence testing, developed there by Albert Coons, to assays of viruses and the antibodies they stimulate.

In 1957, Buckley was recruited by Max Theiler of the Rockefeller Foundation to develop cell culture systems for their virus laboratories. Using her cell culture systems, she tenaciously characterized numerous viruses that had been sent for identification from their far-flung associated laboratories, and developed plaque assays and neutralization tests for virus identification. Buckley submitted to the Arbovirus Catalogue editor an inventory of cells susceptible to the many viruses she encountered. She systematically studied mosquito cell lines, particularly the C6/36 cell line derived from *Aedes albopictus* mosquitoes by K.R.P. Singh, which have become so useful in amplifying dengue viruses. She showed that these cells would support the replication of viruses from mosquitoes but not viruses from ticks and that they could be used to detect viruses that later could be amplified in mammalian cells.

In 1969 Buckley isolated Lassa fever virus in cell culture and that virus then was recognized as the etiologic agent of Lassa fever. This was no small accomplishment when working with such a highly pathogenic agent. Not only was Jordi Casals hospitalized after being ill because of infection with Lassa virus. A young laboratory technician who worked with Casals had gone to visit family in an adjacent state but did not return the following Monday; it was later learned that he had died from infection with Lassa virus. This was a true nightmare scenario, and Buckley and those who continued to work under the less than adequate safety facilities of the time were truly heroic. Buckley stayed at Yale University until she retired in 1983.

During the period when laboratory studies of Lassa fever were being investigated at Yale University Wilbur Downs was on a train to New Haven one morning, having purchased a book to make the time pass. As he read the book, "The Andromeda Strain" by Michael Crichton, he told me, his hands began to shake, and he imagined the worst. He said that the remainder of that train ride was the worst time of his life.

After an enormous amount of field and laboratory research, it is now known that Lassa virus is found in West African rats. It is not yet certain which species of *Mastomys* are principally associated with Lassa virus, but rats of at least two *Mastomys* species carry the virus in Sierra Leone. *Mastomys* species rodents breed frequently, produce large numbers of offspring, and are numerous in the savannas and forests of West, Central, and East Africa. In addition, they readily invade and colonize human homes. Taken together, these factors contribute to the relatively efficient spread of Lassa virus from infected rodents to humans.

There are a number of ways in which Lassa virus may be transmitted to humans. The rodents shed Lassa virus in urine and feces, as well as in saliva, so the virus can be transmitted through direct contact with these materials, through touching objects or eating food contaminated with these materials, or through cuts or sores. Because multimammate rats may live in and around homes and scavenge human food remains or poorly stored food, transmission in this manner is common. Contact with the virus also may occur when a person inhales tiny particles in the air (aerosols) contaminated with rodent excretions. Finally, because these rodents are sometimes consumed as a food source, infection may occur via direct contact when they are caught or when they are prepared for food. Some evidence suggests that Lassa virus may be transmitted through person-to-person contact, such as in hospitals and clinics (nosocomial infections), where staff may come in contact with bodies, blood, and vomit. That seems to have been the method by which the three missionary nurses were infected: caring for patients and participating in autopsies. As mentioned, both a laboratory technician and Casals, a physician of great skill and renown, became infected. How they became infected remains unknown, but their attempts to inoculate mice with blood from the people in Nigeria who nursed the original patients might have created infectious aerosols or, more likely, the inoculated mice themselves created infectious aerosols.

Signs and symptoms of Lassa fever typically occur 1-3 weeks after the patient is infected with the virus. These include fever, retrosternal pain (pain behind the chest wall), sore throat, back pain, cough, abdominal pain, vomiting, diarrhea, conjunctivitis, facial swelling, proteinuria (protein in the urine), and mucosal bleeding. Neurological problems have also been described, including hearing loss, the most common complication of Lassa fever, tremors, and encephalitis. Because the symptoms of Lassa fever are so varied and nonspecific, clinical diagnosis is difficult, except during epidemics.

Lassa fever has been recognized in Guinea, Liberia, and Sierra Leone, as well as Nigeria, all in West Africa. However, because the rodents that carry the virus are found throughout West Africa, the actual geographic range of the virus and the disease it causes may extend to other countries in the region. In areas where the disease is endemic, Lassa fever is a significant cause of morbidity and mortality.

While this infection may cause mild or no observable symptoms in about 80% of people infected, the remaining 20% have a severe multi-system disease. Lassa fever is also associated with occasional epidemics, during which the case-fatality rate can reach 50%. Approximately 15% to 20% of patients hospitalized for Lassa fever die from the illness. However, only about 1% of infections with Lassa virus result in death. Death rates are particularly high for women in the third trimester of pregnancy, and for fetuses, about 95% of which die in the uterus of infected pregnant mothers. Evidence suggests that arenaviruses are not as pathogenic for their rodent hosts as they are for humans. This also is true for other rodent-borne and for bat-borne viruses, probably an indication of the meaning and significance of "reservoir host".

The number of Lassa virus infections per year in West Africa has been estimated at 100,000 to 300,000, with approximately 5,000 deaths. Unfortunately, such estimates are crude, because surveillance for cases of this disease is erratic at best. In some areas of Sierra Leone and Liberia, it has been shown that 10%-16% of people admitted to hospitals have Lassa fever, a statistic that indicates the serious impact of the disease on the population of this region.

The CDC highly recommends taking precautions when caring for patients with Lassa fever. Such precautions include wearing protective clothing, including masks, gloves, gowns, and eye-protecting goggles; using infection control measures, such as complete equipment sterilization; and isolating infected patients from contact with unprotected persons until the disease has run its course. Taken together, the precautions are called VHF isolation precautions or, more often, "barrier nursing methods". Use of BSL-4 facilities is always suggested where such facilities are available. If they are not available, it is probably best to do nothing except to request rapid assistance from appropriate sources and prevent nosocomial infections as best as possible.

Still other highly pathogenic arenaviruses have been found more recently. These include Guanarito virus, the cause of Venezuelan hemorrhagic fever, which is transmitted as a zoonotic agent from rodents (Alston's cotton rat, *Sigmodon alstoni*); Sabiá virus, the cause of Brazilian hemorrhagic fever, which causes hepatic necrosis and hemorrhagic manifestations; and Chaparé virus which, as does Machupo virus, causes a hemorrhagic fever in Bolivia. The natural reservoirs of Sabiá virus and Chaparé virus, although assumed to be rodents, are as yet unknown.

In a paper published nearly 40 years ago, Andrew A. Arata and Norman G. Gratz associated biogeographic information (locations of rodents) with recognized distribution of arenaviruses. Their principal conclusion, albeit preliminary because of scarcity of data at the time, was that there are associations between arenaviruses and their specific host rodents, i.e., certain species and families. By now, it is clear that, although "spill-over" occurs from time to time, each arenavirus is associated with rodents of a single species. What is more, those viruses are restricted to geographic areas where those rodents occur. That has been shown to be the case for hantaviruses (and all rodent-borne viruses) as well.

Hantaviruses

Donald E. Carey: In 1961, this physician-staff member of the Rockefeller Foundation was assigned to the Virus Research Centre (now National Institute of Virology) in Poona (now Pune), Maharastra, India. The center was jointly supported by the Indian Council of Medical Research and the Rockefeller Foundation. After three months of orientation Carey and his family moved to Bagayam, a small village near Vellore (Tamil Nadu), where a field station had been established and where they lived on the campus of the 1000-bed Christian Medical College and Hospital. Carey began collaborative work on herpes, mumps, lymphocytic choriomeningitis, and on the arboviruses causing dengue, chikungunya, Japanese encephalitis, West Nile, and other diseases, working with Ruth M. Myers (Christian Medical College), Korshed M. Pavri and F.M. Rodrigues, both of the Virus Research Center, Pune), Paul Arnstein (CDC, Atlanta on assignment to the

G.W. Hooper Foundation, University of California Medical Center, San Francisco), and many others.

Korshed Minocher Pavri: Born in Bombay (now Mumbai), Pavri obtained a Ph.D. degree from the University of Bombay, then a Fulbright Fellowship to focus her interests in virology, training first at the New York State Department of Health laboratories and then at the Rockefeller Foundation.

On her return to India she joined the Virus Research Centre at Pune as an assistant research officer in the mid-1950s. In 1978 she was named Director of what became the National Institute of Virology, continuing with her interests in arboviruses, such as Japanese encephalitis, chikungunya, dengue, and other arboviruses endemic in India. Pavri was a member of the W.H.O. Expert Panel on viral diseases and taught many students over the years. Eventually, Pavri decided to draw more attention to HIV/AIDS in India. Even after retiring in 1989, she continued to work as Project Director of the (Indian) Centre for AIDS Research and Control and edited a newsletter regarding AIDS.

Pavri was as interested in arboviruses as were Carey and Myers, and worked closely with them in the isolation and identification of many unidentified and previously unrecognized viruses from mammals and birds, but it was primarily Carey who persisted with this work. Carey's son Ted, who was 12 years old at the time and working with his father during a school vacation, trapped shrews at Thottapalayam, near Vellore, dissected them and collected specimens to be inoculated into mice for virus isolation. Virus isolation from vertebrates at the time was done by the standard method of intracranially inoculating clarified tissue suspensions into newborn mice. One of the newly isolated viruses was from a suspension of spleen tissue from an Asian house shrew (*Suncus murinus*) captured in 1964 and was named Thottapalayam virus. Because Carey et al. were unable to identify it as being related to any known virus, it was sent to Robert Shope at the Rockefeller Foundation in New York for further studies. He also was unable to identify it and the particulars of those attempts were published in the Indian Journal of Medical Research as *Thottapalayam virus: a presumptive arbovirus isolated from a shrew in India.* Their presumption was incorrect. Some 25 years later Hervé Zeller et al., using reagents acquired from Joel Dalrymple at the United States Army Medical Research Institute of Infectious Diseases, showed that Thottapalayam virus was very distantly related to the hantaviruses and, indeed, was a member of that complex of viruses (confirmed genetically by Dalrymple), thus belonging to the family *Bunyaviridae*, genus *Hantavirus*, which includes no arboviruses. Until that discovery, all hantaviruses had been isolated from or detected only in rodents. Thottapalayam virus was from a soricomorph, an insectivore, not a rodent, the first of many shrew- and mole-borne hantaviruses to be recognized.

At the suggestion of Jean-Pierre Digoutte, then Director of the Pasteur Institute of Cayenne, French Guiana, Zeller had traveled with his family from Cayenne to spend a short time at the CDC in Fort Collins. His assigned task was to attempt to at least partially identify viruses that had not been identified but which were registered in the Arbovirus Catalogue as "unclassified". He accomplished so much and his stay was such a successful one that he stayed with us for three delightful years.

After Ottis Causey retired from his position as Director of the Virus Research Laboratory at the University of Ibadan in Nigeria, Carey became its director in 1970. The Ibadan laboratory had been established in 1964 as part of the Rockefeller Foundation network of laboratories studying yellow fever and other diseases caused by arboviruses. Yellow fever investigations, always a priority under Causey, continued, and in 1969 Carey, along with Graham Kemp and Vernon Lee of the Ibadan laboratory, as well as Robert Shope of Yale and Paul Bres (Figures 53 and 90), then the Director of the Pasteur Institute of Dakar, investigated an outbreak of yellow fever occurring among rural villagers living on the Jos Plateau near the center of Nigeria. Although the official nationwide case count was 209 that year, Carey and his colleagues found 252 cases during a survey of only seven hospitals, and Carey estimated that there had been more than 100,000 cases in the affected region. It was shown by John Boorman of the West African Medical Council laboratory in Ibadan and also by Dorothy Moore and Vernon Lee that in this epidemic the vector of yellow fever virus was not *Aedes aegypti* but *Aedes luteocephalus*, a mosquito found in cut stumps of cactus used as hedgerows around homes. Once again yellow fever virus had found a way to persist and survive in peridomestic habitats.

Hemorrhagic fever with renal syndrome (epidemic hemorrhagic fever, Korean hemorrhagic fever): A hemorrhagic disease with renal involvement was described by Japanese military physicians in China hundreds of years ago ("epidemic hemorrhagic fever") and by Russian physicians in the 1930s ("epidemic hemorrhagic nephroso-nephritis" or "Far eastern hemorrhagic fever"). A similar disease was described in the United States during the American Civil War; other clinical syndromes that might match modern reports also have been reported. Both Russian and Japanese studies designed to characterize the disease (by incubation period, persistence of immunity, etc.) were done using human subjects. In spite of this, hemorrhagic fever with renal syndrome was not accurately described until 1951 during the Korean War. Some of the United Nations troops there suffered from an acute febrile illness characterized by prostration, vomiting, a variety of hemorrhagic manifestations, proteinuria, renal failure, and shock, sometimes culminating in death. Many hypotheses were advanced as to the cause, but, though humans were known to be susceptible to whatever it was, no laboratory indicator systems (cell cultures or rodents) were found to be useful to isolate the etiologic agent.

At that time, Ho-Wang Lee (Figure 127), a South Korean physician who had obtained a Ph.D. at the University of Minnesota, described the disease in detail. While his studies continued, the United States military initiated its own research, expending considerable resources in doing so. Although the cause of hemorrhagic fever with renal syndrome had eluded numerous excellent scientists, it did not elude Lee. After many years, working with Karl Johnson, who at the time was at the United States Army Medical Research Institute of Infectious Diseases, he was able to isolate the virus from humans and identify the virus associated with the disease and from rodents collected in South Korea. They named the virus Hantaan virus, as the rodents from which they obtained the virus were collected near the river of the same name. The principal host of this rodent-borne virus was identified as the striped field mouse (*Apodemus agrarius*). This original finding, of course, initiated more studies, including those of the epidemiology and transmission of the virus, characterization of clinical disease, determination of attack rates, and characterization of the virus itself. When other, related, viruses were shown to cause identical or similar diseases, it became clear that a cluster of related viruses of rodents existed, viruses that were transmissible to humans and able to cause severe or mild hemorrhagic fevers. Because of their molecular characteristics, they were considered to constitute a new genus, *Hantavirus*, in the virus family *Bunyaviridae*. Seoul virus was isolated by Lee and colleagues from the brown or Norway rat (*Rattus norvegicus*); the bank vole (*Myodes*, [formerly *Clethrionomys*] *glareolus*) was shown to be the reservoir for Puumala virus; and the yellow-necked field mouse (*Apodemus flavicollis*) was shown to be the reservoir host of Dobrava virus. These viruses occur in unique one virus-one host relationships in Europe and Asia and are associated with rodents of various species, wherever those rodents are found.

Figure 127. Ho-Wang Lee
(image courtesy of Ho-Wang Lee)

Figure 128. C. J. Peters (1940 -)
(image courtesy of C. J. Peters)

Hantavirus pulmonary syndrome: In 1993, a newly recognized hantavirus, Sin Nombre virus, was found to cause a disease called hantavirus pulmonary (or cardiopulmonary) syndrome, first recognized among young Native Americans in the Four Corners area of the United States, where New Mexico, Colorado, Utah, and Arizona meet. Sin Nombre virus was identified with remarkable speed by expert virologists at the CDC and the United States Army. Initial clinical, epidemiologic, and molecular characterizations also were quickly completed, due to the efforts of C.J. Peters (Figure 128), Thomas Ksiazek (Figure 129), James Childs, Stuart Nichol (Figure 130), James Mills (Figure 131), and others at the CDC. Connie Schmaljohn (Figure 132) and her Army team were, however, first to isolate and identify the virus. Terry Yates, Brian Hjelle and others at the University of New Mexico, including Karl Johnson, who had "retired" to that area, conducted epidemiologic evaluations. To determine the geographic distribution and natural history of this virus, large-scale longitudinal surveys were established at multiple sites in New Mexico, Colorado, Arizona, and Montana. Over the next 13 years, Ksiazek and colleagues led data collection efforts, which were coordinated by Mills, an experienced and knowledgeable ecologist, excellent editor, and insightful biologist. Data collection is still continuing in Montana. These longitudinal studies yielded information useful for understanding the fundamentals of transseasonal transmission, epizoology, epidemiology, evolution, epidemic potential, prevention, and control of hantaviruses in the western United States and

Figure 129. Thomas Gary Ksiazek (1946 -)
(image courtesy of Brian Bird, U.S. Centers for Disease Control)

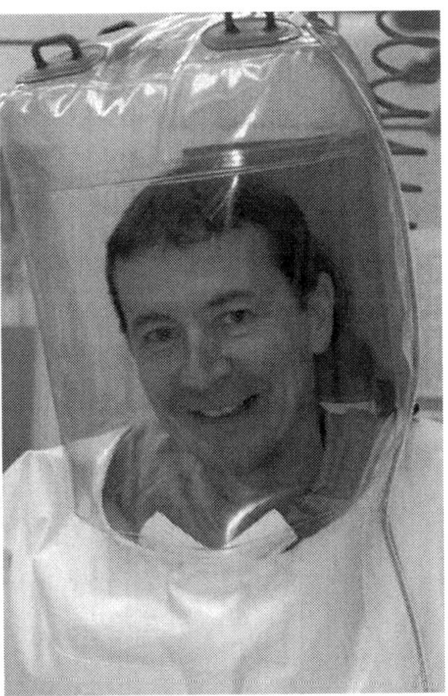

Figure 130. Stuart Thomas Nichol (1955 -)
(image courtesy of Brian Bird, U.S. Centers for Disease Control)

Figure 131. James Norman Mills (1948 -)
(image courtesy of James Mills)

Figure 132. Connie S. Schmaljohn (1952 -)
(image courtesy of Connie Schmaljohn)

elsewhere. Mice of various species, sizes, shapes, and colors have been central, if involuntary, participants in these hantavirus studies.

Using a combination of clinical findings, serologic surveys, and molecular tools devised specifically for such studies, attempts were made to find hantavirus pulmonary syndrome cases outside the Four Corners area. Other newly discovered hantaviruses, detected in rodents of other species, were shown to cause hantavirus pulmonary syndrome in both the United States and Canada. When international collaborative surveillance efforts were extended to include Latin America, even more hantaviruses were detected, some associated with hantavirus pulmonary syndrome and some not. At present, at least 74 hantaviruses have been detected in rodents, soricomorphs, and bats, most in the Western Hemisphere. This total likely is owing to intensive efforts to find them in the years following recognition of hantavirus pulmonary syndrome (Table 3).

The first hantavirus isolated was Thottapalayam virus, found in 1965 in tissues of a shrew captured in India but not identified as a hantavirus until 1989. Recent and on-going studies by Richard Yanagihara and his collaborators have shown that shrews and moles (order Soricomorpha) serve as hosts for many newly recognized soricomorph-only hantaviruses, demonstrating the fascinating existence of another branch on the hantavirus family tree.

Shortly after hantavirus pulmonary syndrome was recognized in 1992, the CDC began detailed surveys of rodents near cases of clinically-defined hantavirus pulmonary syndrome cases wherever they were reported, supporting laboratories hemisphere-wide with CDC personnel when invited, conducting and supporting symposia, sending reagents, and confirming testing results. That comprehensive effort showed that, if one looked hard enough at rodents anywhere, a new hantavirus could be found.

Of the more than 4,600 species of mammals, about 44% are rodents. Thus, at least hypothetically, there might be more than 2,000 distinct hantaviruses. Considering that subspecies are known to occur for most rodent species, many more than 2,000 different hantaviruses might exist. Furthermore, 10% of all species of mammals are insectivores and hantaviruses have been isolated only from a few insectivores, which suggests that we have not come close to the end of hantavirus discovery. The same could be said for arenavirus discovery in rodents and other mammals and of other viruses in bats.

Filoviruses

Marburg virus disease: Kidney cells from monkeys have been used for virus isolation, neutralization tests, and other studies for many decades. Those were the cells that Jonas Salk, Albert Sabin, and Mikhail Chumakov used to prepare their poliomyelitis vaccines. There are two types of monkey kidney cells: primary cells, which are obtained fresh from the kidneys of a recently killed (but apparently healthy) monkey and serially propagated cells (cell lines) that were established as primary cells but became immortalized by passage under the proper in vitro conditions. As one can imagine, obtaining primary monkey kidney cells weekly is an arduous and never-ending task, whereas obtaining a monkey kidney cell line takes no more than a phone call to a commercial source or a request to a colleague for a flask of them, so the latter are used more often, even though they might have chromosomal abnormalities and could cause malignancies if they should manage to invade a human (by accidental inoculation).

In August 1967, workers at a laboratory in Marburg an der Lahn, Germany, were preparing monkey kidney cell cultures for use in preparing a poliomyelitis vaccine. Other workers were doing the same thing in a laboratory in Frankfurt am Main, Germany. Clinical manifestations of a hemorrhagic fever occurred in some workers who had been processing tissues of African green monkeys (*Chlorocebus* [formerly *Cercopithecus*] *aethiops*) imported from Uganda, and in others had been involved only in killing these same monkeys, in conducting post-mortem examinations of the carcasses, or in handling the cells or the glassware that contained the cells. Over a 3-week period, a total of 20 people in Marburg and Frankfurt began to display signs and symp-

Table 3. Recognized hantaviruses[a] (family *Bunyaviridae*, genus *Hantavirus*), listed alphabetically by host taxon.

Virus	Natural source[b]	Country of origin	Human illness
order Rodentia, family Muridae, subfamily Murinae			
Amur/Soochong	Korean field mouse (*Apodemus peninsulae*)	Russia/ South Korea	HFRS[c]
Da Bie Shan	Chinese white-bellied rat (*Niviventer confucianus*)	China	none recognized
Dobrava	yellow-necked mouse (*A. flavicollis*)	Slovenia	HFRS
Hantaan	striped field mouse (*A.agrarius*)	South Korea	HFRS
Sangassou	African wood mouse (*Hylomyscus simus*)	Guinea	none recognized
Saaremaa	striped field mouse (*A. agrarius*)	Finland	HFRS
Seoul	brown rat (*Rattus norvegicus*)	South Korea	HFRS
Serang	Asian house rat (*R. tanezumi*)	Indonesia	none recognized
Thailand	bandicoot rat (*Bandicota indica*)	Thailand	none recognized
order Rodentia, family Cricetidae, subfamily Arvicolinae			
Bloodland Lake	prairie vole (*Microtus ochrogaster*)	U.S.A.	none recognized
Hokkaido	grey red-backed vole (*Myodes rufocanus*)	Japan	none recognized
Isla Vista	California vole (*M. californicus*)	U.S.A.	none recognized
Khabarovsk	Maximowiczii's vole (*M. maximowiczii*)	Russia	none recognized
Luxi	Yunnan red-backed vole (*Eothenomys miletus*)	China	none recognized
Muju	royal vole (*My. regulus*)	South Korea	none recognized
Prospect Hill	meadow vole (*M. pennsylvanicus*)	U.S.A.	none recognized
Puumala	bank vole (*My. glareolus*)	Finland	HFRS
Topografov	Siberian brown lemming (*Lemmus sibericus*)	Russia	none recognized
Tula	common vole (*M. arvalis*)	Russia	HFRS
Vladivostok	reed vole (*M. fortis*)	Russia	none recognized
order Rodentia, family Cricetidae, subfamily Neotominae			
Blue River	white-footed mouse (*Peromyscus leucopus*)	U.S.A.	none recognized
El Moro Canyon	western harvest mouse (*Reithrodontomys megalotis*)	U.S.A.	none recognized
Limestone Canyon	brush mouse (*P. boylii*)	U.S.A.	none recognized
Monongahela	deer mouse (*P. maniculatus*)	U.S.A.	HPS[d]
New York	white-footed mouse (*P. leucopus*)	U.S.A.	HPS
Rio Segundo	Mexican harvest mouse (*R. mexicanus*)	Costa Rica	none recognized
Sin Nombre	deer mouse (*P. maniculatus*)	U.S.A.	HPS
order Rodentia, family Cricetidae, subfamily Sigmodontinae			
Alto Paraguay	Chacoan marsh rat (*Holochilus chacarius*)	Paraguay	none recognized
Anajatuba	Fornes' rice rat (*Oligoryzomys fornesi*)	Brazil	HPS?
Andes	long-tailed pygmy rice rat (*Ol. longicaudatus*)	Argentina	HPS
Ape Aime	montane akodont (*Akodon montensis*)	Paraguay	none recognized
Araraquara	hairy-tailed bolo mouse (*Necromys lasiurus*)	Brazil	HPS
Bayou	marsh rice rat (*Ol. palustris*)	U.S.A.	HPS
Bermejo	Chacoan pygmy rice rat (*Ol. chacoensis*)	Bolivia	HPS
Black Creek Canal	hispid cotton rat (*Sigmodon hispidus*)	U.S.A.	HPS
Calabazo	short-tailed cane mouse (*Zygodontomys brevicauda*)	Panama	none recognized
Caño Delgadito	Alston's cotton rat (*S. alstoni*)	Venezuela	none recognized
Castelo dos Sonhos	(a pygmy rice rat) (*Ol. utiaritensis*)	Brazil	HPS
Catacamas	Coues's rice rat (*Oryzomys couesi*)	Honduras	none recognized
Central Plata	yellow pigmy rice rat (*Ol. flavescens*)	Uruguay	HPS
Choclo	fulvous pygmy rice rat (*Ol. fulvescens*)	Panama	HPS
Juquitiba	black-footed pygmy rice rat (*Ol. nigripes*)	Brazil	HPS
Lechiguanas	yellow pigmy rice rat (*Ol. flavescens*)	Argentina	HPS
Leguna Negra	small vesper mouse (*Calomys laucha*)	Paraguay	HPS
Maciel	Argentine bolo mouse (*Necromys benefactus*)	Argentina	none recognized
Maporal	arboreal rice rat (*Oecomys speciosus*)	Venezuela	none recognized
Muleshoe	hispid cotton rat (*S. hispidus*)	U.S.A.	none recognized
Oran	Chacoan pygmy rice rat (*Ol. chacoensis*)	Argentina	HPS

Pergamino	Azara's grass mouse (*Ak. azarae*)	Argentina	none recognized
Playa de Oro	Coues's rice rat (*O. couesi*)	Mexico	none recognized
Rio Mamore	small-eared pygmy rice rat (*Ol. microtis*)	Bolivia	none recognized
Rio Mearim	Amazonian marsh rat (*H. sciurus*)	Brazil	none recognized
order Soricomorpha, family Soricidae, subfamily Soricinae			
Amga	Laxmann's shrew (*Sorex caecutiens*)	Russia	none recognized
Ash River	masked shrew (*So. cinereus*)	U.S.A.	none recognized
Boginia	Eurasian water shrew (*Neomys fodiens*)	Poland	none recognized
Camp Ripley	northern short-tailed shrew (*Blarina brevicauda*)	U.S.A.	none recognized
Cao Bang	Chinese mole shrew (*Anaurosorex squamipes*)	Vietnam	none recognized
Jemez Springs	dusky shrew (*So. monticolus*)	U.S.A.	none recognized
Kenkeme	flat-skulled shrew (*So. roboratus*)	Russia	none recognized
Qiandao Lake	striped-back shrew (*So. cylindricauda*)	China	none recognized
Seewis	Eurasian common shrew (*So. araneus*)	Switzerland	none recognized
Xinyi	Taiwanese mole shrew (*An. yamashinai*)	Taiwan	none recognized
order Soricomorpha, family Soricidae, subfamily Crocidurinae			
Azagny	West African pygmy shrew (*Crocidura obscurior*)	Côte d'Ivoire	none recognized
Imjin	Ussuri white-toothed shrew (*Cr. lasiura*)	South Korea	none recognized
Jeju	Asian lesser white-toothed shrew (*Cr. shantungensis*)	South Korea	none recognized
Tanganya	Therese's shrew (*Cr. theresae*)	Guinea	none recognized
Thottapalayam	Asian house shrew (*Suncus murinus*)	India	none recognized
order Soricomorpha, family Talpidae, subfamily Talpinae			
Asama	Japanese shrew-mole (*Urotrichus talpoides*)	Japan	none recognized
Dahonggou Creek	long-tailed mole (*Scaptonyx fusicaudus*)	China	none recognized
Nova	European common mole (*Talpa europaea*)	Hungary	none recognized
Oxbow	American shrew mole (*Neurotrichus gibbsii*)	U.S.A.	none recognized
order Soricomorpha, family Talpidae, subfamily Scalopinae			
Rockport	eastern mole (*Scalopus aquaticus*)	U.S.A.	none recognized
order Chiroptera, family Vespertilionidae, subfamily Vespertilioninae			
Mouyassué	banana pipistrelle (*Neoromicia nanus*)	Côte d'Ivoire	none recognized
order Chiroptera, family Nycteridae			
Magboi	hairy slit-faced bat (*Nycteris hispida*)	Sierra Leone	none recognized
Unknown			
Hu39694		Argentina	HPS

[a] The taxonomy of hantaviruses is a fluid situation. An increasing number of hantaviruses and hantavirus subtypes are being discovered as epidemiologic investigations of hantavirus pulmonary syndrome are conducted, particularly throughout the Western Hemisphere. Indeed, many of the South American viruses listed in this table may be subtypes of Andes virus. Because hantaviruses (and arenaviruses) have "one virus-one host" relationships and rodents comprise 40%, chiroptera 20%, and soricomorphs 10% of all present day mammals, this table simply provides an indication of the present situation. Rather than using percent nucleotide sequence identity, cross-neutralization tests would be useful to distinguish these viruses because it is the amino acid sequence identity which is critical for cross-protection. However, because molecular techniques now are used for hantavirus and other virus identifications, virus isolations are not attempted or are difficult to do. Clearly, recognition of additional hantaviruses is certain, as this complex table demonstrates.

[b] Common names change from time to time and personal preferences for common names differ. Also, note that rodents belonging to certain species appear to have yielded more than one hantavirus. Given the one virus-one host hypothesis, it is likely (or known) that different subspecies of a particular rodent may be infected with a different hantavirus subtype or even with a different hantavirus.

[c] HFRS indicates hemorrhagic fever with renal syndrome. Some of the viruses so noted cause severe, moderate or mild HFRS and are not distinguished here because if you die from a disease it does not matter whether it has been classified as mild or severe.

[d] HPS indicates hantavirus pulmonary syndrome (also known as hantavirus cardiopulmonary syndrome)

Thanks to Ric Yanagihara for assistance with this table.

toms of what was diagnosed initially as infections with an enteric bacterium, perhaps a shigella.

When hemorrhagic symptoms appeared, the provisional diagnosis was changed to an infection caused by a spirochete (bacterium) of the genus *Leptospira*. The German patients were admitted to the University Hospital Marburg an der Lahn, where a physician accidentally punctured his skin with a contaminated hypodermic needle and became infected, as did a nurse treating patients. In all, 23 case-patients, including five fatalities, were recorded from the outbreak in Marburg and four case-patients plus a physician and a pathology assistant, including two fatalities, were observed in Frankfurt. It is now known that the incubation period is 5 to 10 days and the onset of the disease is sudden and is marked by fever, chills, headache, and myalgia. About five days after onset of symptoms, a maculopapular rash, most prominent on the trunk (chest, back, stomach), may occur. Then nausea, vomiting, chest pain, a sore throat, abdominal pain, and diarrhea may appear. Symptoms may become increasingly severe and may include jaundice, pancreatitis, considerable weight loss, delirium, shock, liver failure, massive hemorrhaging, and multi-organ dysfunction.

In September of 1967, hemorrhagic fevers similar to those in Germany were diagnosed in a veterinarian and his wife, both employees of a national laboratory in Belgrade, Yugoslavia (now Serbia) that was producing poliomyelitis vaccines by use of monkey kidney cells. The monkeys with which they worked also were from Uganda. The veterinarian had been infected while conducting necropsies on the monkey carcasses, and his wife became infected while caring for him. Both patients survived after receiving convalescent serum from survivors of the Frankfurt outbreak.

Months later, a woman whose husband had been one of the original patients but who had completely recovered clinically from his illness was admitted to that hospital. Shown to have the same virus infection by laboratory tests, it is now thought that she acquired it through sexual intercourse with her husband, whose sperm was subsequently shown to be infected with the virus responsible for the outbreak of what was called Marburg disease, also known as "green monkey disease".

All the monkeys involved in this series of episodes had come from the same monkey exporter in Uganda. Because of hostilities in the Middle East at the time, there was confusion as to exactly where the monkeys came from in Uganda and where those monkeys might have acquired their infections. The original source of the virus is unknown.

The virus causing this dreadful illness was isolated in baby hamster kidney cells and then in a variety of primary cell cultures and cell lines, some with cytopathic effects and some without. By electron microscopy, Marburg virus is a filamentous particle, not comparable to any previously recognized virus. Other outbreaks of Marburg virus disease were subsequently recognized in Zimbabwe, Kenya, the Democratic Republic of the Congo (formerly Zaire), Angola, Gabon and Uganda. Another outbreak occurred in Russia, caused laboratory accidents that occurred while working with the virus. Case-fatality rates in various outbreaks have ranged from 20% to 80%, so that the occurrence of this disease, particularly in places where medical facilities are suboptimal, has a powerful effect on local human populations and serious impacts on economies, travel, health regulations, utilization of hospital facilities, socialization, and public perception of risk. Epidemic outbreaks of Marburg have taken a heavy toll on human life in Central Africa and devastated large ape populations in Gabon and the Democratic Republic of Congo.

Ebola hemorrhagic fever: Unrecognized until 1976, ebola hemorrhagic fever was first observed among patients in a mission hospital in Yambuku, near the Ebola River in the Democratic Republic of the Congo (formerly Zaire). As with Marburg virus, this VHF has been associated with remarkably high case-fatality rates, up to 90% in some epidemics and nearly that in all epidemics. Initial investigations of the outbreak were done by French medical investigators. When it became clear that secondary cases, i.e., cases among patient contacts, were occurring and that no end to this expansion was in sight, the W.H.O.

organized a team of investigators, the International Medical Commission for the Study of the New Hemorrhagic Fever of Zaire". The virus causing this disease, eventually but temporarily named "Ebola virus", was isolated and partially characterized very quickly by scientists at CDC in Atlanta and named by the team of experts sent to Zaire by the governments of the United States (CDC), Belgium, Canada, France, and South Africa and by the W.H.O. Karl Johnson led this team of experts, which included Joel Breman and Joseph McCormick of CDC, Peter Piot and Guido van der Groen of Belgium, Pierre Sureau of France, and many others. In the laboratories at CDC Luanne Elliot, James Lange, Patricia Webb, Herta Wolff and, prominently, Frederick Murphy, aided by a task force at CDC which included outstanding epidemiologists Philip Brachman, Lyle Conrad, John Bryan, Lawrence Schonberger, David Sencer (Director of CDC and Assistant Surgeon General at the time), and William Foege (who became Director of CDC). Each has her or his own story to tell but many of those views can be found by ferreting through the scientific literature, magazine articles, and popular books (some good, some inaccurate; none overblown), and popular films, and will not be detailed here.

A very brief outline of the taxonomy of this virus and related viruses and of Marburg virus here will be helpful. Marburg virus was unlike any other virus known at the time of its discovery, so it was considered an "unclassified virus". The word "unclassified" is unsettling to compulsive types, therefore such a category does not usually last long. When "Ebola virus" was recognized as such, it was not known that other viruses, related but distinct from it, were soon to be discovered. Indeed, at about the same time the Yambuku outbreak was discovered, an outbreak of the same disease was occurring in Maridi, Sudan. Clinical signs and symptoms of this hemorrhagic fever were essentially identical in the two areas and were thought to be extensions, one of the other; however, the Zairian virus was shown to differ from the Sudanese virus. When both were shown to be more closely related to each other than to Marburg virus, though related to Marburg virus nonetheless, they were considered all members of a newly recognized

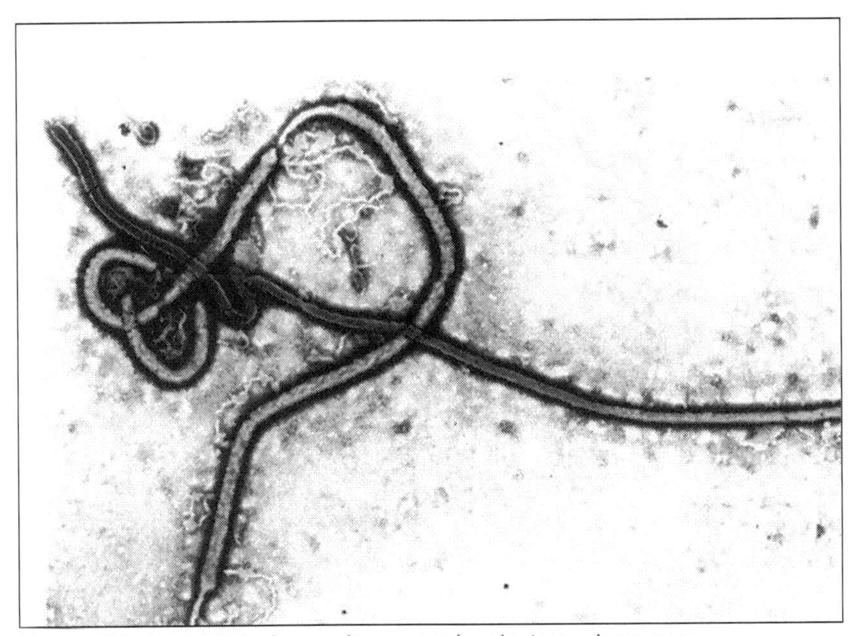

Figure 133. Zaire ebolavirus as it appears by electron microscopy
(image courtesy of Frederick A. Murphy)

family of viruses, the filoviruses, so named because of their filamentous morphologies revealed by electron microscopy (Figure 133). Eventually, they composed the virus family *Filoviridae* and the genera *Marburgvirus* and *Ebolavirus*. Any virus closely related to the original Marburg virus is spoken of as "a marburgvirus" and any virus closely related to the original "Ebola virus" is spoken of as "an ebolavirus". The diseases they cause are called Marburg hemorrhagic fever and ebola hemorrhagic fever, respectively. Each of the many ebolaviruses now has a distinct name, related to the location where it was first observed.

Signs and symptoms of infection with the Zaire and Sudan ebolaviruses may begin with mild "flu-like" symptoms but suddenly progress to include abdominal pain, fever, headache, bloody vomit (hematemesis), diarrhea, maculopapular rash, malaise, joint and muscle pain, sore throat, clotting aberrations, chest pain, and central nervous system signs. Additional bleeding abnormalities and low blood pressure are observed as the disease progresses. The ebolaviruses cause hemorrhaging by interfering with functioning of the endothelial cells lining the interior surfaces of blood vessels and with blood coagulation. As the blood vessel walls become damaged and eventually destroyed, platelets are unable to participate in coagulation and patients bleed, succumbing to shock from decreased blood volume. A physician with direct and long clinical experience with hemorrhagic fever patients told me that when he first saw a patient with this disease he was "scared shitless!" because the patient seemed to be dissolving before his eyes, he had no idea what was causing all this or where it had originated, and had no idea how to stop it from happening. Friends and caregivers of such patients can acquire the infection by contact with blood, saliva, or any other body fluid. Secondary cases are not rare, and therefore containment is a special problem. At least one patient who was admitted to hospital because of a broken leg died of hemorrhagic fever. It seems he had been given a bed in which a hemorrhagic fever patient had died and the bedding had not been changed! Reuse of needles and syringes used to administer antibiotics also has been shown to transmit filoviruses, as well as human immunodeficiency virus, hepatitis viruses, and other infectious agents. Following simple barrier nursing protocols and extensive hand-washing ordinarily prevent transmission of viruses, even these particularly frightening ones.

At present, two marburgviruses (Marburg virus and Ravn virus) and five ebolaviruses (the original Zaire virus, once again called Ebola virus; Sudan virus, Taï Forest virus, Bundibugyo virus, and Reston virus) are recognized. In addition, a virus recently detected in bats in Spain, Lloviu virus, has been shown to be related to the other ebolaviruses and a new genus, *Cuevavirus*, has been established for it. An astonishing amount of personal risk, effort, money, and expertise has been invested in obtaining a large amount of useful information about these viruses.

By 1989, public interest in these relatively recently recognized viruses had decreased and news about them had virtually disappeared from newspaper headlines when an outbreak of a hemorrhagic disease was recognized at a commercial colony of crab-eating macaques (*Macaca fascicularis*) in Virginia, near Washington, D.C. Both simian hemorrhagic fever virus and a filovirus were detected in these dead and dying primates, but no human infections were observed and the simian hemorrhagic fever was determined to be a confounding distraction, although possibly the cause of the hemorrhagic manifestations. That same year other hemorrhagic fever cases were seen in monkeys in a biological facility in Texas; all were monkeys imported from a single commercial source in the Philippines. In 1992 similar cases of hemorrhagic fever appeared in monkeys at a facility in Italy and in 2008 among pigs in the Philippines.

The virus was named Reston virus after the location of the original observations. When the Virginia monkey colony outbreak was recognized, Philip K. Russell and C.J. Peters, then of the United States Army Medical Research Institute of Infectious Diseases, and Frederick Murphy and James Hughes of CDC were immediately called in to investigate. A team of expert virologists, many of whom proudly call themselves "arbovirologist" and all of whom have made it their life work to prevent exotic diseases, included Nancy and Gerald Jaax, Peter B. Jahrling, Thomas W. Geisbert, Eugene D. Johnson, David Huxsoll, David Franz, and Ernest Takafuji of the United States Army Medical Research Institute of Infectious Diseases, Joel Breman, Heinrich Feldmann, Joseph McCormick, Anthony Sanchez, and Thomas Ksiazek of the CDC, and Karl Johnson (by then "retired" but still called upon because of his experience, innovative ideas, and useful suggestions). The building in which the outbreak occurred in Virginia was demolished in May 1995.

During a 1994 survey for viruses in chimpanzees in Ivory Coast (Côte d'Ivoire), West Africa, necropsies revealed some gross pathologic abnormalities of heart and lung. Microscopic studies revealed lesions similar to those observed in human patients during the 1976 ebolavirus outbreaks in Zaire and Sudan. Other chimpanzees, found dead in the forest, were shown to have ebolavirus infections. A veterinarian performing the necropsies contracted an ebolavirus infection and within a week developed symptoms similar to those cause by dengue viruses and considered to be just that. She was evacuated to

Switzerland for treatment, discharged from hospital after two weeks, and had fully recovered six weeks after onset of the infection. That ebolavirus eventually was named Taï Forest virus.

Two other ebolaviruses have been detected since then. Bundibugyo virus was shown to be the cause of a new ebola hemorrhagic fever in Uganda in 2007 to 2008. By the time the epidemic ended, there had been 116 confirmed and probable cases with 39 deaths (34%). The other new filovirus, Lloviu virus, was detected in feces and liver samples from insectivorous Schreiber's long-fingered bats (*Miniopterus schreibersii*) found dead in a cave in Spain. The reason for the investigation was that there had been a die-off of these bats only, among bats of many species. The virus has been shown to be related to the ebolaviruses but because of the genetic distance between them, a new genus has been proposed for Lloviu virus. Fortunately, no human infections with this virus or unusual illnesses have been reported by any of the numerous tourists who visit this cave each year. "Why not?" is an appropriate question to ask.

The role of bats in virus transmission and as virus reservoirs: As summarized by Calisher, Childs, Field, Holmes and Schountz in 2006 and by Wong, Lau, Woo and Yuen in 2007, bats (order Chiroptera) have recently been demonstrated to serve as reservoir hosts of many viruses. Representing more than 25% of the more than 4,600 recognized species of mammals, billions of bats help control insects, reseed cut forests, and pollinate plants that provide food for humans and other species; their guano is used as fertilizer and for manufacturing soaps, gasohol, and antibiotics. Whereas bats in general are extremely common, some of them are in danger of disappearing as ecologic conditions and habitats change or are changed.

Every so often in the past a virus would be isolated from a bat, usually incidental to other studies, for example when a bat would fly into a net being used to capture birds. People who study bats, chiroptologists, are quite protective of their favorite mammals because of the poor reputation bats have acquired through no fault of their own. Thus virologists, most of whom have little knowledge of bats, and chiroptologists, most of whom have little knowledge of viruses, rarely have spoken, much less collaborated, until quite recently. The recognition that certain medically important viruses are harbored by bats is changing all that.

It has long been known that rabies virus can be transmitted by bats, but the recent emergence and recognition of other human, livestock, and wild vertebrate pathogens associated with bats has brought about a vigorous expansion of the study of these vertebrates as reservoirs for pathogens. More than 100 viruses now have been detected in bats and bats of at least 16 families are known to harbor viruses. It is likely that some of these viruses detected in bats may be only incidental infections and do not provide evidence that bats are their reservoir hosts. However, it is also likely that the more studies that are done, the more bat-virus associations will be revealed. This work is being done by virologists, including arbovirologists and others trained in dealing with pathogens at the highest level of biocontainment. Work done with viruses in the past 100 years has, step by step, improved our capacity to study them and to do so with greatly improved safety.

No reservoir hosts for Marburg virus or for ebolaviruses were identified until recently, when bats were shown to carry Marburg virus and Zaire ebolavirus. In addition, severe acute respiratory syndrome (SARS) was shown to be caused by a coronavirus and bats were later shown to be the natural reservoir for this virus. Infection with those and other viruses does not appear to affect the bat hosts, just as Sin Nombre and many other zoonotic viruses do not appear to substantially affect their natural hosts.

Hendra, Nipah, and Menangle paramyxoviruses: These viruses recently emerged in Australia and south Asia and have been shown to be bat-borne. The circumstances of their emergences are instructive because they were, at the time, so startling in regard to location, clinical illness, and cause. Hendra virus was the first of the three to be recognized.

In 1994 a horse trainer in Hendra, a suburb of Brisbane in south-east Queensland, became critically ill with a respiratory syndrome. Coincidentally, a meeting of the Australian Society for Microbiology was about to begin in Melbourne. John Mackenzie, then the president of that society, organized a conference call to include Australian and foreign virologists who had just arrived in Melbourne to attend the meeting. During the conference call the proximal medical history of the patient was reviewed. A few days prior to the onset of his illness, the trainer had attempted to force a bolus of food down the throat of an anorexic horse and had scratched his arm on the horse's teeth. His conditioned worsened, and he became pre-mortem. None of those attending the conference call could say with any certitude that the illness appeared to be one with which they were familiar. The only useful comments were that those who were handing the patient and who would be handling the body should take every possible care not to expose themselves to body fluids or tissues and to thoroughly cleanse any surfaces that might be contaminated. The patient died, and a paramyxovirus was isolated at the Australian Animal Health Laboratory in Geelong from material collected at his autopsy. The virus was first named "equine morbillivirus", then re-named Hendra virus. An assistant of the trainer also had been ill with a severe respiratory infection but survived. Furthermore, horses at a property from which the first sick horse had come had died in the recent past, but nothing was detected in the remains of those disinterred horses and no clue as to the origin of the virus was obtained from virus and serologic surveys of horses, dogs, cats, rodents, birds, or other vertebrates in the Hendra area.

A month after the first human death, another outbreak occurred in Mackay in central Queensland and a single fatal equid death occurred near Cairns in North Queensland in 1999. Infected horses typically show signs of respiratory involvement, but both the second and third human fatal cases had encephalitic signs. Including the original human case-patient, at least four humans (of seven known infections) and 30 horses have died after Hendra virus infection.

Fruit bats, known in Australia as "flying foxes", are common in some parts of Australia, as they are elsewhere in Australasia. Because they were common in the Hendra area, these animals were surveyed, as were rodents, cats, dogs, sheep, pigs and others. Test results indicated that pteropid bats (Order Chiroptera, Suborder Megachiroptera, Family Pteropodidae, genus *Pteropus*) were involved in the natural cycle of Hendra virus. More than 25% of pteropids, including bats representing the four principal species in eastern Australia (the grey-headed flying-fox, *Pteropus poliocephalus*; the black flying-fox, *Pteropus alecto*; the little red flying-fox, *Pteropus scapulatus*; and the spectacled flying-fox, *Pteropus conspicillatus*) had antibody to the virus.

In 1997 another paramyxovirus (genus *Rubulavirus*) was isolated from stillborn piglets at a large commercial piggery near Menangle in Australia; a nearby fruit bat colony and the piggery had co-existed for 29 years before the incident. Although most sows carried their litters to term, abortions occasionally occurred and there were large numbers of within-litter fetal deaths at a variety of gestational ages. Affected litters included mummified, autolyzing, fresh stillborn and live piglets. Teratogenic defects, frequently seen, included arthrogryposis, brachygnathia and kyphosis. Internally, part or all of the brain and spinal cord was absent in most piglets and there was malacia and non-suppurative inflammation of the brains and spinal cords of some. Non-suppurative myocarditis and hepatitis also were present in some piglets.

Two of 250 humans in contact with the infected pigs had high titers of antibodies to the new virus, named Menangle virus. Both reported a febrile illness with a measles-like rash but neither reported having direct exposure to flying foxes. Individual bats living seasonally in a large, mixed colony of grey-headed flying foxes and little red flying foxes and roosting within 200 m of the affected piggery had neutralizing antibodies, as did flying foxes of other species from other colonies thousands of km distant, during and prior to the outbreak at Menangle (H. E. Field, pers. comm., 2011). Vertebrates of other species in the vicinity of the affected piggery were seronegative. Although attempts to isolate virus from flying foxes were unsuccessful, paramyxovirus-like virions labeled with antibody to Menangle virus from a convalescent sow were seen by electron microscopy in flying fox feces collected beneath the roost near the piggery. In 1999 Tioman virus, a rubulavirus distinct from Menangle virus, was isolated from variable flying foxes (*Pteropus hypomelanus*) in Malaysia. Little is known about the host range or pathogenesis of this newly recognized rubulavirus.

Then, in 2009, Marsh et al. isolated another henipavirus from urine of pteropid bats in Queensland, Australia. This virus, named Cedar virus, has many characters in common with other henipaviruses but is not pathogenic for ferrets and guinea pigs, both of which are known to be susceptible to infection and disease with Nipah, Hendra, and other henipaviruses. In addition, the coding strategy of the Cedar virus P gene was shown to play an important role in evading the host immune system. Further studies of this virus might cast light on the pathogenetic mechanisms of henipaviruses and, perhaps, lead to disease intervention. That henipavirus-like genome sequences occur in African bats and antibody to henipaviruses in bats in China likely indicate that more henipaviruses exist and that more information about these fascinating paramyxoviruses will be forthcoming.

In 1999 an outbreak of respiratory disease with encephalitic complications was observed in Malaysia in adult male Malaysians of Chinese descent and in their pigs, which suffered from pneumonia, characterized by rapid and labored breathing and a harsh and explosive ("mile long") cough. Initially, the Malaysian government attributed the outbreak to Japanese encephalitis virus. However, it was pointed out that that virus is transmitted by mosquitoes, which do not selectively feed on adult male Chinese pig farmers. What is more, Japanese encephalitis vaccination programs in Malaysia have a history of effectiveness so that most Malaysians are protected from that disease by the time they reach adulthood and the few cases that do occur are found in children, who were not in the affected population during the outbreak. Antibody to Japanese encephalitis virus detected in the Malaysian patients likely was a "red herring", the result of vaccination or past infection with that virus. As an increasing number of pigs became involved, the Malaysian government instituted a program to cull pigs, and millions of them were killed at great financial cost. Furthermore, there were associated infections and some deaths in those who were hired to kill these animals. This epizoodemic had a disastrous effect not only on the Malaysian human (40% case-fatality rate) and pig populations, but of those of nearby countries; cases in Singapore abattoir workers also occurred, the result of exportation of infected pigs from Malaysia. The number of cases eventually declined due to culling and severe restrictions on movement of pigs, and the virus was contained.

In light of the Hendra experience, bats were studied for a possible role in the natural history of this disease, and once again a paramyxovirus was isolated from both humans and pigs. This virus was shown to be related to, but distinct from Hendra virus, establishing the genus *Henipavirus* in the family *Paramyxoviridae*. The virus was named Nipah virus, after Sungai Nipah, the village where the disease was first observed. Of 265 reported human cases, 105 were fatal. The large flying fox (*Pteropus vampyrus*) and the variable flying fox were found to be natural and reservoir hosts for Nipah virus.

Since 2001, sporadic outbreaks of Nipah virus-associated disease in humans have been identified in Bangladesh. Although many characteristics of this disease were similar to the Malaysian outbreak, including initial delayed recognition, a primary presentation with fever and central nervous system signs, and a high case-fatality rate, in Bangladesh the human cases were not associated with disease in pigs, and there was evidence suggesting human-to-human transmission. Serologic surveys of domestic and wild animals undertaken after the 2001 and 2003 outbreaks in Bangladesh provided evidence of Nipah virus infection only in Indian flying foxes (*Pteropus giganteus*). Concurrent serologic surveillance of Indian flying foxes in India in 2003 found that 54% had neutralizing antibodies to Nipah virus, suggesting that Nipah virus or a closely related virus was widespread across the range of Indian flying foxes. It has now been reported that Nipah virus infections occur in humans in India and neutralizing antibodies to Nipah virus have been detected in large flying foxes in Indonesia and Cambodia. Nipah virus also was isolated from Lyle's flying fox (*Pteropus lylei*) in Cambodia. Thus, the henipaviruses likely occur across the entire global distribution of pteropid bats, which either migrate or otherwise move long distances. Although the risk that humans might become infected with Nipah virus from bats may be low, once the virus escapes its natural cycle, its epidemiologic characteristics could be quite a different story.

In the Bangladeshi and Indian outbreaks, consumption of fruits or fruit products (e.g., raw date palm juice) contaminated with urine or saliva from infected fruit bats appears to be the most likely source of infection of humans. Outbreaks of Nipah virus have been shown to coincide with the date palm sap harvesting season and drinking raw date palm sap is a risk factor for human Nipah virus infection. In an effort to understand the epidemiology of this virus, infrared cameras are now being used in Bangladesh to determine how and when bats gain access to date palm sap.

During later outbreaks in Bangladesh and India, Nipah virus spread directly from human-to-human through close contact with people's secretions and excretions. In Siliguri, India, transmission of the virus was also reported within a health-care setting, where 75% of cases occurred among hospital staff or visitors. From 2001 to 2008, about half of reported cases in Bangladesh were due to human-to-human transmission.

Rhabdoviruses

Rabies virus-related viruses: L.R. Boulger and James Porterfield isolated a virus from a straw-colored fruit bat (*Eidolon helvum*) at Lagos Island, Nigeria. They named it Lagos bat virus but they were unable to determine a relationship with any other virus, so they sent it to colleagues in many laboratories around the world, asking for help in identifying it. Other apparently chance occurrences led to the isolation of many other "unclassified" viruses. For example, Jack R. Schmidt at the United States Naval Medical Research Unit in Cairo isolated obodhiang virus from *Mansonia uniformis* mosquitoes in Sudan, and Graham E Kemp, Vernon H. Lee, Dorothy Moore, Ottis Causey at the Virus Research Laboratory at the University of Ibadan, at the time supported by the Rockefeller Foundation, isolated kotonkan virus from culicoids (midges) and Mokola virus from shrews (*Crocidura* species) and from humans with rabies-like disease in Nigeria. Kemp was a veterinarian who, at the time, was particularly interested in bovine ephemeral fever, caused by bovine ephemeral fever virus (family *Rhabdoviridae*, genus *Ephemerovirus*), which is transmitted by culicoids, and Lee was an entomologist interested in the culicoids themselves because they are vectors of that virus and of bluetongue viruses (family *Reoviridae*, genus *Orbivirus*). At the Yale Arbovirus Research Unit, Shope had shown that Lagos bat, Mokola, and Obodhiang viruses were related antigenically. In collaboration with others, Shope and Tesh also were attempting to classify rhabdoviruses from vertebrates. David I. H. Simpson in England had sent Lagos bat virus to Murphy, asking him to determine the morphology of that virus by electron microscopy. Murphy reported to Simpson and to Shope that Lagos bat virus was a rhabdovirus. Because of certain similarities in virus shape and location of intracyoplasmic inclusions in cells infected with Lagos bat virus to those infected with rabies virus, Murphy suggested that Shope determine whether it was antigenically related to rabies virus (family *Rhabdoviridae*, genus *Lyssavirus*). It was, and a rabies virus-related group of viruses was established. Independently, Dorothy Moore, also at the Ibadan laboratory, found that kotonkan virus was related to Mokola virus, and kotonkan virus was subsequently shown to be morphologically similar to obodhiang virus. At that point they had a certain vertebrate pathogen, rabies virus, related to a virus from mosquitoes, another from culicoids, another from shrews, and yet another from a bat! All related to rabies virus? Perhaps at first difficult to understand, these viruses provide for us clues to the evolution not only of rhabdoviruses in general but of rabies viruses in particular. Gregory H. Tignor and Shope immunized laboratory mice against rabies vaccine virus or against rabies virus from a monkey in Trinidad and challenged them with Lagos bat virus and Mokola virus as well as with the standard Pasteur strain of rabies virus. Their results confirmed the previously recognized interrelations of these viruses and asked whether failure of rabies vaccine to protect people from that disease might have been due to the people having been infected with a rabies virus-related virus, rather than with rabies virus itself.

In South Africa, C.D. Meredith, A.P. Prossouw, and H. van Praag Koch had published what they called an unusual case of rabies. The patient, who had been bitten on the lip, died. The virus isolate they obtained from the patient's brain tissue did not react in the rabies immunofluorescence test. This newly recognized virus was named Duvehage virus, another rabies virus relative.

Although Australia is ostensibly free of rabies, what is meant is that "street rabies" virus is not present there, in spite of a few importations of that virus in people who acquired it elsewhere. Nonetheless, the so-called Australian bat lyssavirus is endemic in certain Australian fruit bats and causes a rabies-like disease in humans. Antibody to rabies virus is protective against infection with Australian bat lyssavirus, and rabies vaccine protects against this disease. Given that "rabies" is not a virus but a disease caused by a virus (rabies virus), the term "rabies-free" is inaccurate insofar as Australia is concerned. That, however, is an issue to be taken up by those who protect international trade matters, not those interested in virological facts.

Calisher and Nick Karabatsos (CDC/Fort Collins), Lee Thompson of U.S.D.A., and Jean S. Smith of CDC (Atlanta) immunized adult mice with rhabdoviruses that had been shown to be at least slightly cross-reactive with rabies virus by immunofluorescence and challenged those mice intraperitoneally with rabies virus. At least some of those immunized with Mokola (15/25), Puchong (11/24), Sandjimba (7/25), and Kolongo (3/25) were protected against such challenge but those immunized with the Australian rhabdoviruses Berrimah and Adelaide River viruses and Bivens Arm virus from the United States were not (0/25 each). This further complicated the question "What is a rabies virus-related virus?"

Since those fundamental findings, other rabies virus relatives have been detected in bats and arthropods, providing interesting and confounding information regarding the evolution of these viruses. It is not at all clear why certain ephemeroviruses share antigens with certain lyssaviruses but, according to Peter J. Walker, CSIRO Livestock Industries, Australian Animal Health Laboratory, Geelong, Victoria, Australia (pers. comm. 2010), antibody to a sequence of six to eight conserved amino acids can recognize a cross-reactive epitope. Walker has shown that such sequences occur in Adelaide River virus N protein at sites homologous to rabies virus N sequences to which even commercial rabies virus monoclonal antibodies bind. The rhabdovirus N protein is relatively, if minimally, conserved in some regions, so it is not unlikely that such short peptides could be the source of confusion. For example, ephemeroviruses cross-react strongly in complement-fixation or indirect immunofluorescence tests and may show low level cross-reactions by indirect immunofluorescence with viruses of the genus *Lyssavirus*. However, sequence comparisons with other rhabdoviruses indicate that in evolutionary terms the ephemeroviruses are closer to vesiculoviruses than to members of other genera in the family. Nevertheless, it is clear that obodhiang, kotonkan, Puchong, Berrimah, Malakal, Kimberley and Adelaide River viruses are ephemeroviruses, not lyssaviruses, and therefore are not rabies virus-related viruses in the true sense of that term, notwithstanding the findings of Shope and others and of Calisher, Karabatsos, Thompson, and Smith. Whether all of these are true arboviruses or not, the evolutionary development of the rhabdoviruses will make a truly fascinating story when more data become available. Kemp had suspected that kotonkan virus causes a bovine ephemeral fever-like disease of cattle, showing both the importance of phenotypic studies of viruses and the necessary involvement of investigators with varied interests from many parts of the world as the basis for noteworthy collaborations.

Perspectives

The drama and public awareness associated with any of these outbreaks puts them in the spotlight for a time ("The disease of the week"). Then they fade from public view as yet another deadly agent is discovered or reoccurs or a story of more immediate importance surfaces, such as the marriage of a starlet or of a football player. This is the usual state of affairs with news media and even with the world-wide web. The scientific community, however, does not forget these matters. Small groups of investigators often spend years, decades, or even entire careers continuing what was begun under epidemic, urgent, frightening, and critical conditions. Putting one foot after another, following a path or putting what might seem to be finishing touches on a thesis that will never be completed, questions are answered, new questions are asked, new methods devised or older ones improved, and what can be called "progress" is made and small victories declared. Then another terrifying incident occurs and the cycle begins anew. This likely will continue to be so because of how we are changing the environment and what we destroy and create.

Viruses, particularly viruses with RNA genomes, will continue to evolve. Areas of the world that had been left undisturbed will come under the saw, the ax, the plow, and the drill and soon another virus, new to human society or to now-stressed wildlife, will burst into highly noticeable outbreaks or epidemics. If we cannot avoid these occurrences, and it appears we cannot, at the least we can try to predict them and attempt to be prepared to counter them. The only way to do that is to have available well-trained and experienced people. Many, if not most, of the investigators of hazardous non-arboviral diseases are arbovirologists, people trained to investigate infectious diseases and their natural cycles, people who had had experience with highly pathogenic viruses in the past, who were willing to put themselves at risk to save others, to learn first hand something new, to answer questions that had been gnawing at them for years, to, inevitably, ask new ones and apply their intellects to all this. Arbovirologists are uniquely prepared to study viruses that jump from the "natural world" to human populations and to livestock and wildlife. The diverse nature of arboviruses, with their malleable RNA genomes providing the capacity to adapt to multiple hosts and to develop unique transmission mechanisms, gave arbovirologists an ecologic perspective of diseases and provided them with the experience necessary to study such conditions and situations.

The efforts of the Rockefeller Foundation and various government agencies to find and identify viruses causing tropical fevers and encephalitides led to the recognition of hundreds of previously unknown viruses. If not completely unexpected, the sheer numbers and varieties were astonishing. What all this meant, where each virus fit in and where it would take medical virology was troubling. Obtaining virus isolates was not a mere stroke of luck, or accidental, it was the purpose of this work. Still, when a virus was isolated, the question had to be asked, "What should we do next?" Next, of course, always was to identify it to determine whether it had already known relatives. When no relatives could be found immediately, the only reasonable next step was to put it back in the freezer and make a note to pick it up again at some time in the future and try again, compare it with viruses that had been discovered in the interim. This is the nature of the work, part slogging along day by day and part serendipity.

CHAPTER 14

The diverse transmission cycles of arboviruses and other viruses

Arboviruses do not comprise a single class of viruses but are rather a category of viruses that are grouped together because of their biological characteristics. The same can be said for the various viruses causing hemorrhagic fevers and hantavirus pulmonary syndrome, which themselves are distinctly diverse. Such weak and irresolute descriptions are inherently unsatisfying to the scientific mind. In addition, certain arboviruses are related evolutionarily to viruses that are not transmitted by arthropods, and some viruses replicate in vertebrates, but do not do so as a part of their natural cycles and do not depend on vertebrates to persist in nature. In this chapter, the remarkable variety of complex transmission cycles of these viruses will be presented. If viruses are "mistletoe on the Tree of Life", as Duncan J. McGeoch has said, why should they have everything in common?

A major complexity of arbovirus transmission in general is the requirement for the virus to replicate in at least two phylogenetically disparate organisms: afebrile or febrile vertebrate hosts with body temperatures at or higher than the temperature at which the vector exists and the arthropod vector, usually existing at a lower temperature. That vertebrates produce antibody that can select against certain virus variants (mutants) and yet allow other virus variants to be amplified makes all this something like a biological amusement park and the cell not much more than a milieu for the expression of genes.

There is no attempt here to be fully inclusive of the many and various natural cycles used by vector-borne pathogens or of the details of their transmission. The comprehensive book, The Biology of Disease Vectors, edited by William C. Marquardt et al., contains abundant information and references for those who would seek more. What follows are brief specific examples of general principles of the variety and complexity of virus transmission cycles.

Transmission via Arthropods

Mechanisms of transmission of viruses by mosquitoes are numerous and varied. These include direct biological transmission (female mosquito to vertebrate), vertical transmission (infected female to her female and male progeny), and venereal transmission (male infecteing vertically to uninfected female or infected female to an uninfected male). Non-biological transmission to vertebrates can be accomplished via virus on vector mouth parts and by infected and uninfected vectors co-feeding on a vertebrate host. Considering the multitude of mosquito species and the thousands of kinds of vertebrates that could serve as virus hosts, the many and varied ecologic conditions in which arboviruses are transmitted, the tenuous circumstances of the cycles themselves, and other factors that adversely affect maintenance of the viruses in nature, these apparently fragile cycles are much more stable than might be expected. The proof of this is that the viruses occur, somehow.

Beginning with the recognition that yellow fever virus is transmitted from human to human by mosquitoes and the subsequent recognition of the "jungle yellow fever cycle" (i.e., monkey-to-monkey by other mosquitoes), studies of transmission of other arboviruses led to the recognition of other types of cycles and have revealed their remarkable diversity. As mentioned in Chapter 6, RNAi also can participate in this remarkable complexity by selecting against certain virus variants and allowing other variants to replicate and be transmitted. Following are a few details of a simple, human-mosquito-human cycle.

Chikungunya and o'nyong-nyong viruses: Both these viruses were discovered in the 1950s in Africa. They are closely related members of the family *Togaviridae,* genus *Alphavirus* and are members of the Semliki Forest virus complex, which also includes Bebaru, Getah, Mayaro, Ross River, Semliki Forest, and Una viruses, each of which can cause headache, fever, rash and arthralgia in humans. The vertebrate wild hosts (reservoirs?) of chikungunya virus in Africa are primates, including baboons, but no wild vertebrate host or reservoir of o'nyong-nyong virus has been identified. The sylvatic cycle of chikungunya virus in Africa includes wild primates; the virus is transmitted among them and to humans by *Aedes luteocephalus* and *Aedes furcifer-taylori* mosquitoes. In Asia this same virus is transmitted among humans by *Aedes aegypti* mosquitoes, but neither sylvatic cycle nor reservoir host has been identified or is suspected to exist. It is because of these observations that chikungunya virus is thought to have originated in Africa. A recent change in the RNA of that virus, allowing it to replicate in the Asian, invasive *Aedes albopictus* mosquitoes on Indian Ocean islands near Africa and in Europe, has been demonstrated by means of viral genetics, which does not alter this view. During epidemics, o'nyong-nyong virus is transmitted among humans by *Anopheles funestus* and *Anopheles gambiae* mosquitoes. No reservoir host or sylvatic vector of this virus has been recognized.

Chikungunya and o'nyong-nyong are very closely related viruses that cause similar if not identical diseases. Chikungunya virus is transmitted by aedine mosquitoes and o'nyong-nyong virus by anopheline mosquitoes, chikungunya virus continued to cause infections in humans, but o'nyong-nyong virus had not been detected since an epidemic nearly 40 years before, when it caused many hundreds of thousands of human infections. Chikungunya virus occurs enzootically throughout much of rural Africa while o'nyong-nyong virus occurs in urban settings in Asia. The apparent absence of o'nyong-nyong virus for more than three decades is proof of how little we know about this virus because this virus likely was being transmitted between vectors and hosts (humans? small mammals?) at a low and undetected rate.

Ann Powers, Aaron Brault, Robert Tesh and Scott Weaver, noting that these two viruses have been reported to differ somewhat biologically which suggests that they belong to different lineages, conducted phylogenetic studies on isolates of each of these viruses from Africa and Asia. Two distinct chikungunya virus genetic lineages were recognized: one from western Africa and the other from southern and East Africa and from Asia. Moreover, the Asian strains, although more closely related to the southern and East African strains than to the western African strains, appeared to be of a single genotype. Further molecular analyses might provide supportive evidence for the biological differences among these chikungunya virus genotypes. These researchers estimated that chikungunya virus and o'nyong-nyong virus diverged from each other thousands of years ago. This span of time certainly is sufficient for what could be a single mutation to have occurred, one that would explain many of these phenotypic differences. In sum, the molecular analyses of a variety of chikungunya virus isolates from Africa and Asia and of o'nyong-nyong virus isolates from 1959 and from 1995 indicate that the African and Asian isolates of chikungunya virus are substantially different from each other and that the recent o'nyong-nyong virus isolates are not substantially different from the 1959 isolates of that virus. Obviously, these viruses are transmitted to humans by mosquitoes but their complete natural cycles are not yet fully understood. Further information is needed regarding the occurrence of as yet unidentified virus mutations and evolutionary changes which allow the maintenance and expansion of these closely related viruses in unidentified wild vertebrate hosts and vectors.

Transmission of rodent-borne viruses among rodents

Transmission of most rodent-borne viruses has been shown to occur principally among their rodent hosts, with transmission to humans being only occasional and "accidental" events. Transmission between rodents occurs seasonally among those fighting for food, territory or females (virus infection rates usually are higher in male than in female rodents). Vertical transmission of these viruses also has been recognized and, for some of them, is an important mechanism.

Hantaviruses: When, after decades of attempts, the relentless Ho-Wang Lee, along with Pyung Woo Lee and Karl Johnson, finally isolated Hantaan virus, the etiologic agent of what is called in Korea "Korean hemorrhagic fever", they solved a quandary and answered some important questions. The methods used to detect Hantaan virus included testing lung and other tissues from striped field mice (*Apodemus agrarius*) by immunofluorescence with sera from patients convalescing from Korean hemorrhagic fever. The research team observed similar immunofluorescence with lung tissues of striped field mice and sera from patients acutely ill with that disease. They also serially propagated the agent in adult striped field mice, showed that they could observe immunofluorescence in the tissues from lungs and other organs of experimentally infected striped field mice, and determined the time to appearance and persistence of virus in the rodents. They were able to isolate the virus in Vero E6 (monkey kidney) cells but failed to amplify the virus in a variety of other cell cultures and laboratory hosts. These findings have served as the basis for subsequent identifications and biological characterizations of the 60 or so hantaviruses isolated or otherwise identified to date (Table 3). In fact, without the methods developed by Lee, Lee, and Johnson, far fewer of the hantaviruses would have been detected and fewer associations of hantaviruses with rodent hosts and human diseases would have been made.

When the work of Lee, Lee, and Johnson revealed the association of rodents and Hantaan virus (the prototype virus of the family *Bunyaviridae,* genus *Hantavirus*), other investigators saw an opportunity to identify the Korean hemorrhagic fever-like illnesses in their region of interest. Investigators associated nephropathia epidemica with Puumala virus; others showed that epidemic hemorrhagic fever (China) and hemorrhagic fever with renal syndrome (Russia) have viral causes identical to Hantaan virus. Seoul virus was isolated from urban rats; laboratory infections with Hantaan virus were documented; and serologic evidence for the presence of hantaviruses was recognized. Evidence mounted for a one hantavirus-one (principal) host relationship in nature, which led to convincing epidemiologic evidence that hantaviruses are each associated with a rodent or insectivore of a particular species.

When the polymerase chain reaction assay was incorporated into the diagnostic armamentarium, hantaviruses could be detected without isolating them, such that it was possible to recognize the insectivore branch of the hantavirus tree. Keep in mind that of viruses in the five genera of the family *Bunyaviridae* (*Orthobunyavirus, Phlebovirus, Nairovirus, Tospovirus* and *Hantavirus*) only the hantaviruses are strictly rodent-borne or insectivore-borne; the others are arthropod-borne, with vertebrates or plants (tospoviruses) as amplifying hosts. This knowledge provides details useful in devising evolutionary hypotheses. The search for hantaviruses is not yet closed and likely will not be closed until far into the future. It is fascinating to note not only the geographically widespread nature of hantaviruses but the sophisticated mechanisms by which they have evolved in one virus-one host relationships and by which they maintain their individual transmission mechanisms. It likely is important that hantaviruses are not pathogenic for their rodent hosts. That they do not appear to infect rodents other than their primary hosts but may be highly pathogenic for humans is an incongruity that will be clarified in the future by immunologists and pathologists.

Arenaviruses: The classical and prototypical arenavirus is lymphocytic choriomeningitis virus. Its natural cycle comprises house mouse (*Mus musculus*)-to-house mouse transmission, but causing the occasional human infections, mostly defined as mild febrile illnesses but also associated with pregnancy-related infection leading to congenital hydrocephalus, chorioretinitis, mental retardation, and fetal teratogenesis. Mice infected with this virus may carry and shed it through their lives while remaining asymptomatic but such persistent infections have not been reported with humans.

As H. Weigand and J. Hotchin proposed, the age of the mouse when first exposed to the virus determines its immune response. If lymphocytic choriomeningitis virus infection in the mouse occurs *in utero* or within the first few hours of life (i.e., before the immunologic responsive period), the mouse develops immune tolerance. The virus continues to proliferate for an indefinite time. However, if a mouse is infected after the neonatal period, when the immune system is responsive, the immune response is active. This immunological conflict can result in one of three outcomes: immunological paralysis, significant or complete suppression of virus with immunity to reinfection, or death. C.J. Peters and co-workers have emphasized the teratogenic effects of this virus in mice.

Equally dramatic, Machupo virus is used here as another example of arenavirus epidemiology because it is associated with more natural settings, selected from many possible arenaviruses. The natural cycle of this virus appears to be relatively simple, spread rodent-to-rodent, as with hantaviruses, though a closer look suggests otherwise.

During the 1958 epidemic of Bolivian hemorrhagic fever caused by Machupo arenavirus, relevant rodent control was applied and the epidemic declined soon after that practice began. However, it was not known whether those efforts were the cause of the decline or whether they were coincidental. Patricia Webb, Gustavo Justines, and Karl Johnson conducted experimental infections of laboratory-reared large vesper mice (*Calomys callosus*), the rodent host of this virus, and infected them with Machupo virus to determine the effects of the virus on them. The virus induced a viremic, immunotolerant infection in suckling large vesper mice for more than 150 days and an intermediate response in those more than 9 days of age. The tolerant infection was found to be associated with hemolytic anemia and splenomegaly as well as lesions they had not observed in those mice that had cleared their viremias. The mice produced circulating neutralizing antibodies. Although neutralizing antibodies were present in parenterally infected adult animals, animals born to, and in contact with, an infected female did not produce such antibodies. Furthermore, these researchers were able to produce an increase in the proportion of those with tolerant response by decreasing the virus dose or by inbreeding the rodents. Their conclusion, later proven with other arenavirus-rodent model systems, was that long-term effects of tolerant infection include mild runting, decreased survival time, and "almost total sterility among females, largely caused by fatal virus infection of embryos".

Which then was the determining factor in the ebbing of this Machupo virus epizootic, the virus or the host? If attributes of the host play a significant role in this scenario, then the ebb and flow of rodent population density, a determining factor in the epizoology of rodent-borne viruses, is the determining factor in virus prevalence. However, the population density of the rodent host in this instance is, at least in part, determined by the rate at which Machupo virus causes sterility in female mice; those investigators reduced the large vesper mouse population as part of their efforts to control the epidemic.

More than likely, the rodent genotype and the rodent's response to the virus are interdependent. Comparisons of arenavirus phylogeny with rodent host phylogeny and taxonomic relationships have shown that virus-host co-speciation occurs, indicating a long and relatively benevolent relationship between the host and its viral parasite. Human pathogenic arenaviruses are not monophyletic, which suggests that the pathogenic phenotype has arisen in multiple independent events during virus (and host) evolution.

The periodic dramatic increases (irruptions) sometimes seen in rodent population densities generally are associated with climate events resulting in abundant food supplies and prolonged reproductive conditions. Thus, as with hantaviruses and their rodent hosts, perhaps it is less important to virus persistence that the rodent hosts of arenaviruses survive the virus infection than that they are affected in ways at least as impactful on their populations as they are detrimental to the virus in the short term.

As only one demonstration of the complexity of rodent-borne viral epidemiology, the potential effects of one variable, diet, on virus shedding by rodents are presented in Tables 4 and 5). Table 4 shows results of studies of the effect of various diets on water intake, urinary pH, and urinary output of large vesper mice (unpublished data courtesy of Gustavo Justines and Karl Johnson, formerly of the Middle America Research Unit), and Table 5 (shown as Figure 134) is the effect of various diets on water intake and urinary pH of deer mice (*Peromyscus maniculatus;* unpublished data, Jeffrey B. Doty and Calisher).

The data in Tables 4 and 5 are not comparable because, among other factors, large vesper mice are not deer mice, the diets were not comparable, and the goals were not the same, but they are instructive. The vesper mice fed bananas, apples, or lettuce, which have high water content, drank very little water and had high daily urinary outputs, whereas those fed corn, rice or laboratory chow, which have low water content, drank a great deal of water and had low daily urinary outputs. Urinary pH varied among diets and, in the case of the mice fed corn and rice, decreased to 6.1-6.2. Virus concentration in those fed bananas (high urinary output) was higher than virus concentration in those fed rice (low urinary output). Thus, not surprisingly, urinary output was greatest by mice fed diets with high water content. Justines and Johnson concluded that during the rainy season in the Machupo virus epidemic zone, when many of the foods that large vesper mice eat are of high water content, infected large vesper mice there may shed somewhat more virus than they do during other seasons.

Table 4. Effects of diet on water intake, urinary pH, and urinary volume of large vesper mice *(Calomys callosus)* [a]

Diet	Water intake (ml)/day	Urinary pH	Urinary output (ml)/day
Banana	<0.5	8.6	13.5
Apple	<0.5	6.7	13.4
Lettuce	<0.5	6.6	13.0
Corn	5.9	6.1	2.2
Rice	5.0	6.2	1.7
Lab chow	4.7	7.4	1.0

[a] Data presented are means of 4-day collections from four large vesper mice. These rodents were from a colony of large vesper mice infected with Machupo virus when less than a week old. All became immune tolerant, with persisting viremias and no neutralizing antibody. Two days after they began to be fed the respective diets they were placed in metabolic cages with wire floors and urine was collected for four days. Urine samples also were collected each morning to determine pH (and infectivity).

Table 5. Effects of diet on urinary pH[a] and water intake[b] of deer mice fed laboratory chow (pellets), kale (*Brassica oleracea,* green vegetable) or insects (mealworms, the larval form of the mealworm beetle, *Tenebrio molitor,* and crickets, *Acheta domestica,* with dietary change (from kale to insects or insects to kale) at day 20.

Day	Lab chow	Kale	Insects
0	8.2	8.4	8.1
1	8.1	8.1	8.1
2	8.0	8.1	8.0
3	8.2	8.1	8.0
5	7.9	8.1	8.2
13	7.9	7.9	6.4
14	7.9	7.6	6.4
15	7.8	7.3	6.3
16	7.9	7.3	6.2
17	7.9	7.3	6.2
18	7.8	7.2	6.2
19	7.8	7.5	6.2
20	7.9	7.5	6.2
21	7.7	6.2	7.4
22	7.7	6.0	7.5
23	7.8	6.1	7.5

[a] Urine samples were collected each morning to determine pH. On the fifth day some of the deer mice were taken off the laboratory chow diet and fed kale or insects and on day 20 those deer mice fed kale were switched to an insect diet, and vice versa.
[b] Overall, deer mice fed kale drank half as much water as deer mice fed insects

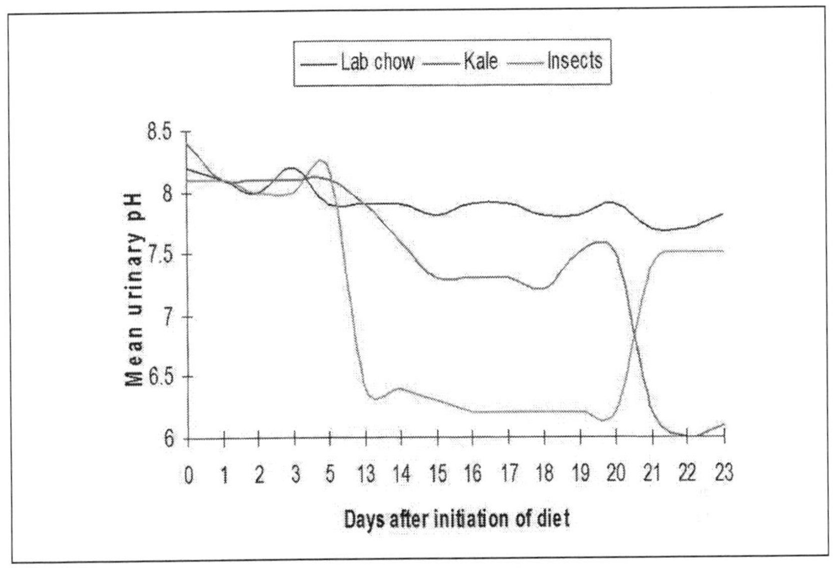

Figure 134. Effect of diet on deer mouse urinary pH

The relatively scant data derived from feeding deer mice various diets and switching those diets in mid-course suggest that a low protein, high water content diet (kale) did not decrease urinary pH relative to the urinary pH of mice fed laboratory chow and that deer mice fed the high water content diet drank about half as much water as those fed the high protein diet (insects), whereas the urinary pH of those fed the high protein, low water content diet was quite low (6.0-6.4), a pH range over which bunyaviruses are known to become unstable and therefore less infectious. Thus, during droughts, when vegetation is scarce and deer mice use readily available insects as a food source, even if they are infected the mice do not shed viable virus. But after a climatic event, when vegetation reappears, the virus with which they are infected might be less likely to be inactivated and more likely to be infectious, a hypothesis that corresponds chronologically and climatologically with field observations of seroconversions to Sin Nombre virus in deer mice. Should such a hypothesis be correct, one would be justified in wondering just how complex natural cycles are, how dependent they are on multiple variables, and what all those variables are.

Transmission of viruses among bats

Relatively recently, bats (order Chiroptera) have been shown to be infected with a wide spectrum of viruses and to be of epidemiologic significance. There are at least 1,116 species of bats, representing about 25% of the more than 4,600 recognized species of mammals. At least 100 distinct viruses have been isolated from or detected in bats, but these have come from bats of only 103 species (no viruses detected in bats of 1,013 species!), which suggests that additional investigations of bats would reveal the presence of many more viruses.

Isolating a virus from or detecting its genomic nucleic acid in an arthropod or a vertebrate is not proof that that arthropod or vertebrate is a natural host of that virus. Arthropods can acquire a virus in a blood meal taken from a viremic vertebrate by mechanical means, a wild vertebrate can acquire a virus from an arthropod by mechanical, rather than biological, means or even by ingesting it (e.g., by cannibalism of an infected host, by incidental contact with virus in excreta from an infected vertebrate, or by exchanging body fluids with an infected vertebrate). In addition, even if a virus is acquired by biological means, the arthropod might serve as a host and even transmit the virus yet not be an important part of the natural cycle of the virus, simply an accidental spillover host. So, too, isolation of a virus from or detecting its genomic nucleic acid in a bat or a rodent or another vertebrate is not indicative of its being a natural host of that virus. Mosquitoes feed on their preferred vertebrate hosts but they will feed on other hosts if available. A great deal of effort is required to prove vector status of a virus source, to confirm host participation in natural cycles, and otherwise demonstrate relevance of such findings.

Reasons for the previous paucity of studies of viruses of bats are that (1) bats of many species are "endangered" or "threatened" and bats of certain species are protected and it is therefore illegal to capture them; (2) it is difficult to capture bats; (3) few investigators who are knowledgeable about bats are also knowledgeable about viruses and vice versa; (4) until recently, bats were not considered as possible hosts when epizoological studies of viruses were planned; (5) viruses appear to have few pathogenic effects on bats; and (6) finding sick or dead bats is an unusual occurrence, as their carcasses usually do not last long in the wild.

Unlike vector-borne and rodent-borne pathogens, very little is known about the transmission cycles of bat-borne viruses. Bats are highly evolved ancient life forms. They are no less diverse than rodents, birds and other common vertebrates. It is convenient but no more reasonable to lump them together as "bats" as it is to call all rodents "rats" or "mice". Bats may live for 10 to 30 years; they have small and few litters each year and frequently cluster in colonies. Bats move vertically and horizontally, and some migrate great distances. Transmission of bat rabies virus from infected mother to uninfected fetus has been documented, suggesting that evidence for vertical transmission of many other viruses may one day be shown. In addition, many bats cluster closely in colonies, suggesting the possibility that viruses may be horizontally transmitted among them. Research on bats has emphasized their biology, not their health, but it is now obvious that studies of diseases of wildlife should include bats so that we may understand and protect them as well as determine the role they play in maintenance of viruses and in zoonotic virus emergence. The ability of bats to coexist with viruses may be the result of rapid control of viral replication early in the immune response. Some evidence suggests a role in all this for interferon, particularly interferon gamma. In sum, as represented by the dramatic examples below, bats may serve as previously unrecognized reservoir hosts of many human, livestock and wildlife pathogens.

Filoviruses: When the first recognized cases of ebola hemorrhagic fever were recognized in Zaire in 1976, the experienced epidemiologists engaged in determining the source of the infection had noted bats roosting in the attic of the cotton factory where many cases occurred, which suggested to them that the factory itself might have been the focus of the prime source of the infections. Given that bats are found in many buildings as well as in cracks in walls, trees, caves, and other locations that provide shelter, and that the first bats found infected with the newly isolated Zaire ebolavirus did not have detectable antibody to that virus, researchers turned to other possible sources, including potted seedlings of weeds and crop plants of 24 species, vertebrates (pigeons, multimammate mice, laboratory mice, and field-collected frogs, toads, geckos, snakes, tortoises), cockroaches, ants, spiders, millipedes, and leafhoppers, as well as bats of three species. With the notable exception of the bats, none appeared to support the replication of Zaire ebolavirus. In both fruit bats and insectivorous bats, virus replicated and circulated at high titer without the bats becoming obviously ill.

Investigators in many countries of Europe, Africa, and North America (Brian R. Amman, Daniel Bausch, Christian Drosten, Jonathan H. Epstein, Pierre B.H. Formenty, Jean-Paul Gonzalez, William B. Karesh, Thomas G. Ksiazek, Eric M. Leroy and Pierre E. Rollin, Robert Swanepoel, Jonathan S. Towner, and many others), collaborating on field work under arduous, sometimes harrowing, conditions, attempted to identify the source of ebolaviruses and Marburg virus in nature, but at first mostly negative data were obtained. Complementary conceptualizations of studies and laboratory expertise provided by others (Thomas Briese, Peter Daszak, W. Ian Lipkin, Stuart T. Nichol, and Sherif R. Zaki) eventually provided definitive results that are useful in understanding the overall situation, as discussed in Chapter 13.

Shortly thereafter, additional cases of hemorrhagic fevers caused by ebolaviruses were identified in Sudan and, eventually, elsewhere, and their etiologic agents identified. In searching for virus reservoirs, the initial suspects were primates, including chimpanzees and gorillas, as well as antelopes that were either found dead or suspected because ebola hemorrhagic fever patients had eaten meat from them. These were dismissed as possible sources of virus because natural hosts are not usually affected by viruses. Suspicion returned to bats, as did the research.

The finding of Marburg virus RNA and IgG antibody in Egyptian rousette fruit bats (*Rousettus aegyptiacus*) in Gabon by Jonathan Towner, Xavier Pourrut, César Albariño, Chimène Nkogue, Brian Bird, Gilda Grard, Thomas Ksiazek, Jean-Paul Gonzalez, Stuart Nichol, and Eric Leroy was the first definitive evidence for the presence of a filovirus in bats, and the first evidence of infection of a filovirus in non-primates. This finding served to stimulate further investigations, which have been fruitful. Many questions remain to be answered: Are bats incidental hosts of filoviruses or are they reservoir hosts? The fact that they do not appear to be affected by filoviruses would argue for the latter. Can bat viruses be amplified in the bat tissue cell lines being developed and then be used to detect even more bat viruses? Because the use of exquisitely specific polymerase chain reaction assays to detect a particular virus precludes detection of RNA from other viruses, virus isolation by amplification in cell cultures might reveal the presence of more viruses than are presently recognized. Given the staggering impact of ebolaviruses on humans in Africa and on African primates, what will be the long-term effect on populations of these harassed, endangered, or threatened animals? Biologists such as William B. Karesh, Peter Daszak and Jonathan Epstein, all of EcoHealth Alliance (formerly "Wildlife Trust") in New York, are involved in field studies intended to answer this and related questions. Will economies in areas where filoviruses are enzootic improve sufficiently to wean inhabitants from the dangerous custom of eating anything containing protein; i.e., will "bush meat" be a thing of the past before the grand parade of wildlife is stilled? Investigating all the issues involved in the spread of filoviruses that lead to epidemic diseases in humans involves studying viruses of bats, transmission to wild primates, and subsequent transmission to humans. This is truly a race against time and against the complexity of the situation.

Nipah paramyxovirus: The outbreak, then epizoodemic, of Nipah virus first recognized in Sengai Nipah village in Malaysia in 1999 is a classic in terms of an emerging disease of previously unknown etiology and source. Of course, once an etiologic agent is identified, defining the source usually follows rather quickly, as it did in this situation. Isolation of Nipah virus from humans by Kaw Bing Chua and Ken (Sai Kit) Lam was followed by identification and pathologic studies of the virus and its effects by Chua, Lam, William J. Bellini, Peter Daniels, Brian Eaton, Hume E. Field, Thomas Ksiazek, Sherif Zaki and numerous others, not only in Malaysia but in Australia and the United States. Antibodies against henipaviruses have been identified in bats of the genus *Pteropus* wherever they have been tested, including Cambodia, Thailand, India, Bangladesh, and Madagascar. Nipah virus was isolated from urine specimens collected underneath variable flying fox (*P. hypomelanus*) roosts in Malaysia and since then from other flying foxes. Once these studies were accomplished a containment and control plan was implemented.

At the outset of this episode, many humans and pigs were seriously affected or died following infection with Nipah virus. Little was understood about the natural history of this virus, because the usual complications accompanying the recognition of an emerging disease were present, and because of certain socio-political complications, so that it was difficult to anticipate how far this virus and disease would move, whether it would somehow be transported through Thailand and Myanmar to China and perhaps to other countries of Asia, what specific treatments could be applied to patients, whether portions of the human population other than adults would become infected, and even whether it could be stopped at all. The impact of the virus and its complications on the local economy was one consideration but the psychological impact on people in the entire area was also profound, as is usual whenever and wherever an epidemic of any disease is first identified.

Nipah virus is closely related to Hendra virus of Australia, and Hendra virus had been detected in fruit bats, so fruit bats were obvious targets for virus detection efforts. Nipah virus was soon detected in fruit bats, but it was the ecologic characteristics of areas near pig farms that proved significant.

The rapid expansion of pig farming, as profitable a business in Malaysia as it is elsewhere, led to clearing of forested land that had long been used as roosting sites for fruit bats. However, where hillocks existed, many of the trees were not cleared, leaving islands with clusters of trees suitable as fruit bat habitats, some of which were in close proximity to the pig farms. Bats then had easy access to the foods fed to the pigs and therefore, from time to time, came into contact with the pigs; some bats even were eaten by those pigs. Thus, Nipah virus of bats became Nipah virus of pigs and of pig farmers.

Malaysia comprises a mélange of religious and ethnic groups, including Muslims, who do not eat pork; many of them are in the Malaysian military. When Malaysian military personnel were sent to the affected areas to reduce the pig populations, they were exposed to the blood of Nipah virus-infected pigs; Muslim soldiers also became infected. It did not take long to develop an epidemiologic picture of this disease and its infectious potential. After discussions, it was determined that using a combination of depopulation of pigs, public education, and governmental oversight, the epizoodemic could be ended. It was, but not before 258 people (mostly pig farm workers) developed encephalitis, 104 of whom died, and 1 million pigs had been slaughtered. Subsequent outbreaks of this disease in India and Bangladesh have been associated with fruit bats under somewhat different circumstances.

Lin-fa Wang and associates at the Australian Animal Health Laboratories in Geelong have made noteworthy progress in development of diagnostic systems, including bat cell line production, and in increasing our understanding of the molecular mechanisms by which Nipah virus and related henipaviruses infect, circulate and persist in nature.

It is clear by now that transmission of viruses, whether by arthropods, rodents, or bats, is unique and dependent on the complexity of the peculiarities of the natural cycles of the virus. This is what makes epidemiology so challenging but also so important and, in a peculiar way, entertaining, if sometimes a bit frustrating.

Sexual transmission of Marburg virus and Zika virus, an arbovirus; are these common mechanisms or oddities?

Months after the original Marburg disease epidemic, a woman whose husband had been one of the original patients but who had completely recovered from his illness was admitted to hospital. Husband and wife were confirmed to have had infections with the same virus. It is now thought that she acquired it through sexual intercourse with her husband, whose sperm was subsequently shown to be infected with the virus responsible for the outbreak.

Isolated in 1947 from a febrile rhesus monkey (*Macaca mulatta*) captured in the Zika Forest near Entebbe, Uganda, Zika flavivirus had, until recently, also been isolated only from mosquitoes in Africa and from a scant few laboratory workers who had been infected accidentally. Antibody to this virus, however, has been found in humans not only in Africa but in Asia. Described as causing an illness presenting with fever and rash, this virus is one of many flaviviruses and other viruses that had been essentially ignored, so that resources could be expended on more pressing public health concerns. In 2007, however, an outbreak of non-hospitalizable illness characterized by rash, conjunctivitis and arthralgia had occurred among residents of Yap Island, Federated States of Micronesia, some 1,500 km (850 mi.) east of Mindanao in the Philippines. It has now been estimated that nearly 75% of island residents older than 3 years of age had been infected, establishing this as the first recognized transmission of Zika virus other than in Africa and Asia.

Sexual transmission of Zika virus recently occurred. During a 2008 mosquito-sampling project in southeastern Senegal, two United States scientists contracted Zika virus infections. Epidemiologic evidence suggests that the infections were acquired in Senegal, rather than elsewhere on their journey home. Irrespective of place of acquisition, both patients became ill 6–9 days after their return to the United States. Both experienced signs and symptoms consisting of swollen ankles, maculopapular rash on the toso, extreme fatigue and headache but no fever. The day after the onset of symptoms, one of these patients experienced the same symptoms plus light-headedness and chills, wrist and ankle arthalgia, and symptoms of prostatitis (perineal pain and mild dysuria), nonetheless remaining afebrile. Fatigue and rash decreased the following day, with only residual wrist arthralgia, headache, and prostatic symptoms persisting. On the third day after onset, two aphthous ulcers appeared on his lip and the next day he and his wife observed signs of hematospermia (red–brown fluid in his ejaculate) that lasted for four days. Both patients recovered uneventfully but the wife of the patient who had had prostatic symptoms and hematospermia developed much the same set of clinical signs and symptoms, also without fever, the same day that she and her husband observed his hematospermia.

Acute-phase and convalescent-phase serum samples were obtained from the three patients; all three were shown by multiple assays to have seroconverted to Zika flavivirus. Virus isolation attempts were unsuccessful, as were reverse transcription PCR assays with multiple sets of primers. The conclusions were that: (1) all three patients had experienced Zika virus infections; (2) one of the two patients who had been in Senegal also had transmitted this arbovirus to his wife after his return home; and (3) direct contact was the transmission route, most likely as a sexually transmitted infection.

Thus another mode of transmission of a virus that until now was thought to be only arthropod-borne has been documented. Because of the rarity of reports of sexual transmission of arboviruses between humans, it is unlikely that this mode of infection is epidemiologically important for arboviruses but the publication describing this experience adds to the extensive literature on sexual transmission of infectious agents, including viruses.

CHAPTER 15

Taxonomy leading to specialization in arbovirology

What has happened to arbovirology? Where did it go? Did it go? The short answers to the last two questions are "nowhere" and "no". Arbovirology has not disappeared. Because arboviruses are not members of a single family or other specific taxonomic group, expertise in arbovirology, with some notable exceptions, now is divided into its constituent parts, or at least into most of its constituent parts: flavivirologists, togavirologists, rhabdovirologists, orbivirologists, and so on. Other scientists have focused on techniques applicable to many viruses. As a case in point, electron microscopic examination of viruses now is used as one of many diagnostic tools. Many laboratories have electron microscopists on staff, but the exquisite expertise needed to authoritatively describe electron microscopic findings remains in the hands of a relatively few eminent experts who are interested in many viruses but usually focus on just a few of them, or only on pathogenesis, or only on improving techniques. In 1961 Telford Work, at the time still at the Rockefeller Foundation, published a paper in which he said, "We are perhaps where the map makers were three centuries ago, before the chronometer made possible the precise determination of longitude. Even though the celestial constellations had been known and used by seafarers from before the time of Copernicus, the invention and intelligent use of the chronometer was necessary to determine accurately a point on the globe to which a captain could sail his ship."

Work went on to suggest that because Casals had already formed many viruses into constellations ("groups"), we needed to develop techniques and understanding of basic mechanisms which will enable us to navigate our laboratory and field investigations toward more certain objectives. He surmised that the points to be plotted will eventually form the chart for more successful diagnosis, treatment, control, and prevention of the plethora of new arthropod-borne virus infections which we can now see not only as humanitarian, but also as economic, developmental, and medical problems in the tropics.

Clearly the obvious problems (putting together a community of like-minded investigators, finding viruses, determining their interrelationships, developing research tools, understanding the epidemiologies of these viruses, controlling disease outbreaks, etc.) have multiplied since then but there is more to do and proportionately less funding with which to do it. Better techniques are available, and our understanding of basic mechanisms of virus replication and of diseases has improved considerably. Still, there is much work to be done if we are to predict disease outbreaks and prevent illnesses, so it is critical that studies of arboviruses be continued, no matter what those studies are called.

Robert B. Tesh: Only a few laboratories conduct antigenic and serologic studies; these include the World Reference Center of Emerging Viruses and Arboviruses at the University of Texas Medical Branch at Galveston. Directed by Robert B. Tesh, and aided by Amelia Travassos da Rosa and their colleagues, and by visiting scientists and trainees, its work continues along the same path begun by Shope, Tesh and their predecessors at the Rockefeller Foundation, beginning in 1928. Work at that superb resource in Texas continues to follow the philosophies and practices that came from the Yale Arbovirus Research Unit when then-Director Robert Shope and Tesh moved from there in 1995, taking with them the huge collection of viruses and serum samples they and their predecessors had accumulated. Following the death of Shope, Tesh continues to expand that collection. Today, Tesh, one of the "true believers" in arbovirology, fully understands its remarkable history and its usefulness and proceeds from there, superimposing his interest and training in medicine to conceive and design experimental inquiries.

As are so many of the luminaries of arbovirology, Tesh is a physician. He obtained a B.S. degree in Zoology from Franklin and Marshall College, an M.D. degree from Jefferson Medical College, did an internship at San Francisco General Hospital, was a resident in pediatrics at Gorgas Hospital in the Canal Zone, a Peace Corps physician in Recife, Brazil, an NIH a post-doctoral Fellow at Tulane University School of Medicine, and head of the Epidemiology Section at the NIH Middle American Research Unit in the Canal Zone. Somehow he found time to fit in a Master of Science in epidemiology degree from Tulane University. He was a staff member of NIH's Pacific Research Station in Honolulu, working with Leon Rosen, and then moved to Yale University.

From intrathoracically injecting sandflies, to studies of transovarial transmission of viruses, to pathogenesis of viral infections, his studies have been meticulous and seminal, shaping our approaches to research and our views of viral pathology. In 1995, Tesh and Shope moved to Galveston, Texas, to the University of Texas Medical Branch. Tesh's primary research interests include the epidemiology and pathogenesis of arboviruses and hemorrhagic fever viruses. That covers a wide range of possible topics, but his emphasis remains on human illnesses.

Of all the living arbovirologists, it seems fair to say that Tesh is the least narrowly focused. With others, of course, he has published on a dizzying array of arboviruses and other viruses: studied vesiculoviruses (family *Rhabdoviridae,* genus *Vesiculovirus*) and their vectors in many countries; studied the biology and vectorial capacity of phlebotomine flies as well as the phleboviruses (family *Bunyaviridae,* genus *Phlebovirus*) and orbiviruses (family *Reoviridae,* genus *Orbivirus*) isolated from them, many of which were new to science; studies insect densoviruses (family *Parvoviridae,* subfamily *Densovirinae,* genus *Brevidensovirus*); determined the occurrence of transovarial transmission of California serogroup bunyaviruses, dengue, Japanese encephalitis and yellow fever flaviviruses, and Toscana phlebovirus; and determined the prevalence of antibodies to alphaviruses in southeast Asia and certain Pacific islands. He also investigated an epidemic of Ross River alphavirus in American Samoa; characterized Ockelbo alphavirus disease in Sweden; identified newly recognized coltiviruses (family *Reoviridae,* genus *Coltivirus*) in Indonesia; conducted numerous detailed investigations of Venezuelan equine encephalitis and Mayaro alphaviruses and Oropouche orthobunyavirus; discovered new hantaviruses and arenaviruses and worked on studies of the pathogenetic progression of these viruses in their rodent hosts and in humans. Tesh found St. Louis encephalitis flavivirus in Argentina; characterized the geographic distribution of Japanese encephalitis flavivirus genotypes and the molecular lineages of chikungunya and o'nyong-nyong alphaviruses, as well as the geographic distributions of North Central and South American subtypes and genotypes of eastern equine encephalitis alphavirus. He determined the antigenic relationship of Rift Valley fever virus with other phleboviruses and determined the relationships between the orthomyxoviruses (genus *Thogotovirus*). Tesh conducted important experimental infections and pathological studies of numerous viruses, including West Nile and yellow fever flaviviruses and monkeypox virus (family *Poxviridae,* subfamily *Chordopoxvirinae,* genus *Orthopoxvirus*); and developed improved diagnostics. All of this was done with an obvious preference for understanding the source, the virus, the clinical illness, and the pathologic consequences of virus infections. His extensive expertise and viral polymathic skills are the result not only of his intelligence and hard work but of his field and laboratory experiences with mentors such as Leon Rosen and Robert Shope, as well as his own individual character traits (persistence, ability to focus, determination to expose the unknown, outspokenness, honesty).

An excellent writer and editor, Tesh has published more than 300 detailed papers and more than 30 book chapters. His work is indispensable and, along with his colleagues, he has set standards for the rest of us and devised models for our understanding of the ecology of many important, exotic and highly pathogenic viruses. His laboratory is the source, usually the sole source, of reagents from the World Reference Center, which he directs. A reviewer for many journals, a helpful member of various editorial boards, a popular guest lecturer, and a virological renaissance guy, Tesh continues to be a valuable source of support for arbovirologists everywhere. Still, the shrinking funding for research of this kind, no matter how valuable its contributions, likely will eventually mean the end of that living museum, that irreplaceable reference resource, and someday in the future someone inevitably will ask "Why did we not save all that?".

Figure 135. James Wayne LeDuc (1945 -)
(image courtesy of James LeDuc)

A remarkable assemblage of top virologists now works in the Galveston laboratories. With considerable foresight and scientific and administrative acumen, David H. Walker, former post-doctoral trainee with Frederick Murphy at CDC, physician and Chair of the Department of Pathology and Director of the Center for Biodefense and Emerging Infectious Diseases has attracted many of the most experienced, innovative, accomplished and brightest bulbs in the lamp of science. Among them have been Tesh, C.J. Peters, Frederick Murphy, Thomas G. Ksiazek, Alan D.T. Barrett, James W. Leduc (Figure 135), Stephen Higgs, John C. Morrill, Charles F. Fulhorst, Mary

L. Milazzo, Slobodan Paessler, Joan B. Geisbert, Thomas W. Geisbert and others. In concert, this team constitutes what now may well be the greatest collection of arbovirologists and other virologists in the world, comprising a national and international resource available in case of a need for epidemic response, even at the highest levels of hazard, no matter the virus, no matter the location.

Thomas G. Ksiazek: Ksiazek is able to provide clinical, epidemiological, virological, ecological or basically any other relevant expertise called for. Having been awarded undergraduate and doctorate of veterinary medicine degrees at Kansas State University, Ksiazek obtained a Master's degree from the University of Wisconsin with Thomas Yuill, studying viremias and antibody responses to La Crosse virus in gray squirrels *(Sciurus carolinensis)* and eastern chipmunks *(Tamias striatus)*. After that, he obtained a Ph.D. at the School of Public Health, University of California, working with James Hardy and William Reeves and then moved to United States Army Medical Research Institute of Infectious Diseases, Frederick, Maryland. From there he moved to the United States Centers for Disease Control and Prevention in Atlanta, where he succeeded C.J. Peters as Chief of the Special Pathogens Branch. Now at the University of Texas Medical Branch at Galveston, Ksiazek has accumulated experiences world-wide, having had long-term assignments in Egypt, Indonesia, and Taiwan and outbreak experience in Asia, Africa, and South America, in addition to his experiences in North America. Along the way, Ksiazek has been involved in the discoveries of the viruses that cause hantavirus pulmonary syndrome, Nipah encephalitis, severe acute respiratory syndrome, Venezuelan hemorrhagic fever, Bundabugyo hemorrhagic fever and pathogens causing other lethal diseases. He has investigated Rift Valley fever and influenzavirus A H1N1 outbreaks, has written and consulted on a wide variety of topics of interest to virologists working with high containment facilities, and is, simply put, one of the very few people who can do everything needed and solve nearly every virological or epidemiological problem. Rather than classifying him as an arbovirologist, Ksiazek might better be considered simply a virologist, but he began his infectious diseases career as an arbovirologist and maintains a strong interest and participates in all things arbovirological.

Specific tools applied to wide-ranging problems: Most virology laboratories now depend on molecular tools for their diagnostic needs. The motives are that molecular techniques have been improved and made more readily available than in the past, genotypic characterization is the only specific way in which a virus can be identified with exactness, and determining genotype is the way in which epidemiologic origin and spread can be followed. Superb molecular biologists, such as Scott C. Weaver at the Galveston laboratories, have shown the way to the future by incorporating the biology of viruses in the description of viruses. Weaver's understanding and appreciation of arbovirologic history have been very helpful, not only to him but to others in our attempts to comprehend the natural cycles of viruses and eventually to prevent or control arbovirus diseases. He is an exemplar of the difference between molecular chemists and molecular biologists. All are highly skilled but some of the former seem to me to be more focused on the results than on the meaning of the results, although this subset grows smaller as time wears on.

The use of commercial "kits" and highly specific tools yielding highly specific results does have drawbacks. For example, when determining whether a particular virus is in a sample from a particular host, such as a bat, most specific and sensitive polymerase chain reaction assays will reveal only the presence of that particular virus, missing the presence of other, even closely related, viruses. This means that researchers must make additional collections and test new samples for other viruses. Fortunately, newer techniques using degenerate primers, mixtures of primers with similar sequences, are useful in identifying previously unrecognized nucleic acid sequences that are similar to nucleic acid sequences of known viruses. Their utility lies in their lack of absolute specificity. Many other novel and innovative methods have been and are being developed in numerous laboratories, brilliantly so by Lipkin and Briese at Columbia University in New York City.

When kits make testing easier than in the past or make virus discovery possible when it had not been, and when genomics is a goal of modern virology, as it should be, the little picture can get lost in the big picture. For those of us interested in studying diseases of humans, livestock, and wildlife, "the field is the patient". Without continuous studies of naturally occurring viruses where they naturally occur (enteroviruses in diapers or in sewer systems, hantaviruses in rodents, orphioviruses in tulips, filoviruses in bats, La Crosse virus in chipmunks and mosquitoes, Colorado tick fever virus in ticks, yellow fever virus in monkeys, etc.), all we can have are viruses that have been stored in freezers, to be studied completely out of context. Yes, we can know a great deal about a particular virus, but we will not know where it fits in the great jigsaw puzzle that is its natural history.

Nonetheless, the constraints caused by lack of funding (or, perhaps, misdirected funding) are a seemingly uncontrollable practical problem for virologists, as for everyone else. In times past, universities, foundations, and other organizations provided funds to outstanding scientists for research. There was little competition for such funds because few people were competing. In those naïve days, one wrote a letter asking for a small amount of money for a laboratory need or for a trip to a meeting and, if the request was approved, a check was written. In addition, studies of yellow fever, Nairobi sheep disease, African horse sickness and other classic diseases were really studies of the easiest diseases to study. These are, of course, important and important diseases always will and should be studied immediately. However, the viruses that cause them are not difficult to isolate or to identify, partially because techniques were developed relatively quickly and partially because of the seminal contributions by innovative investigators. The virologic pioneers did not have the tools that are available today; they relied on observation, knowledge, innovation, intuition and a great deal of hard work. Today diseases are practically thrust upon us and outbreaks or epidemics are recognized promptly, reported widely (c.f. "ProMED-mail"), and addressed as soon as possible. As the inevitable results of human population expansion occur and the attendant impacts on habitats or ecosystems follow, there will be more epidemics and more viruses to study, resulting in sadness for many and job security for some.

Today, governmental organizations hold the combination to the safe and what are advocated as national priorities are key to obtaining funding. Committees, sometimes huge committees, review grant proposals and make their decisions based on suggested recommendations by invited and ostensibly unbiased and impartial reviewers. Most often this system works well but, when it does not, an innovative and potentially valuable study is unfunded and, therefore, undone. Competition for funding undercuts or at least negatively influences the natural collegiality of scientists, such that some communications are withheld, data not shared, and simultaneous discoveries not recognized, so that investigators are, in effect, rewarded for working in greater isolation, rather than in conjunction. In many ways, this takes us backwards 100 years or more and may be putting the greater population at increased and avoidable risk.

A large number of investigators still pursue studies of arboviruses, but emphasis and funding are placed on immediate responses to disease outbreaks. Arboviruses are still with us, causing illnesses and deaths, moving hither and yon (easier these days), and existing in places we have not yet disturbed or destroyed. The lack of sufficient field work creates an artificial perspective among laboratory researchers. The lack of sufficient historical knowledge and laboratory experience makes for a limited perspective. Fortunately, some younger virologists "get it" and will continue along the path laid down by our predecessors. It is they, after all, who will expand that to the next horizon.

One major contribution of arbovirology to our understanding of disease spread has been the relatively recent recognition that zoonotics comprise the majority of newly emerging diseases. Arbovirologists, of course, have known for many years that arboviruses are found in cycles that include arthropods and vertebrates, two very different hosts. Such a capacity on the part of a virus requires that the virus replicate in hosts that have very different core temperatures, cellular components, and general biological peculiarities. The realization that zoonotic viruses, whether arthropod-borne or not, must somehow be able to "jump" between very different sorts of hosts (bats to humans, horses, pigs, and civets; ticks to people and deer; migrating waterfowl (somehow) to chickens and then to people; mosquitoes to frogs; rodents to people; and so on. The permutations and combinations appear to be endless. The scientific community now seems to have rediscovered the more than 70 years' data vis-à-vis yellow fever and other arboviruses and has become more focused not only on virus discovery, which is not difficult when people, pigs or horses are dying, but on epidemiology, natural cycles, and host-switching. Workshops and entire books containing data and perspectives on the occurrence and possible mechanisms of cross-species transmission have been devoted to the subject.

What is more, by rather superficially and later much more rigorously characterizing the habitat where arboviruses were found, arbovirologists have contributed to our understanding of the indirect and direct effects of climatologic events on virus transmission. The effects of global climate changes, trophic cascades, changes in rainfall patterns, and human effects on habitats (drilling, grading, road building, conversion of farmland to housing units, dams, and more) finally have been recognized as necessary for study in order that diseases can be prevented from emerging and spreading. A recent and long overdue innovation is the "One Health Initiative" [http://onehealthinitiative.com/]. The One Health Initiative is intended to build collaborative efforts among physicians, veterinarians, osteopaths, dentists, nurses, and other health and environmentally related disciplines, including the American Medical Association, American Veterinary Medical Association, the American Society of Tropical Medicine and Hygiene, the CDC, the USDA, and the United States National Environmental Health Association. Many prominent scientists, physicians, and veterinarians worldwide have endorsed the initiative of this growing organization and movement. In view of the recognition that about 70% of emerging or re-emerging infections are zoonotics, it is imperative that workers in human and veterinary medical practices speak with each other and share observations and insights. A dead cow (bovid, moose, whale, or other) might indicate only an accident or a singular peculiarity, but it might also be the indicator case of a zoonotic epidemic. By the very nature of arbovirology, this recognition is not news. One of the organizers and visionary enthusiasts of the One Health Initiative has been Thomas Monath, an arbovirologist if there ever has been one.

The most recent examples of arbovirus emergence and discovery always gain prominence in the scientific literature and sometimes are slipped into the popular press as well. For example, during late summer 2001 in Austria, a series of deaths occurred in birds of several species, and, because of the similarities with the initial outbreak of West Nile virus in the United States two years previously, Weissenböck, Kolodziejek, Url, Lussy, Rebel-Bauder and Nowotny conducted routine necropsies of the dead birds and pathology and immunohistology of the dead birds. The results suggested a West Nile virus infection, but subsequent identification and partial characterization of virus isolates from the birds did not support that preliminary diagnosis. The isolates exhibited 97% identity to Usutu virus, a mosquito-borne flavivirus of the Japanese encephalitis virus complex. Usutu virus had been isolated from mosquitoes in South Africa in 1959 by Bruce McIntosh and isolated by others from mosquitoes, birds and a rodent in other countries of Africa. Usutu virus had been associated with a febrile rash syndrome in a human in the Central Africa Republic but had never been associated with fatal disease in vertebrates. The virus has now been isolated from birds in Hungary (2005) and Switzerland (2006) and likely will spread to other countries in Europe. Indeed, Buckley et al. have obtained serologic evidence that Usutu virus has infected birds in the United Kingdom. In all, no great damage thus far, but it is disturbing that Usutu and other viruses could establish themselves far from their apparent origins and that they can do so imperceptibly, at least at first. Unless a virus kills its first vertebrate host in the country it invades, the index case almost certainly will be missed. In fact, even if it does kill that first vertebrate host, it is unlikely to be detected.

In April 2010, a severe outbreak of duck viral infection, with "egg drop" (decreased egg production), feed uptake decline, and ovary-oviduct disease spread through major duck-producing regions in eastern China. A virus was isolated from affected ducks and genomic sequencing of the virus showed that it is closely related to Tembusu virus (a mosquito-borne, Ntaya group flavivirus of no previously recognized significance), with 87% to 91% nucleotide identity of the partial E (envelope) proteins to that of Tembusu virus and 72% of the entire genome coding sequence with Bagaza virus, the most closely related flavivirus with an entirely sequenced genome and also a flavivirus of no previously recognized significance. Named Baiyangdian virus, the investigators fulfilled Koch's postulates and warned that this virus could have disastrous effects on Chinese and other duck-producing areas.

Later in 2010, Agüero and co-workers reported that an unusually high number of wild game birds (partridges and pheasants) had died in Cádiz in southwestern Spain and that molecular detection and virus isolation revealed flavivirus infections in the birds. Sequence analysis identified the causative agent as Bagaza virus, a flavivirus with a known distribution that includes sub-Saharan Africa and India.

The extension of the range of West Nile virus to the Americas, Japanese encephalitis in Australia, Usutu virus in Europe, Baiyangdian virus in China, and Bagaza virus in Spain, each associated with a disease of some sort, and each a flavivirus, may indicate that changes in climate, increased travel, better diagnostic tools, or more assiduous clinical observations have brought these viruses to our attention.

It is not only flaviviruses that have spread and become apparent. A newly recognized phlebovirus (family *Bunyaviridae*) was found in China in 2009. Increased and improved surveillance for acute febrile illnesses in that huge and varied country revealed the existence of severe fever with thrombocytopenia syndrome, a life-threatening illness. By inoculation of cell culture with blood samples from patients meeting a case definition the virus was isolated and its RNA detected by PCR. Characterizing the virus by electron microscopy and its RNA by nucleic acid sequencing and using enzyme-linked immunosorbent assay, indirect immunofluorescence assay and neutralization testing to detect and ascertain virus-specific antibody in patients' serum samples; a clear assessment of the epidemiology of this disease has not been obtained. The causative virus, awkwardly named severe fever with thrombocytopenia syndrome virus, was isolated from patients with fever, thrombocytopenia, leukocytopenia, and multiorgan dysfunction. Evidence for the presence of viral RNA or of antibody to the virus was detected in 171 patients from six provinces. Serologic assays revealed a virus-specific immune response in all 35 pairs of serum samples collected from patients during the acute and convalescent phases of the illness. The virus and disease have now been found in Japan and South Korea.

The very recent discovery of an apparently new arboviral disease in Western Europe exemplifies the continuing emergence of viruses from zoonotic sources. In November 2011 farmers in Schmallenberg, Germany, noticed that some of their dairy cows were febrile and were producing less milk than normally. Within two months the virus causing this illness was isolated by investigators at the Friedrich-Loeffler-Institute and provisionally named Schmallenberg virus. The illness that began to be detected in cattle and goats on farms in Germany has spread to Belgium, the Czech Republic, England, Estonia, Ireland, Finland, France, Italy, Luxembourg, Netherlands, Norway, Spain, and Sweden. Adult cows are affected, and stillbirths and birth defects have been observed in calves, lambs, and newborn goats. In some herds 20% to 50% of lambs have congenital malformations, including hydranencephaly and scoliosis; most are born dead.

The virus has been shown to be an orthobunyavirus (large, medium, and small circular RNAs comprise their genomes) of the Simbu serogroup; these viruses are mainly transmitted by culicoids and mosquitoes and are known to infect ruminants. At first Schmallenberg virus was suspected to be closely related to Akabane virus, discovered in Japan by Akira Oya in 1965, but also found in Australia and Kenya. With data available at present, it appears that Schmallenberg virus is a reassortant of the Simbu serogroup viruses Shamonda (S and L segments) and Sathuperi (M segment) viruses. Shamonda virus was first isolated from cattle and culicoids in Nigeria and from sentinel cattle and culicoids in Japan; Sathuperi virus was first isolated from mosquitoes in India, then from cattle in Nigeria.

Because the affected livestock in Germany were first observed in autumn of 2011, it is likely that infections had occurred in the summer but fetuses that were exposed to the virus in utero were not born until several months later. The first cases of lambs with congenital malformations such as hydranencephaly and scoliosis appeared before the end of the year. Additional cases were diagnosed in cattle in 2012, likely the result of infection of the fetuses in autumn 2011 and born in February and March 2012.

Evidence thus far indicates that *Culicoides obsoletus* is the principal vector of this teratogenic virus. As of yet, no human illnesses have been attributed to Schmallenberg virus, even though culicoids feed on humans, albeit less often than do mosquitoes. Still, many questions come immediately to mind: Surveillance of culicoids for bluetongue viruses has been on-going for many years in Europe. If the vector is shown to be a culicoid, how could this virus have been in Europe without having been found before now? Of immediate and vital importance is the determination of the origin of this virus. Has it been in Europe for many years? Was it recently introduced? Was the introduction unintentional? Because Schmallenberg virus contains an RNA segment of Shamonda virus, which was not known to occur in Europe, are current arbovirus surveillance procedures in Europe adequate? It is safe to assume that further epidemiologic studies will be done and will answer these and other questions. These examples from recent times emphasize the on-going nature of arboviral amplification. It is not expected that this evolutionary progression will end any time soon.

A very few rhetorical questions:

How many arboviruses and hemorrhagic fever viruses have yet to be discovered? Mora et al. have estimated that in addition to the 1.2 million species of recognized eukaryotes, another ~6.5 million species (±1.3 million S.E.) may be sharing our plant, of which ~2.2 million (±0.18 million S.E.) are marine. In other words, only 14% of existing life forms on earth and only 9% of oceanic life forms are known at this time. In view of the fact that individuals of each eukaryotic species have been shown to be infected with at least one virus, are we not to expect that thousands, perhaps millions, more viruses could be found, if we looked?

How quickly do RNA viruses, with no obvious capacity to proof-read their replication, mutate, survive, and amplify as competent pathogens?

How many more hectares of land can be cleared and other natural areas drilled, cultivated with plants of invasive species, used to provide forage for livestock, or cemented over before we stumble across yet another new arboviral or other pathogen or they stumble across us and our livestock? Because we are monumentally and irreversibly altering former natural areas, are dependent on oil and other extractive industries (some of which make a mess of the environment), because we require increasing amounts of food for an increasing human population, and because we have not allocated sufficient resources to properly determine "what is out there", are we not likely to have the answers to these questions come knocking on our doors? The answers to these questions are critical to both human and veterinary medicine and to virology and epidemiology as important, even life-saving, fields of study.

Thousands of viruses have been detected in sea water, some of which have been partially identified, most of which have not. Their origins and significances are unknown, but these viruses are numerous. When Rockefeller Foundation investigators went looking for yellow fever virus, they inadvertently discovered many scores of other arboviruses as well. And when any competent investigator today examines tissues from people with infectious diseases, by polymerase chain reaction, virus isolation, electron microscopy, or other methods, or conducts serologic surveys, processes fleas from sea mammals, studies road kill on Amazon forest highways, collects ticks and blood from polar bears (obtaining the convalescent sample is the trick), bleeds people with rashes or small mammals that were minding their own business, takes throat swabs from zoo animals or coughing dogs, or otherwise engages in the business of virus detection, they almost always find something. What they find is not usually as important as that they find something. Who doubts that we have merely made a deep scratch in the surface of viral detection and that there is a world of undiscovered viruses? Should Hollywood write and film the movie and just fill in the blanks later? More practically, will an ebolavirus cause an epizootic in the zoo of a large city? Will coronaviruses adapt to a new host and be carried to your neighborhood? Will a hantavirus switch hosts and begin to kill cattle? Will Rift Valley fever strike in Iowa or Brazil or Germany or China or Australia? Nightmare scenarios are easy to devise, it is reality that is difficult to predict, so we should be prepared for anything; an impossibility.

The days in which those yellow fever investigators cast their wide nets are no more, at least for the time being, or until the administrators who hold the purse strings realize what an excellent and useful endeavor that was – work no longer likely in these days of impoverished governments. Emphasis is now only on pathogens, not on finding the many more viruses that surely exist in the wild, which is not in the least unreasonable at this time and under these economic conditions. Should we spend valuable and shrinking resources to look for an unknown and probably irrelevant virus when we have to deal with human immunodeficiency virus, chlamydia, tubercle bacilli, malarial parasites, multiply antibiotic resistant bacteria, *E. coli* 0157:H7, noroviruses, hepatitis viruses, Lyme disease borrelia, and a laundry list of other pathogens we know are important? That's a political question, not a scientific one. Bat conservationists are overly protective (they don't think so) of bats, and there is a staggering lack of information about bat health and about the pathogens with which they might be infected and which they might be transmitting. Impediments other than short-sighted administrators and funding shortages also stand in the way, but the fact is that we no longer actively look for viruses as we did in the past. That cannot be a good thing. It is clear that studies of arboviruses and hemorrhagic fever viruses must continue to depend on collecting fresh material, not only from people during epidemics or outbreaks and from peridomestic vertebrates. From such a continuing flow will come fascinating viruses from which we will continue to learn. As samples accumulate and data are generated, we surely will accumulate information useful in understanding the diseases, the relationships of the viruses and the genetics of these charming and fascinating, if sometimes deadly little beasties.

What must be done under current conditions is what should have been done decades ago: (1) We must develop a long-term and comprehensive plan to study arboviruses, rodent-borne viruses, and bat-borne viruses. This would include field studies as well as laboratory studies, with first-rate molecular biological expertise, first-rate field workers and first-rate epidemiologists involved and committed. Lack of funding for field studies and for training of young field workers is a problem to surmount. (2) Areas undergoing rapid population, housing, and agricultural changes should be a first priority for pre-emptive studies. Many areas that have undergone rapid human population expansion have shown sad and dangerous results. It is illogical to assume that the human population of this planet can continue to grow as it has and still be supported in terms of foodstuff, energy, clean air, and clean water. Infectious diseases will continue to cast a specter over humans and over our livestock and other agricultural needs. (3) The layman's view of a museum is that it is a dusty old place, one which exhibits the carcasses of animals which have been dead for decades. Reference laboratories, often viewed as museums, as static collections, are anything but that. They are epidemiologically useful as sources of stored materials to be compared with recently collected materials. Funding for these critical collections needs to be readjusted to fit the needs. Administrators and even scientists should be educated to understand the value of reference collections. (4) We must improve the ease with which reagents can be safely exchanged among research laboratories. This will require changes in laws and regulations. (5) Training of microbiology students must continue to improve so that additional, even improved, diagnostic tools will become available to meet the challenges we surely will face in the future. (6) We should encourage laboratory research on pathology caused by viruses and on studies of pathogenetic mechanisms (for development of preventatives). If we are not prepared to plan for the future, we will awaken each day to face new and increasing numbers of disease problems. As Tom Monath has suggested, the consequences of inaction are continued surprises: limited capacity for surveillance; reliance on humans, livestock, wild animals and crops to serve as disease sentinels; finding only what we look for; accumulation of incomplete information on disease ecology; static reference and reagent collections; and the appearance of even more regulations and restrictions on international collaborations. Lack of action is at our own peril.

CHAPTER 16

Some personal recollections of people and travels

This book is a history, not *the* history of arbovirology, because it contains not only facts but also my own perceptions. Following are a few brief accounts of experiences I have had during my nearly 50 years in arbovirology. They are included not as a recruitment tool (although I hope that some might consider moving from what they are doing to the exciting field of viral epidemiology) but simply for enjoyment. I hope each illustrates the surprising complications, intellectual challenges, unexpected friendships, and pure joy of being an arbovirologist.

Telford Hindley Work: In 1964, as the person largely accountable for the federal response to disease discoveries, Work, then at CDC, directed and participated in epidemiologic investigations of clusters and outbreaks of La Crosse virus infections in many Midwestern states. Born in California, Work enjoyed outdoor activities and eventually attended Stanford University as a Biological Sciences major. While there he published his first scientific paper, "The nest life of the turkey vulture". Continuing his interest in wildlife, he focused on birds of an endangered species, the California condor (*Gymnogyps californianus*), for which he held a warm spot in his heart for the rest of his life. It was through his efforts and the efforts of others that that bird has been rescued from extinction.

Work attended Stanford University Medical School and, graduating in 1946, went on active duty with the United States Navy. His first assignment was aboard an oil tanker that took him to the Persian Gulf, Sri Lanka, and Japan, through the Suez Canal to the east coast of New York and from Venezuela to Cuba. Released from military service, he pursued an interest in tropical medicine and exotic diseases, attempting to become involved in epidemiologic studies, uniquely considering, as he put it, "the population as the patient". After meeting and at the urging of Hugh Hollingsworth Smith, a virologist at the Rockefeller Foundation who had played a significant role in developing the yellow fever vaccine, Work earned a doctorate in Tropical Medicine and Hygiene at the London School of Hygiene and Tropical Medicine and then spent two years with Sir Philip Manson-Bahr in Fiji studying various aspects of the epidemiology of filariasis and, as he put it, "learning to think like a mosquito". Never one to avoid new and challenging experiences, Work then accepted a Rockefeller Foundation fellowship to study at Johns Hopkins University School of Hygiene and Public Health, receiving a Master of Public Health degree in 1952 and then an appointment to the Rockefeller Foundation staff. Five months later he was assigned to work with Richard M. Taylor at the Naval Medical Research Unit 3 in Cairo.

After he, Herbert Hurlbut, and Richard Taylor had isolated West Nile virus from birds in the Nile River delta, helped to formulate the role of wild birds in the ecology and distribution of this virus, isolated Sindbis virus from mosquitoes, and searched for yellow fever virus in Sudan, Work was transferred to the Rockefeller Foundation's Virus Research Institute in Poona (now Pune), India. Those laboratories developed C6/36 (*Aedes albopictus*) cells for use in what have become essential to studies of arboviruses, studied Jamshedpour fever (caused by hepatitis E virus), documented the first recognized outbreak of

Reyes syndrome and discovered the presence of Japanese encephalitis in southern India. Work and team members recognized and participated in the description of Kyasanur Forest disease and the identification of the virus that causes it. With the noted entomologist Harold Trapido he described natural infections of humans and monkeys and demonstrated that ticks of the genus *Haemaphysalis* transmitted the virus. Efforts and findings by their Indian colleagues R. L. Rao, M.G. Varma, D.P. Murthy, Pravin N. Bhatt (Figure 136), Keerti Shah and others were crucial to the success of these studies.

Figure 136. Pravin Nanabhai Bhatt (1923 -)
(image courtesy of Pravin Bhatt)

Returning to the New York laboratories in 1962, Work helped Taylor establish the Arbovirus Information Exchange, soon becoming its editor. Work later was appointed head of the Virology Section of the United States Centers for Disease Control. An exceedingly productive few years followed, as he led the discovery of Venezuelan equine encephalitis virus subtype II, Everglades virus, and other viruses in the Florida Everglades National Park and elsewhere; led discovery and epidemic studies of La Crosse virus in the Upper Midwest; St. Louis encephalitis virus in Illinois, Florida, and Texas and studied other arboviruses in the United States and world-wide, participating in international collaborations on tick-borne virus studies, and more, much more.

In 1967 Work became Professor of Tropical Medicine and Infectious Diseases at the University of California at Los Angeles, where he taught and, with his devoted wife and professional associate Martine

Jozan Work, began the search for foci of St. Louis encephalitis virus and other arboviruses in arid zones of southern California, demonstrating year-around activities of *Culex tarsalis* mosquitoes in the Imperial Valley.

He was elected President of the American Society for Tropical Medicine and Hygiene, and his Presidential address, given before the 19th Annual Meeting of that Society (San Francisco, California, 1970), entitled "On the Japanese B-West Nile virus complex or an arbovirus problem of six continents", presaged the 1999 incursion of West Nile virus into the Americas. In Work's early view, west Japanese encephalitis and West Nile viruses were restricted primarily to the north of Wallace's Line, which extends southeast from the Philippines to Bali. Based on his careful serosurveys and epidemiologic studies, however, he suggested that West Nile virus might eventually be found on all continents except Antarctica. He was correct.

Work spent a sabbatical year in Australia, where an epidemic of Murray Valley encephalitis was occurring in the Kimberley region. There, he and Martine Jozan Work, a pediatrician with extensive virologic experience, worked with Neville F. Stanley (Figure 137) of the University of Western Australia to understand the complex epidemiologies of the arboviruses of the Kimberley Region of that state, focusing on the Kununurra area. On another sabbatical, this one in Argentina, the Works studied dengue on the border with Paraguay and yellow fever on the border with Brazil. Telford Work exemplified the kind of person who kept arbovirology moving along: highly intelligent, dynamic, widely experienced, widely accomplished, persistent, insightful, a meticulous cataloguer, a tireless virologic proselytizer, and a raconteur extraordinaire, devoted to the improvement of the public's health, demanding, soft-hearted, and literate, perhaps even a bit (or more than a bit) idiosyncratic.

How he could tell a story! Once, on a fishing trip, I asked him the simple question: "Why is she no longer your secretary?" and before he got to the answer two days later he had told me about filariasis in

Figure 137. (l. to r.) Ian David Marshall, Neville F. Stanley and Elizabeth C. Edwards trapping and processing birds for ecological studies of Murray Valley encephalitis virus in the Kimberley region of Western Australia. (image courtesy of John S. Mackenzie)

the Pacific, cattle dogs, baseball box scores, Volvo engines, and a great deal more – all fascinating, at least to me.

Pilottown, Louisiana: One evening in the spring of 1966, Work called me at home and told me to pack; I was going to Pilottown, Louisiana, to help Rexford Lord collect birds migrating from Central and South Americas and process them for viruses and antibody. Our work there was part of a series of studies done as a continuation of earlier studies (bleeding, tagging, and releasing) of birds in British Honduras (now Belize). The intent was to determine whether arboviruses were transported intercontinentally (northward) by migrant birds. Lord, an experienced ornithologist, was the focus of these activities in Belize, Pilottown and along the eastern seaboard of the United States.

It is possible, I suppose, that Work had finally given in to my whining about being stuck in the laboratory, never having the opportunity to get out in the field where the real action was. Whatever his reason, I packed some personal belongings and necessary laboratory supplies and flew from Atlanta to New Orleans, where I was met by the crew of a Plaquemines Parish vector control helicopter and flown to Pilottown, 120 km (74 mi) south of New Orleans. The helicopter hovered low over a wooden dock, and I and my belongings and supplies went out the door onto a wooden walkway. Lord was there to greet me and help me carry everything to where we would be living – a pink houseboat! He then walked me to the bird-netting sites and filled me in on my responsibilities. Although I had no idea how to do most of the assigned tasks (remove birds from the fine Japanese mist nets, identify and bleed the birds, and then band them), I did know how to release the birds, as I was perfectly competent to open my hands. After spending the night scrubbing the houseboat's kitchen, so that I could regain my appetite, we began the work. We had only cold cereal for our meals and a few unidentifiable greenish objects in the refrigerator, so I inquired about obtaining some real food. I was told we had no access to a grocery store and that we would have to fish if we wanted to eat something else. Instead, we rowed into various channels, found crab pots, and stole whatever we could find. This was not the glamorous and exciting government work I had envisioned when I had complained to Work. Nonetheless, after a few days we had bled, tagged, and released hundreds of migrant birds; we returned to Atlanta to process the samples and test the bloods for virus and for antibody.

That certainly was a good introduction to field work for me and, in retrospect, the results of our efforts made any inconveniences just minor nuisances. From the birds we captured, we isolated what we later demonstrated to be South American variants of eastern equine encephalitis virus (one from a blackpoll warbler, *Dendroica striata*, and one from a wood thrush, *Hylocichla mustelina*), and a strain of Mayaro virus from an orchard oriole, *Icterus spurius*. We concluded that, though eastern equine encephalitis virus (and even Mayaro virus) obviously could arrive in the United States from the south, courtesy of migrating birds, it probably arrives too early in the year to become established there, given that viremic birds probably arrive before competent arthropod vectors are abundant. Because Mayaro virus had never been detected in North America, we further concluded that the isolation of that virus likely had been a singular or very rare occurrence. I took a hiatus from whining for quite some time after that adventure.

A meeting at Smolenice Castle: Small, intimate meetings of arbovirologists in pleasant surroundings have been a hallmark of the field since its inception and have been prime means of attracting like-minded and affable researchers, which includes just about all arbovirologists. I was able to attend meetings in Brisbane (Australia), Dubrovnik (Croatia), Moscow (Russia), Belem (Brazil), and many other delightful and interesting venues, thanks to thoughtful and hospitable organizers.

One such meeting was held at the 15th century Smolenice Castle, in the eastern Carpathian Mountains, near the town of Smolenice, Slovakia (formerly Czechoslovakia). Destroyed numerous times by uprisings, during Napoleonic wars, and by World War II battles, it eventually was rebuilt and is now the property of the Slovak Academy of Sciences and is a beautiful and delightful location for meetings. In 1979 I was invited to attend a symposium there, "New aspects in ecology of arboviruses", which was attended by many outstanding scientists, primarily from Czechoslovakia but also from the Soviet Union, Germany, Italy, France and its far-flung laboratories, Poland, The Netherlands, Hungary, Switzerland, Austria, Portugal, Brazil, New Zealand and the United States. I had been asked to present a paper "Antigenic relationships of the arboviruses: an ecological and evolutionary approach" and to co-edit the proceedings with the excellent young Slovakian scientist and fine gentleman Milan Labuda. My experience with international meetings at that time was limited and the surroundings were both impressive and somewhat daunting, given that so many well-known scientists from Europe and other areas were in attendance. I had anticipated it would be a rather formal gathering, given the somewhat icy relations between the governments of at least some of our home countries, and that there would be cool or distant interpersonal relationships between attendees. I was wrong about that.

For one thing, other meetings on the subject of arboviruses had taken place at Smolenice Castle in the past, excellent meetings with outstanding attendees, and many of the 1979 meeting attendees knew each other from other meetings and collaborations. For another, the wine was good and flowed freely. In addition, the fascination of viruses on the part of the attendees surmounted most political differences.

Sophia Ya. Gaidamovich, one of the many reputable Soviet scientists in attendance was an acquaintance of mine for many years. She had visited my laboratory at the CDC in Atlanta and had visited my laboratory after we had moved to Fort Collins. I had once taken her to see the wonderful vistas of Rocky Mountain National Park in Colorado. Not being accustomed to the high altitude and the winding roads, she complained continually that I was driving dangerously fast. I stopped the car, opened her door, and told her either to get out and walk the many miles back to Fort Collins or to quit complaining. She quit complaining.

Marian C. Horzinek: A multilingual, multitalented, and multiaccomplished human of the first order and, as Frederick Murphy calls him, "King of the nonarbo togaviruses", Horzinek also attended the meeting at Smolenice Castle. He was born in Poland but left there in 1946 with his family when he was a young boy, wandering west with them after, as he put it, "the Polish milicja had occupied the family mansion and arrested all of us". After incarceration in a concentration camp, a long trek to the German border in cattle wagons, and erratic train travels in search of surviving members of the family, they arrived in the West. Horzinek studied veterinary medicine in Germany, obtained his Doctor of Veterinary Medicine, and in 1970 a Ph.D. in virology. He began his career in virology at the Public Health Laboratory in Hannover, later helping to establish the Chair of Virology at Hannover Veterinary School, and then spent a year as a research fellow in

Caracas, Venezuela. He returned home as Head of the Exotic Diseases Division at the Federal Research Institute for Animal Virus Diseases in Tübingen, after which he moved to The Netherlands where he was appointed Head of Department and Professor of Virology and Virus Diseases at the Faculty of Veterinary Medicine, Utrecht University. Ultimately, he was appointed Director of Utrecht University's Institute of Veterinary Research; in 1996 he established and directed the Graduate School of Animal Health. Now he has retired from day-to-day activities but edits the online veterinary research journal that he founded, Veterinary Sciences Tomorrow (i.e., "Vetscite"), lectures and consults here and there, and ties his own distinctive bowties, by which he is easily recognized.

Peerless even in 1979, Marian suggested we have a bit of fun in Smolenice Castle. We found some wine, chains (obviously not needed by the groundskeepers; otherwise why would they have been hanging around a gate post?), bed sheets, a candle or two, and some hidden staircases, and proceeded to "haunt" the Castle very late into the night. Focusing on Gaidamovich's room, we tried to frighten her, but the only response received was "Calisher! Go to bed".

Mikhail Petrovich Chumakov: This great Russian scientist was also an attendee, severely handicapped as he was by his catastrophic contact with tick-borne encephalitis virus while in Siberia more than 40 years previously. Perhaps the bravest person I have met, Chumakov might have been physically handicapped, but he had continued his work with enthusiasm and with all the effort he could muster. I was being gently mocked because I was the only one drinking red wine, while everyone else was drinking what they considered a fine Slovakian white wine. Chumakov came to the table where I was sitting with other friends and joined me in drinking the red. He asked my father's name and I told him it was "Leon"; always after that he called me "Charles Leonovich". When the traditional dancing began, with couples holding a handkerchief between them, Chumakov invited me to join him on the dance floor. Imagine! The man could scarcely walk but wanted to participate in this, as in everything else. It was an unforgettable few days and nights, not only scientifically but personally. I might add here that I was on my honeymoon, though my wife was in Croatia, waiting for me. We had gotten married only two days before I left for the meeting, so my wife was placed in the safe hands of Jelka Vesenjak, while I went to Smolenice to evaluate the wine.

An Australian adventure: Between when I retired from CDC in 1992 and when I began a new life at Colorado State University, I completed the few repairs of our home that I was competent to do. That did not take long (mostly because I am no repairman), so I went fishing in the beautiful Rocky Mountains, attended a meeting on positive-strand RNA viruses in Florida, and spent two weeks in China, attending a meeting, on bluetongue viruses. When my wife announced that we were remodeling the house, I went to Australia for three months; an excellent decision.

For many years Australian arbovirologists had been asking me when I was planning to visit their country and I told them I either did not have the time or did not have the money. That was not the case in the fall of 1992, so I accepted all of their kind offers, including a Visiting Fellowship in the Molecular Evolution and Systematics Group, Research School of Biological Sciences, Australian National University, Canberra, offered to me by Adrian J. Gibbs, a plant virologist and long-time correspondent. After a few weeks in Canberra trying to adapt an existing computer program to incorporate arboviruses, with a view towards someday putting online the entire *International Catalogue of Arboviruses and Certain Other Viruses,* I left to visit the Darwin area of the Northern Territory.

Thanks to the generosity of Lorna Melville and her family, I was able to stay in Humpty Doo and work at the nearby Berrimah Veterinary Laboratories, Department of Resources – Primary Industries. For many years, only the most important viruses had been studied; all others had been stored for future study. I welcomed the challenge of facing the identification of many hundreds of viruses and, with assistance from Richard Weir, began this huge task. When I was confident that Richard could carry on for a few days or longer, I took an opportunity to visit Kakadu National Park, east of Darwin and Berrimah. Aboriginal rock paintings, crocodiles, gum (eucalyptus) trees, hundreds of species of birds of which I never had known existed, numerous mosquitoes and flies, and oppressive heat. I have never seen a more interesting place, met more enjoyable people, or had a better time. We identified viruses by the hundreds, some new, some known but not recognized to occur where they had been found, some not previously isolated from mosquitoes of a particular species, etc. This was great fun and we acquired useful information as well.

From Darwin I flew west through Broome, stopping briefly at the cemetery where so many pearl divers are buried, and on to Perth and the University of Western Australia, where I spent a week or so with John Mackenzie, Annette Broom, Cheryl Johansen, Michael Lindsay (Figure 138), and others of that lively and accomplished group, establishing an immunoglobulin M-capture enzyme-linked immunosorbent assay for use in serologic tests for antibody to certain arboviruses in human sera. I was housed in a guest suite at the Queen Elizabeth II Hospital, which was convenient, as in my wanderings around Kings Park I had been bitten by three very large and aggressive ants that looked to me like the alien machines in "War of the Worlds". I am allergic to ant-bites and had to be treated at once. Valuable lesson learned: never sit on bare ground in Australia.

I rented a car with which I was unfamiliar (driver sits on the right side, drives on the left side of the road, or the other way round; I never did figure that out) and off I went, knocking over road hazard warning signs, south through Fremantle, and Margaret River to Augusta, on the Indian Ocean. I arrived in Augusta late on what was Thanksgiving Day in the United States, a time for Americans to give thanks for what we have, gather with family, enjoy each other's company, and eat well. I found the only restaurant that was still open late in Augusta, bought fish and chips, and drove to a picnic area at Cape Leeuwin to eat. That was the first and only time in my life I have been homesick.

Figure 138. Michael David Lindsay (left) and John S. Mackenzie at Marble Bar, Pilbara Region, Western Australia.
(image courtesy of John Mackenzie)

I was about 2,700 km (1,700 mi) from Melbourne, 3,000 km (1,900 mi) from Djakarta, Indonesia, and had I been able to swim or sail directly west, the first land I reached would have been the southern tip of Africa! Nonetheless, I recovered quickly. The next day I saw sunken ships, great white sharks (*Carcharodon carcharias*) circling in the Great Australian Bight, a remarkable variety of birds, red kangaroos (*Macropus rufus*), the largest of all macropods and the largest extant land mammal native to Australia (except for Andrew Bogut). In the "Valley of the Giants", I experienced karris, red tingles, and jarrah eucalyptus trees near Denmark.

After returning to Perth, I flew elsewhere around Australia, visiting friends and colleagues, and seeing many of the sites. All in all a remarkable tour and after so many travels elsewhere, I finally had the good sense to keep a diary and albums of photographs. Made easier in each place by outgoing, intelligent, learned, and relaxed Australian colleagues, my visit was not only personally memorable, it was professionally rewarding. There was not a single place visited where I did not learn a great deal. Thanks to Frank Fenner, Adrian and Pat Gibbs, Ian and Kathleen Marshall, Geoff and Rhonda Gard, Linda Hueston, Richard and Ros Russell, Tony Della-Porta, Lorna and Ian Melville, John and Isobel Mackenzie, Neville and Dawn Hunt, others mentioned previously, and some not mentioned, I have seen heaven and liked it.

John Sheppard Mackenzie: A graduate of the University of Edinburgh, with a Ph.D. from the Australian National University in Canberra, Mackenzie has been as involved as anyone in Australia in studies of arboviral and bat-borne viruses there. He began his professional career as a Fellow in the Public Health Research Institute of New York City, then headed the Department of Genetics at the Animal Virus Research Institute in Pirbright, England, and finally arrived where he belonged, at the University of Western Australia, Perth, as Head of the Department of Microbiology. Serving as Head of the Department of Microbiology and Parasitology at the University of Queensland for five years, Mackenzie became Chief Executive Officer of the Australian Biosecurity Cooperative Research Centre for Emerging Infectious Diseases and then a medical officer at the W.H.O. Geneva. Finally, he returned to the University of Queensland as Professor of Microbiology, then retired so that he could get some work done. At present, he is a technical consultant to W.H.O., a member of the board of Directors of a commercial biological company, a Premier's research fellow and a faculty member of various and far-flung Australian universities. Mackenzie has been deeply involved in studies of highly pathogenic arbovirus and bat-borne viruses and his insights are recognized as highly valuable. His knowledge, experience, wide spread contacts, genial manner, and enthusiasm for collaborative efforts are the reasons he is continually called on when epidemiologic and diagnostic problems arise.

Another of the knowledgeable and expert arbovirologists is John G. Aaskov at the Queensland University of Technology. After obtaining a B.Sc. at the University of Queensland, Aaskov earned a Ph.D. from the University of Leeds, England. As Director of the W.H.O. Collaborating Centre for Arbovirus Reference and Research, Aaskov provides a tertiary arbovirus diagnostic referral service for all Pacific Island countries and a genotyping service for dengue viruses, as well as providing training for scientists throughout the Asia Pacific Region. His service to W.H.O. as a technical advisor takes him to many countries in his area, and his many collaborators have allowed him to develop vaccines, including one for Ross River alphavirus, which at the time of this writing is proceeding through the various trials necessary for acceptance.

Time spent with Frank Fenner: I had met Fenner a few times here and there, at scientific meetings, symposia and under other professional circumstances. When the American Society for Virology held its annual meeting at Colorado State University in 2000, he was in attendance, delivering a superb lecture. Due to medical reasons, it was one of his last trips overseas. We invited him, Fred Brown, Joel Dalrymple, Tom Monath, and Neal Nathanson to dinner at our home. President John F. Kennedy once told an audience of Nobel Prize winners at the White House, "I think this is the most extraordinary collection of talent, of human knowledge, that has ever been gathered together at the White House, with the possible exception of when Thomas Jefferson dined alone." Maybe so, but I would put our guests up against his any day.

When my wife and I visited Canberra some years later, Frank insisted on driving us around the city. Of course, we wanted to take him to dinner, but he insisted on having us to his home instead. Just before 5 P.M., he offered us a drink and snacks, which he said he had every day at that time. Right at 5 P.M. he walked to the front door, opened it and let into the house a Jack Russell terrier, which wagged its tail, lay down on the carpet and promptly went to sleep. When we finished our drinks, Fenner walked to the door, opened it without saying a word and let the dog out. I could not resist asking him what that was all about, and he said that the dog belonged to someone in an Embassy down the street (Canberra is the capital of Australia) and that he joined Fenner every day at 5 P.M. and stayed with him while he had his drink. Obviously, even a neighborhood dog appreciated Fenner's gentle nature and good company. Years later, when collaborating on a book chapter with Fenner, I learned more about the epidemiology, even the philosophy, of viral eradication than had ever crossed my mind.

Joel M. Dalrymple: The inimitable Dalrymple was among the most accomplished, forward-looking, considerate, and fun-loving people in arbovirology. He was born and grew up in Utah, attending the University of Utah. He enlisted in the United States Army in 1968 and spent his entire professional career with the military, first at Walter Reed Army Institute of Research, then as a civilian there and at the United States Army Medical Research Institute of Infectious Diseases at Fort Detrick, Frederick, Maryland. Joel contributed greatly to our understanding of the biological and molecular characteristics and interactions of viruses and to the development of vaccines. Perhaps his greatest contributions were to our understanding of hantaviruses, but he was an arbovirologist through and through and his contributions to our knowledge of alphaviruses and flaviviruses (particularly dengue viruses) are well known. He worked for and with a devoted and expert team, including Phillip K. Russell and with Charles L. Bailey, Walter E. Brandt, Gary G. Clark, Bruce F. Eldridge, Mary K. Gentry, Erik A. Henchal, George W. Korch, James W. Leduc, Kenneth J. Linthicum, George V. Ludwig, Jack M. McCown, Cynthia A. Rossi, Alan L. Schmaljohn, Connie S. Schmaljohn, Ralph F. Tammariello, Franklin H. Top, Jr, Michael J. Turell, Douglas M. Watts, and others in other institutes, including not only those in the laboratory in Bangkok but, as well, David H.L. Bishop, Leon Rosen, R. Walter Schlesinger, Edwin G. Westaway, and a host of others world-wide. Because of his intelligence, energy, and good humor, it was easy and enjoyable to collaborate with him. His collective works on disease epidemiology, use of monoclonal antibodies for diagnostics, virus discovery, mosquito competence, vaccine development, and more made his legacy as valuable as anyone's.

At a long ago meeting of the American Society for Tropical Medicine and Hygiene, Joel and I were asked to chair a session on viruses. These are serious gatherings, in the established scientific tradition. The speakers stood behind a dais on a stage and the co-chairs sat behind a table holding a pitcher of ice water and two glasses, the table and chairs being on two square risers pushed together, each with metal borders. Unbeknownst to us, one riser was missing the metal edge on one side. Each speaker would have the usual 10 minutes to speak and an additional five minutes to respond to questions. Talks would be timed by a large timer, whose hands we could set to 15 minutes. The green light in front of the speaker would change to a flashing red light after nine minutes, and to a steady red at 10 minutes, so that the speaker would know when to stop speaking; we controlled the timer.

Donald A. Burke, then a young Army physician, now Dean of the Graduate School of Public Health and Jonas Salk Chair in Global Health at the University of Pittsburgh, working in collaboration with Ananda Nisalak and Michael A. Ussery in Thailand at the Armed Forces Research Institute of Medical Sciences, Bangkok, was to present a seminal paper on detection of IgM antibodies to Japanese encephalitis virus in cerebrospinal fluid of patients with that disease and why that was a predictor of fatal outcome. We had heard of their results and were looking forward to the presentation. After Burke was introduced by Joel, the latter returned to his chair and set the timer, but he set it to five minutes and, turning to me, winked. When the five minutes were up, the red light in front of Burke began to flash and he began speaking faster and faster and then the red light came on and he looked to us for help. Joel said, "Don't worry. Take whatever time you need.", and burst out laughing.

The next speaker was having difficulty fastening the microphone cord around her neck, so Joel walked over to her to help. When he returned to his chair its leg slipped into the crack left by the missing metal border and as he began to sit he fell onto me. I was about half of his weight, and I grabbed at the table to save myself from falling or being crushed. However, what I grabbed was the tablecloth, so that when he fell on me we ended lying on the floor drenched in ice water among fallen chairs, the timer, and a microphone. We received a standing ovation and for years afterwards people remembered our "performance" with great glee. It was like being at a fraternity party, but without the beer.

In 1993, Joel was planning to attend an International Congress for Virology meeting in Glasgow, Scotland, at a time when I was to be in Yugoslavia. I invited him to travel to Yugoslavia, meet me there and then go to Rome, where we could spend a couple of days and then return home. He could not get to Yugoslavia but agreed to meet me in Rome. Meanwhile, I wrote to the office of the Pope, who when a Cardinal had been conferred an honorary degree from the University of Notre Dame when I graduated from there. I explained that, as I would be in Rome with my friend Joel, it would be nice to see him again, to "catch up" and see what he had been doing since 1961. I received a kind letter from the Holy See's office in New York City, letting me know that "you and your friend Joel are welcome to attend an audience with his Holiness" on such and such a date. I sent the letter to Joel who asked whether we could just pass on all that and come home directly from Yugoslavia, which we did, through Rome. Joel thought the Pope was a friend of mine, and I never told him otherwise.

To provide a glimpse of Dalrymple's personality, I quote here from a memoriam for him written by David L. Huxsoll: "I knew Joel from the time he entered the Army; I had daily contact with him from 1983 to 1990 while I served as Commander of USAMRIID [United States Army Medical Research Institute of Infectious Diseases]. His disdain for administration (and sometimes administrators) assured that my day was never unchallenged. He was a brilliant strategist. During a period of intense research activity, we apparently had difficulty in maintaining a supply of bath towels in the change rooms of the numerous biocontainment suites. After listening to Joel's multiple threats to come out of the shower, through the change room, and into the corridor in the buff dripping wet, I requested an order of towels that would saturate the place, even if it required an 18- wheeler to deliver the order. I never heard from Joel about towels again, but he had successfully coerced me to undoubtedly bend an acquisition regulation."

Connie Schmaljohn: Dalrymple collaborated with and trained many staff members and visitors, including Connie Schmaljohn, who has stayed at USAMRIID in much the same position Joel had filled. She continues and extends the work on hantaviruses and has built an excellent reputation developing sophisticated virus detection and diagnostic methods, mapping genomes, developing and testing vaccines, and studying the immunologic responses to infections with filoviruses. Joel would have been proud.

Schmaljohn obtained a Ph.D. from Colorado State University, supervised by Carol Blair, who had been Dalrymple's research assistant at the University of Utah. Because Dalrymple, by then at USAMRIID, was collaborating with investigators at the CDC in Fort Collins, he and Schmaljohn soon met and Schmaljohn went on to a post-doctoral period of study with Dalrymple at USAMRIID. Her initial efforts at USAMRIID were with studies of Japanese encephalitis virus, which had been her Ph.D. topic, but she soon moved on to study hantaviruses with Dalrymple, first showing that these viruses are members of the family *Bunyaviridae*, then helping to establish the hantaviruses as members of a distinct genus (*Hantavirus*) in the family, then demonstrating how these viruses replicate and eventually working to develop a vaccine against the prototype virus of the genus, Hantaan virus. She works tirelessly to convince administrators that the intellectual ferment created by talented scientists is a strategic and essential necessity to protect United States service members and others from biological threats. Schmaljohn remains at USAMRIID and continues this work.

Patricia Repik: After obtaining her doctorate degree at Rutgers University under David H.L. Bishop and another post-doctoral sojourn at the University of Illinois, Repik was first a post-doctoral student and then was employed under the supervision of Dalrymple at Walter Reed Army Institute of Research. After nine years at the Medical College of Pennsylvania in Philadelphia and another five in a commercial laboratory, she returned to federal employment as a Program Officer at NIH, where she remains, helpful, knowledgeable, and pleasant as always. Both Schmaljohn and Repik are very active and long-term members of ACAV, as was Dalrymple.

When Dalrymple died very prematurely in 1992 a void was created in the arbovirology community, a void that has never been filled. As a matter of course, many other virologists have passed away over time, some younger than others, but most in due course. Dalrymple's death was different – stunning, devastating, and depressing. Arbovirology is a sort of "club", with membership open to everyone, but still is a relatively small club. News of a success or a failure, of an illness or death is noted and circulated rapidly, an affectionate and congenial, if sometimes heartrending bonus to membership.

Circular conversations: Early in my career, on a visit to laboratories in South America at the request of the Pan-American Health Organization, I stopped in the capital of a country whose identity shall not be revealed. I wanted to see the laboratory in which arbovirus studies were being done. I knew they were being done there because the Pan-American Health Organization told me so and had shown me some reports from there, albeit reports that did not contain data. The laboratory director met me and took me to a new-looking building that he had to unlock. No one was inside. I asked how they did virus isolations and he told me in great detail. I asked to see the mouse colony and he told me it was locked and that anyway there were no mice at the time. "When do you have mice?", I asked. "When we have a suspect rabies case.", he replied. "When do you do your work with arboviruses?", I asked. "When we have a suspect rabies case we order them.", he said. "On average, how often is that?", I asked. "We never have rabies cases.", he said. The conversation seemed like falling down a spiral staircase. I learned from the experience that it is best to not take anyone's word for anything and not to bother reading reports that do not contain data. I have not forgotten that lesson.

A visit to West Africa: As a young boy growing up (as much as I have) in New York City, I spent almost every moment of my spare time either playing baseball or passing weekend days at the Carl Akeley Hall of African Mammals at the American Museum of Natural History. The latter fascinated me, and I vowed to see equatorial Africa one day. Unfortunately or fortunately, things have changed since Akeley visited Africa about 100 years ago. Much else has as well.

I was invited by the Government of Nigeria to visit their laboratory in Lagos, a laboratory that for many years had been part of the Rockefeller Laboratory system. Most of the older, established, and accomplished arbovirologists were gone by that time, either retired or deceased, but Abdulsalami Nasidi, M.D., now Director of the Federal Ministry of Health, Nigeria, was the Director of the laboratory. My charge was to transfer from CDC the technology necessary for Nigeria to incorporate the immunoglobulin M and immunoglobulin G enzyme-linked immunosorbent assay, which I had been using for diagnosis of arboviral infections, into the extant diagnostic procedures. With the enthusiastic collaboration of Nasidi, a knowledgeable, experienced, and extraordinarily good humored fellow, I set about doing just that and was quite successful. The night before I was to leave, a party was given in my honor, which was flattering. I was very much looking forward to attending. The night before that, however, I had not gotten much sleep, as the cockroaches on the walls and floors of my hotel room made too much noise, and the rodents watching me from the top of the non-functioning TV seemed both menacing and distracting.

When the party ended I flew to a francophone country in West Africa to teach a W.H.O.-sponsored course on arbovirology. The facilitator assigned to me by W.H.O., a knowledgeable eastern European virologist, saw to my needs with respect to laboratory equipment, hotel, and meals. One afternoon he told me we had been invited by the Director of the laboratory to join him for dinner. Picked up at our hotel by a taxi, we were driven to a somewhat run-down neighborhood and into an alley where we stopped at what appeared to be a garage. When we entered the building, I was unsurprised to find that, although it truly was a garage, it was furnished with tables, chairs, and rugs.

When we were half way through our first beers of the evening, a woman entered, showing us what was in store for us for dinner, a live pangolin (*Manis tricuspis*), a scaly anteater. I apologized as profusely as I could, telling our host that it was against my religion to eat such a thing. He, being more polite than I, accepted my apology and so I spent the evening chatting, pretending to eat monkey paw soup, but partaking only of moldy bread and washing that down with excellent beer. I reckoned a bit of penicillin and alcohol would not kill me. I spent the night and part of the next morning holding the neck of the W.H.O. facilitator over the toilet bowl. I was fine.

Calisher the diplomat: On one extended trip on behalf of the Pan-American Health Organization, I was invited to a dinner party. I am somewhat of a finicky eater and so I always dread such things but, representing an international organization, I did not feel I could refuse to attend. The first course was both unidentifiable and disgusting and I was not planning on eating it when a fellow diner told me that would be extremely impolite of me and that I should at least try it. Rather than that, when the host and hostess were in the kitchen preparing the next disgusting course, I scraped my plate into the bowl of a German shepherd dog on the patio and the food soon disappeared. When the hostess returned to the dining room, the dog vomited out my dinner. Rather than be as undiplomatic as I, and probably wanting to wring my neck, the hostess smiled and said, "We are pleased you like the food.", and brought me another plateful. Since then I have disposed of my neckties, attended to virological matters, and left the diplomacy to others.

A King's ransom: I had not visited Morocco, so when I had the opportunity to attend a symposium on African horse sickness in Rabat, I went. It was a productive and otherwise fine meeting, and I was able to use some available time to visit Fez, Marrakech, and Casablanca in all their historic glory. The last night of the symposium, attendees were invited to a cocktail party and dinner at one of the King's ranches. Walking around the beautiful grounds, I spotted a horse in an unlit stable and walked closer to get a better look. I know nothing about horses except that they have fewer than five legs, but I knew at once that this horse was something special, so I walked to the stable door and scratched the horse's head. From the shadows of the stable a man, then a second man, appeared. One said, "Do you think this is a nice horse, Sir?" I said I did and, jokingly, asked whether it was for sale. When told it was the King's favorite horse, I asked whether the King might be willing to sell it to me for cash, or even take a credit card, although I had no idea how I would get the horse home. Smiling, one of the men said, "As I said, it is his favorite horse. Besides, he does not need the money, so no." I often think of that beautiful animal and think what a pity it was that the King had so much money.

Laboratory infections: I know of at least two arbovirus infections I acquired during my laboratory days. As I have antibody to at least one hantavirus (probably Hantaan virus), I might have had more; might have, because antibody may represent only exposure to an antigen, rather than an infection with the virus itself. Still, it would be interesting to know exactly which virus that antibody was produced against, because I never knowingly worked with Hantaan virus. If it was an "unclassified" or otherwise unidentified virus, it must have been a hantavirus. Too late to determine at this time, I suppose.

The two infections I am certain I had were with Central European encephalitis flavivirus and Bhanja bunyavirus, and I am reasonably certain I know how I became infected with each of them. Both were contracted despite using all available safety procedures available to me at the time. The Central European encephalitis virus infection likely was acquired from an aerosol created when reconstituting a lyophilized live-virus antigen produced some 30 years previously in an attempt to conduct a serodiagnostic test with a sample from a patient who had visited Central Europe, the sample submitted by the California State Health Department. An account of my illness was not published because such accounts had been published many times. In brief, the illness began as a mild headache, which developed into a severe headache with fever, anorexia, myalgias and cognitive dysfunction. After about a week, recovery was well on its way and after two weeks was complete. However, knowing the bimodal nature of a minority of infections caused by tick-borne encephalitis viruses, concern was maintained for months afterwards.

The infection with Bhanja virus probably also was acquired by aerosol. Suspensions of macerated ticks collected in Croatia were centrifuged to remove debris, and the supernatant fluid was used to inoculate suckling mice. Virus was isolated from my blood and antibody to the virus was detected in bloods collected weeks and months after illness onset. Details of this infection and illness were published with our medical officer, Hugh Goodpasture. This first demonstration of human illness caused by Bhanja virus was followed by detection of other human illnesses, one of them fatal, caused by this virus in Croatia.

These experiences are mentioned merely to point out that only the most modern and most secure facilities should be employed when working with viruses or viral reagents, unless those reagents have been certified as non-infectious. Having worked with literally thousands of virus isolates over a period of more than 50 years; having worked in laboratories where eating, drinking and smoking was not restricted; and having used relatively primitive techniques, including "mouth pipetting", I am surprised that I acquired only these two clinical infections. Techniques and training today are much better than they were even 10 years ago, and reagents now used more often consist of polypeptide antigens expressed in *Escherichia coli.* These antigens are not infectious because they do not comprise viral nucleic acid. Still, infectious agents of disease should be handled with the maximum of care. After all, pathogenicity depends on route and dose.

In addition to my laboratory-acquired infections, I became ill while on a field trip in Croatia in February 1972. I was with Jelka Vesenjak-Hirjan on the Island of Brač, trapping rodents and collecting ticks in a particularly strong and cold wind. When I arose one morning I was sick, with signs and symptoms of a serious respiratory infection. Through the judicious medicinal use of some excellent local wine, antipyrexics, and blankets, I managed to survive. When we returned to Zagreb I was put in the care of an expert infectious diseases physician, Dr. Josip Fališevac, at the Hospital for Infectious Diseases, who promptly installed me in a multi-bed ward with numerous young children, all suffering from respiratory infections. It was an eye-opening experience. I and my fellow patients shared a single large room with all the windows open and were made to wear woolen hats and woolen sweaters, blow water from one bottle to another and then back (a practical variant of incentive spirometry), and otherwise do our best to survive. As far as I could tell we all survived. I never knew what caused that illness, but was later told that that particular seasonal wind on Brač was called a bura, famous in that part of the Mediterranean area for bringing with it respiratory illnesses. I was simply pleased to have survived.

In 2002, after a Dubrovnik symposium on arboviruses and hemorrhagic fever viruses, I was having a glass or three of red wine with friends, watching a beautiful sunset, and waiting for a ride to Split. At a nearby table were five Japanese visitors, a very attractive and beautifully dressed young woman and four young men in black suits. I commented on the lady's beauty and one of the people at our table suggested I invite her to join us for a glass of wine. When I approached her table, one of the four men stood and said, "May we help you?" I told him I wanted to invite the lady to join us for a glass of wine and a friendly chat. Informing me that the lady was Princess Sayako, the youngest child of Emperor Akihito and Empress Michiko and the first member of the Japanese royal family to visit Croatia since her parents had vacationed there 26 years previously, and that she was enjoying her inspection of Dubrovnik very much, the other three men stood and managed to let me see the guns in holsters under their jackets. I apologized for my intrusion and said, "Princess? Well then, how about if she joins us for a glass of champagne?" They smiled, she giggled, and I went back to where I belonged, with the drinkers of excellent but inexpensive wines. I glanced at their table only once after that but the Princess was looking at me and smiling, so my attempt at hospitality was not a total failure. I still think she would have had more fun with a group of virologists than with the four men with guns.

Virus and information exchanges; a way to meet people: When I began work at CDC, we were attempting to accumulate arboviruses from wherever we could. Some arrived by mail, others delivered to us in person. Those who sent viruses to us wanted us either to confirm their identifications or to identify them. We did this enthusiastically because it allowed us to enlarge our virus collection as well as to provide a service to the world's scientific community. Bioterrorism was not a matter of concern to us (or even a word) in those days and so when an overseas visitor to CDC brought with her or him a virus, usually lyophilized and in a sealed glass container, carried in a pocket, it was no surprise. During the so-called "Cold War", we received many viruses from people who were supposed to be our enemies. We did not consider this naïve or foolhardy, we considered this international collaboration. One of the many researchers who brought to us and exchanged viruses with us was Dmitri K. Lvov, then a virologist in the

D.I. Ivanovsky Institute of Virology Russian Academy of Medical Sciences, Moscow, later its Director, and now one of the world's experts on epidemic influenza. He and I became friends as well as virological and epidemiological collaborators.

> Attending a 1978 meeting of virologists on the Island of Brač, in what then was part of Yugoslavia, now Croatia, the requisite evening wine-drinking session became a good-natured contest. Dmitri would stand and sing Russian Army chorus songs and I would follow with anti-Soviet jokes (fed to me by Croatian trouble-makers). After I told one particularly cutting joke, Dmitri said that if I would not tell any more jokes he would not sing any more songs and challenged me to swim in the very cold Adriatic Sea. Even the idea of that chilled me but I was not about to appear weak; I intended to hold up my country's honor. We stripped, swam around for a bit, determined that we had not had heart attacks, and emerged from the water, only to find that someone had playfully taken our clothes. We therefore had to walk into our hotel stark naked and ask for our room keys. This was international cooperation at its most productive.

Jelka Vesenjak-Hirjan: That meeting had been organized by Vesenjak-Hirjan, Erika Arslanagič, Volga Punda, and others of the Andrija Štampar School of Public Health, Medical Faculty of the University of Zagreb. After World War II, the United States Government had instituted, through Public Law 480, a program intended to assist countries that had borrowed funds for one reason or another, mostly war debts. Yugoslavia, Poland, Israel, and India participated. However, when a debt is so massive as to be incomprehensible, it simply cannot be repaid (Albert Einstein, when asked what he thought was the most powerful force in the world, said, "Compound interest."). Vesenjak-Hirjan, physician, war hero, former personal physician to Marshall Josef Broz ("Tito"), a fascinating and outspoken woman, a superior scientist, and an individual with remarkable enthusiasm for life, was my counterpart when I was the liaison between the United States and Yugoslavia, and we remained close friends until the day she died.

When I arrived in Zagreb to begin my first meeting with Jelka and her colleagues, I first went to the United States Consulate, as instructed, to collect some dinars, the local currency at the time. I was given a large paper bag full of dinars, but that did not amount to much in dollars. As it seemed that all others on the streets of Zagreb were carrying paper bags, I did not worry that I would be robbed. In any case, as it turned out, I did not need any money. Through Jelka and her generosity, I was unable to pay for anything, not that there was much to buy at the time. Over the years she and I traveled far and wide in Croatia, from Slovenia (then also part of Yugoslavia) and the Hungarian border on the north to Skadar Lake and the Albanian border on the south and to many coastal and inland towns in between. Along the way, in a small Croatian village, Jelka located and commissioned a Croatian "naïve" painter, Ivan Večenaj, to depict the natural cycle of tick-borne encephalitis virus in his own inimitable fashion (Figure 139). The title of the painting is *Šklopec*, vernacular in that part of Croatia for "tick".

While we traveled and ate, she always related to me the history not only of the diseases of the area but of her experiences with each outbreak, even each case, always speaking from a personal as well as a medical perspective. We visited sites where cases of typhus, Q fever, psittacosis, influenza, and hemorrhagic fever with renal syndrome had occurred and she introduced me to survivors, people whose lives she had saved one way or another, and to good food and drink.

> Once, at Skadar Lake, we were close to the Albanian border and I walked through a fence and down a path towards the gate where I assumed the border was. A single shot rang out and kicked up some dirt 10 meters from me. I looked up to see an Albanian border guard with an automatic weapon. "You have passed the border.", he said, "Get the hell out of here"; I did. Jelka thought it was all very funny, if somewhat impolite of the guard.

On another occasion, on the Adriatic Coast, I was invited by some professional fishermen friends of Jelka's to fish with them the next morning. After a long night of drinking excellent "black" (dark red) wine, I was awakened at 3 AM and walked to the boat, where I promptly fell asleep. When I again awoke I could see the shore from the boat, so expected we were not far from the coastal island in Dalmatia from which we had set out. I asked the name of the place we were viewing and was told "Italia!". So, there I was, an American without an Italian visa, in Italian waters, with Croatian fishermen. I sobered up almost immediately.

Through Jelka, my family was able to host a teenager from Brač for a year and to get to know her family on Brač, people who had supported our studies of tick-borne encephalitis virus by generously housing and feeding us and allowing us to handle and test their sheep, which were valued commodities in that formerly poverty-stricken area.

Unconnected experiences in various locations have both educated and fascinated me during my travels; I am certain that all arbovirologists could say the same. In Chile I felt threatened by revolutionary activities when Salvador Allende's government was struggling in vain to overcome what the newspapers were calling "la inflación catastrófica" and a W.H.O. country representative had to drive me to the airport in the middle of the night to keep me from further risks.

In Peru one evening the lights went out in the restaurant where we were dining, a gift of the Sendero Luminoso, a Maoist insurgent guerrilla organization that had destroyed a power station. On another visit to Peru I became violently ill from having ingested a bolus of staphylococcal enterotoxin surrounded by a doughnut. I recovered within a day and traveled to Iquitos to see the monkey colonies and then visited Machu Picchu, the most remarkable place I have ever seen.

I can barely tell one mosquito from another, but I was fairly certain I had recognized *Aedes aegypti* mosquitoes at the airport in Barranquilla, Colombia, on a trip to Bogota. When I arrived in Bogota I asked Carlos Sanmartin and Hernando Groot whether *Aedes aegypti*

Figure 139. Painting by Ivan Vecenaj, Croatia, depicting the natural cycle of tick-borne encephalitis virus. Note the involvement of squirrels, hares, birds, stags, and livestock, and the proximity of this woodcutter's work site to his village. (original painting was in color).

or dengue had been reported in Barranquilla and was told that, as far as they knew, they had not. Less than a year later, I received a cable from Sanmartin which said, "Enormous epidemics of dengue in Barranquilla, Cartagena, and Santa Marta. Hundreds of thousands of cases. Please do not ask about yellow fever."

Francisco de P. Pinheiro and I drove from Belem on the Trans-Amazonian Highway the day before the President of Brazil drove part of it for the official opening. We saw many "agrovillas", small settlements in the rain forest where deforestation was part of the plan and part of the goal. When we stopped for lunch at a small, rather disgusting restaurant, we were pleasantly surprised to come across Joel Dalrymple and others from the Walter Reed Army Institute of Research, who were investigating an unusual human hemorrhagic fever. This eventually was named Lábrea fever, caused by a coinfection or superinfection of hepatitis D or delta virus and hepatitis B virus.

We traveled with them in a convoy, until the evening when we checked into a hotel. Driving on an unpaved road all day, our bodies had become covered with a fine red dust, so showers were in order. Seemingly no matter how long we washed our hair, the water ran red and we eventually ran out of soap. Joel shouted to whoever was within hailing distance, "sopa", after which a very nice young woman came into the communal shower bringing each of us a bowl of soup. Joel suggested that perhaps we should learn some Portugese.

As mentioned above, before attending a meeting on African horse sickness in Rabat, Morocco, I had the opportunity to take a train to Casablanca to look for Humphrey Bogart, Ingrid Bergman, Paul Henreid, Claude Raines, Sydney Greenstreet, Peter Lorre, or even "Rick's Café Américain". Although I did not find any of them, I did notice many Orthodox Jews, which was unexpected. Asked about them, my guide invited me to accompany him to Fez, east of Rabat. The next morning we traveled there to see the oldest degree-granting university in the world, al- Qarawiyyin. Still functioning, this 1,100 year-old Islamic university remains the seat of Moroccan intellectualism. In addiiton to the many early Moslem intellectuals who either were on the faculty or studied there, many non-Moslems studied at al-

Qarawiyyin, including the renowned Jewish philosopher and theologian Rabbi Moshe ben Maimon ("Maimonides"), who studied under Abdul Arab Ibn Muwashah in the twelfth century. I saw many Christians and Orthodox Jews at the university and wondered, as I still wonder, what set of circumstances has occurred to change things so.

In 2008, I attended a symposium on filoviruses sponsored by the Centre International de Recherches Médicales de Franceville, held in Libreville, Gabon. This gave me the opportunity to visit Africa's "Eden". With about five people per km^2, most of whom live in or near the two largest cities, and an abundance of wildlife in a tropical forest setting, this remarkable country is not only a naturalist's dream, it is all a virologist could want, were s/he looking for something to do. That filovirus and arboviral diseases are not uncommon in Gabon should be no surprise.

One's professional experience should be memorable and satisfying but personal experiences should also be worthwhile. A worker in arbovirology either is interested in everything or is a specialist. Robert A. Heinlein (The Notebooks of Lazarus Long) put it well: "A human being should be able to change a diaper, plan an invasion, butcher a hog, con a ship, design a building, write a sonnet, balance accounts, build a wall, set a bone, comfort the dying, take orders, give orders, cooperate, act alone, solve equations, analyze a new problem, pitch manure, program a computer, cook a tasty meal, fight efficiently, die gallantly. Specialization is for insects." It is useful to be at least somewhat familiar with the people living in an epidemic zone, and their characteristics, their local culture, mean education level, mean individual income, mean number of residents per household, household pets, livestock, politics, religions, disease history, altitude, climatic conditions, commerce, arthropod fauna, proximity to water sources, and vaccination levels; the more information, the better. For example, it is impossible or at least difficult to carry out a decent serologic survey when no one understands what you are doing, why you are doing it and, in general, why the hell you have come from a foreign country or a different state to (appear to) ogle the women of the village.

APPENDIX

Long, impersonal lists of names of people involved in arbovirologic studies would not be helpful to the reader and are also boring. Still, some personal information about at least some of these people might provide some flavor. As an alternative to such lists, this Appendix provides a very few details about individuals, where they were educated, and scant reviews of their many accomplishments. It is hoped that these profiles adequately show that teachers teach students who become teachers, continuing that legacy.

Thomas Harry Gardner Aitken: "Tommy" as he liked to be called, was 94 years old when he died in 2007. He obtained a B.S. degree in entomology and zoology and a Ph.D. in medical entomology and parasitology from the University of California - Berkeley in 1940. He joined the United States Army in 1941, and was discharged in 1946 with the rank of Lieutenant Colonel. During his tour of duty, he served in Puerto Rico; in typhus control in Algeria, Egypt, and in Italy; during the typhus epidemic in Naples; and was the Army's Chief Malariologist in the Mediterranean Theater when he received the Bronze Star for controlling malaria in Corsica (France). In 1946 he joined the staff of the Rockefeller Foundation's International Health Division, and was assigned to the malaria eradication project in Sardinia, Italy. This succeeded brilliantly. When he left there in 1951 he was presented with a medal from the Sardinian government. In 1954, after a period of time at the Rockefeller Foundation Virus Laboratory in New York City, Tommy was assigned to the Foundation's Trinidad Regional Virus Laboratory in Port-of-Spain, Trinidad, West Indies, where he spent 12 years identifying and describing newly recognized arthropods, particularly those that vectored disease agents, isolating viruses from them, and carrying out virus transmission studies with them in the laboratory. He also participated in the investigation of arbovirus outbreaks throughout the Caribbean and neighboring parts of South America.

In 1967 Aitken moved to the Foundation's Belem Virus Laboratory in Brazil at the mouth of the Amazon where, besides continuing the same sort of research and field work that he had been doing in Trinidad, he initiated studies of parasitic mites of mammals and birds and studies of rodent botflies. When the Foundation withdrew its staff from Belem in 1971, Aitken went to the Foundation's new headquarters laboratory, the Yale Arbovirus Research Unit at the Yale University School of Public Health in New Haven, Connecticut.

Barry J. Beaty: Born in the thriving metropolis of Richland Center, Wisconsin, Beaty earned B.S. and M.S. degrees in biology from the University of Wisconsin-La Crosse and a Ph.D. in epidemiology at the University of Wisconsin-Madison, under Wayne J. Thompson. Armed with numerous field and laboratory experiences regarding transovarial transmission of La Crosse virus in *Aedes triseriatus*, Beaty accepted a post-doctoral position at the arbovirus nexus at Yale University with Robert Shope. His first paper there indicated that he was being trained in arbovirology from the ground up; with Shope and Delphine Clarke he co-authored a description of salt-dependent hemagglutination with antigens of viruses of the family *Bunyaviridae*. That is how most of the earlier generations of arbovirologists were trained, starting with the very basics of neurovirology, rather like an apprenticeship.

After working with Aitken, Shope and others in that productive ferment, he then joined the faculty at Colorado State University in Fort Collins. Beaty eventually rose to the rank of University Distinguished Professor because of his outstanding scientific accomplishments and became founding Director of the Rocky Mountain Regional Center of Excellence for Biodefense and Emerging Diseases, among other appointments, and was the recipient of a John D. and Catherine T. MacArthur Fellowship. These are unrestricted fellowships given to talented individuals who have shown extraordinary originality and dedication in their creative pursuits and a marked capacity for self-direction.

It does not take long for an intelligent and hard-working investigator to get the picture and have ideas of his or her own. After further experiences and with considerable insights, Beaty investigated gene coding assignments of orthobunyaviruses and arenaviruses with David H.L. Bishop (Figure 140) and Shope, the role of the M RNA segment in the molecular basis of orthobunyavirus transmission by mosquitoes, and application of these and other findings to detection of La Crosse virus in mosquito pools using enzyme immunoassays. That was a turning point in Beaty's career. Having developed the necessary tools, he focused on La Crosse virus in close collaboration with Bishop, Shope, Barry R. Miller, Steven W. Hildreth, James M. Meegan, Christine L. Frazier, Sonja Buckley, and Thomas Aitken, with whom he and others also investigated the susceptibility of laboratory-reared *Aedes aegypti* mosquitoes inoculated with the rabies virus-related Mokola lyssavirus. They demonstrated that Mokola virus replicated slowly. They maintained the virus for 340 days by monthly passage in mosquitoes and observed that virus in many mosquito tissues, including salivary glands, but transmission of the virus to vertebrate hosts was not demonstrated. While they observed transovarial transmission of Mokola virus in mosquitoes, and viremia in infected newborn mice, ticks exposed to these mice did not become infected.

Figure 140. David Hugh Langler Bishop (1937 -)
(image courtesy of Polly Roy)

Because of his experience in the discovery of the mechanism of transovarial transmission of La Crosse virus and elucidation of various characteristics and manifestations of that phenomenon, Beaty moved on to other aspects of virology from the viewpoint of an entomologist/epidemiologist, homing in on dengue as a disease to be controlled. Rather than approach the immediate and usual practical aspects from the perspective of mosquito control, he and his colleagues Carol Blair, Kenneth Olson and William C. Black IV at Colorado State University combined field and laboratory studies with their Mexican colleagues Jose A. Farfán-Ale, Ildefonso Fernandez-Salas, Norma Gorrochotegui-Escalante, Maria A. Loroño-Pino, Saul Lozano-Fuentes, Carlos Machain-Williams, Maria de

Lourdes Munoz, Isabel Salazar-Sanchez, and Irma Sánchez-Vargas as well as many graduate students and post-doctoral fellows, such as the Colombian Francisco J. Diaz, in an attempt to eliminate the mosquito vectors of dengue viruses by ingenious means. This demanding work has been in collaboration with many outside of Colorado State University, of course, including the molecular geneticist Anthony A. James of the University of California at Irvine. Their work appears to have been successful, in that they have made sufficient progress to allow development of methods to produce *Aedes aegypti* mosquitoes carrying a conditional dominant lethal gene, with which they intend to control the transmission of dengue viruses by vector population suppression.

They determined geographic barriers to mosquito gene flow, analyzed vector (*Aedes aegypti*) competence, genetically analyzed vector mosquitoes collected in Mexico and genetically manipulated mosquitoes. In this way they have reduced the competence of the mosquito to transmit dengue viruses. They identified viral genome-derived RNA segments that are expressed in mosquito midguts and salivary glands and engineered them to eliminate homologous virus replication and transmission. By combining these and other facets of the natural intracellular history of these viruses with conventional epidemiology, these arbovirologists expect to interrupt transmission of dengue viruses and thereby prevent dengue diseases.

Beaty's career path was classic: obtain a university education, work on fascinating and important projects, acquire a post-doctoral position with the best arbovirology laboratory in the world, and then strike out on your own. Not everyone has the capacity to do this, of course, and one could take other paths, but Beaty's route proved to be a conduit to success. It is my opinion that his enthusiasm for honest, rapid, and detailed sharing of information with colleagues world-wide has been a critical facet of his success.

In the ensuing decades, Beaty built and managed the Arthropod-borne and Infectious Diseases Laboratory at Colorado State University, along with Carol D. Blair and Kenneth E. Olson, arbovirologists with extensive experience in studies of Japanese encephalitis, dengue, and other viruses. Beaty continues to devise innovative studies of viruses, their replicative steps in mosquitoes, and their effects on vertebrate and arthropod hosts.

Trygve Obert Berge: His father was a school teacher who came from Norway to the United States to pay off a debt which he had not incurred. He married a woman who also had come from Norway to Wisconsin when she was 16. After they had had three children he died of meningitis when Trygve was three-years old. His mother rented a house, made one floor into a restaurant and fed 30 men three meals a day for many years. Although he barely managed to accumulate enough money to stay in school, Trygve attended the University of Wisconsin, then went to medical school, from which he had to drop out. Eventually he earned a Master's degree from that university and moved with his young family to Fargo, North Dakota, taking on the only position of bacteriologist at North Dakota Agricultural College (now North Dakota State University). Not satisfied with teaching, Berge moved with his family to Montana to the national labs in Hamilton, then into the Army when World War II broke out. After that it was to The Philippines, then to Japan, then to Ft. Baker near San Francisco, then to Ft. Detrick, the American Type Culture Collection, and finally to Colorado State University.

Berge had been one of the first Americans into Tokyo after the war ended. Tokyo's soil was badly contaminated and he was assigned to study Japanese encephalitis (then called Japanese B encephalitis to distinguish it from von Economo's encephalitis, also known as encephalitis lethargica) and typhus; part of the work done in Japan for the U.S. Army medical research laboratory in Tokyo eventually constituting his Ph.D. thesis at the University of California at Berkeley. His work with others to develop a Venezuelan equine encephalitis virus vaccine might have been the touchstone of his career but his other efforts included studies of Q fever, epidemiology and pathology of various diseases, and development of other vaccines, in addition of serving at Editor of the Arbovirus Catalogue. To the end he was a distinguished, meticulous, honorable, and conscientious scientist and a man justifiably proud of his accomplishments.

Delphine Harriet Clarke: A graduate of Wellesley College and of New York University College of Medicine, Clarke was an important part of the Rockefeller Foundation virus investigations team. She worked with Max Theiler on parasite-host interactions in chickens infected with *Plasmodium gallinaceum,* then with John P. Fox on hemolysis produced by *Rickettsia prowazekii.* Later she started a long series of detailed studies that were to become fundamental to arboviral diagnosis. With Pierre Ardoin and Claude Hannoun, Downs, and Shope she studied virus chromatography and the effects of sonication and trypsin in developing methods for arboviral antigen preparations; with Beaty and Shope, studies of salt dependency of bunyavirus hemagglutinins; with Casals, hemagglutination and hemagglutination-inhibition; with Frank L. Black, neutralization; with Theiler and Buckley, the use of antibody adsorption to differentiate primary from secondary infections with related tick-borne flaviviruses, differentiated alphaviruses by fluorescent antibody assays, and reported antigenic variation among West Nile virus isolates from discrete geographic areas. The most influential of these was a paper that Clarke published with Casals in 1958, the widely cited "Techniques for hemagglutination and hemagglutination-inhibition with arthropod-borne viruses".

George Brownlee Craig, Jr.: Craig graduated from the University of Indiana in 1951 with a B.A. in zoology and received both M. S. and Ph.D. degrees in entomology from the University of Illinois in 1952 and 1956, respectively, working under the renowned mosquito biologist-entomologist William R. Horsfall. While still a graduate student, he served in the military with the United States Army Preventive Medicine Detachment at Fort Meade, Maryland, in 1954 and as a research entomologist with the United States Army Chemical Center in Maryland from 1954 to 1957. He joined the biology faculty at the University of Notre Dame in 1957, beginning a 38-year career there, eventually being named Clark Professor of Biology, where he established the Vector Biology Laboratory and serving as a personal and scientific mentor for 40 Ph.D. students and 39 post-doctoral students. Among them were the accomplished John Beier, Richard Berry, William Black IV, Christopher Bosio, Durland Fish, Paul Grimstad, Robert Gwadz, William Hawley, William Hickey, Greg Lanzaro, Leonard Munstermann, Roger Nasci, Mark Niebylski, Robert Novak, George O'Meara, Sally Paulson, Jeffrey Powell, Donald Shroyer, Michael Sinsko, James Truman, Edward (Ned) Walker and Dawn Wesson, each of whom continued in Craig's footsteps by making significant contributions.

Scott Halstead: After graduation from Yale University in 1951, from Columbia University with a M.D. in 1955, and two years training in Internal Medicine, Scott B. Halstead was drafted into the United States Army Medical Corps, where he served for 11 years at the Department of Virus and Rickettsial Diseases, 406th Medical General Laboratory, Zama,

Japan, at the Department of Virus Diseases, Walter Reed Army Institute of Research, the Virology Department, South-East Asia Treaty Organization Medical Research Laboratory, Bangkok, Thailand and the Yale Arbovirus Research Unit, New Haven, Connecticut. In 1968, he was appointed Professor and Chair, Department of Medical Microbiology and Tropical Medicine, University of Hawaii School of Medicine. In 1983 he joined the Rockefeller Foundation, serving successively as Associate, Deputy and Acting Director of the Health Sciences Division. He retired from there in 1995 and was appointed Scientific Director, Infectious Diseases Program, United States Navy, Bethesda, Maryland and as Senior Scientist, Department of Molecular Microbiology and Immunology, School of Hygiene and Public Health, Johns Hopkins University, Baltimore, Maryland. Halstead is a recognized world leader in research on dengue and other arthropod-borne viral infections. He was co-founder of the Children's Vaccine Initiative and coordinator of the International Clinical Epidemiology Network and has served since 1967 as consultant to the World Health Organization. As one would expect, Halstead has published and edited widely, consults with private and public agencies, has been the recipient of many awards, served as President of the American Society of Tropical Medicine and Hygiene and the International Federation for Tropical Medicine, is a member of the American Academy of Microbiology, and has been awarded honorary degrees.

One of many reasons he is so widely respected is the novel mechanism called antibody-dependent enhancement that Halstead postulated was responsible for dengue viruses causing dengue hemorrhagic fever and dengue shock syndrome (DHF/DSS) rather than uncomplicated dengue fever. He hypothesized that antibody produced during primary infections with a dengue virus augmented the immunologic response to subsequent infections with another dengue virus and that that was the basis for the severe pathogenesis of dengue hemorrhagic fever and dengue shock syndrome. These are characterized by increased vascular permeability and abnormal blood clotting, leading to disseminated intravascular coagulation, which may be mediated by circulating virus-antibody complexes, activation of complement, and release of vasoactive amines. During immune elimination of infected cells, proteases and lymphokines may be released to activate complement coagulation cascades and vascular permeability factors. Because of this "antibody-dependent enhancement" phenomenon, vaccination against any one or more (but not all four simultaneously) of these viruses simply primes the immunologic pump and establishes a basis for the occurrence of dengue hemorrhagic fever when the vaccinee was next infected with a dengue virus, a solution perhaps worse than the problem. No useful and approved anti-dengue vaccine is available at this time, although many attempts have been and are being made to produce one.

Jean-Pierre Digoutte and **Vincent Deubel:** Born in 1927 in Damascus, Syria, Digoutte studied military health in Lyon and received his doctorate of medicine there. His first assignment was to Mauritania, but he joined the Pasteur Institute in 1966 and stayed with that remarkable organization until he retired. From 1966-1972 he was Director of the Pasteur Institute Bangui, Central African Republic. From 1972 to 1977 he directed the Pasteur Institute French Guiana, in Cayenne. In 1979, after a time as Managing Director of Overseas Pasteur Institutes and Scientific Cooperation, he was made Director of the Pasteur Institute Dakar, Senegal, a position he held until 1995. He guided Vincent Deubel who succeeded him as Director of the Dakar laboratories and is one of the world's experts on molecular biologic studies of viruses in general and of West Nile virus and dengue viruses in particular.

Throughout his career, Digoutte's work focused primarily on tropical virology. His contributions to that specialty in general, and to arbovirology in particular, were numerous and recognized world-wide. He was principally responsible for establishing a W.H.O. Collaborative Center for Arbovirus and Hemorrhagic Fever Virus Reference and Research in Dakar, where hundreds of thousands of mosquitoes, ticks, and other arthropods, as well as humans, livestock, wildlife, and other vertebrates were tested for viruses. Under his supervision, more than 5,000 viruses were identified, the work reported, information stored in a huge data base, and the samples stored for later studies by workers at the Pasteur Institute laboratories and elsewhere. Digoutte strongly supported reagent and information exchange and proved to be a knowledgeable and charming collaborator. Focusing on the natural history, epidemiology, movement, and emergence of African viruses, he studied yellow fever, dengue and Rift Valley fever viruses, as well as dozens of newly recognized viruses. After retiring officially, he continued to guide the Pasteur system as his interests and abilities prompted him; he died in 2005.

Deubel, born in 1948, graduated with a degree in biophysics from the University of Orleans and was awarded a Ph.D. in biophysics in 1973. He worked for 4 years on sexually transmitted diseases. Beginning in 1979, he studied the molecular virology of yellow fever virus and other viruses at the Pasteur Institute Dakar, Senegal. Deubel obtained a Doctorate in Sciences in virology from the University of Paris VII in 1985, then worked at the Centers for Disease Control laboratories in Colorado for two years to conduct research on dengue viruses, then returned to the Pasteur Institute in Paris where he headed the Unit of Arboviruses and Hemorrhagic fevers from 1987 to 2000. He became the Director of the Merieux-Pasteur Research Center in Lyon and the scientific director of the Jean Merieux P4 laboratory from 2000 to 2004.

In 2004 Deubel began serving as acting Director General of the Pasteur Institute Shanghai, Chinese Academy of Science, supervising 130 people collaborating on virologic research in 12 laboratories. The Institute rapidly gained recognition for the quality of its research programs. It developed several medical partnerships with hospitals, biomedical institutions, and the Chinese Centers for Disease Control and has participated in research projects and training within the international network of Pasteur Institutes, particularly those in Asia.

Deubel's research has focused on flaviviruses and zoonotic viruses causing hemorrhagic fever and encephalitis. He has contributed to the development of novel diagnostic tests, virus classification based on viral genome sequence data, and to our understanding of the mechanisms of viral pathogenesis. He has used recombinant gene expression systems and animal models to develop novel preventive measures against viral infections. Currently, he is collaborating with several international networks on epidemiology, diagnosis, and basic research of respiratory infections and encephalitis. In addition, he has developed a platform of "viromics" for the identification of newly emerging and re-emerging viruses. His studies of exotic viruses in laboratories in Paris and Lyon have served the world virologic and medical communities in multiple ways. At present, Deubel is assigned to the Pasteur Institute Cambodia (Phnom Penh), an entity created in a 1992 agreement between the royal government of Cambodia (now Kampuchea) and the Pasteur Institute. Originally created in 1953, the Pasteur Institute Cambodia was re-opened in 1995. Deubel now is the President of the Pasteur Institute International Network Executive Bureau.

I first met Deubel when he served as a Visiting Scientist in the CDC laboratories in Fort Collins while I was still there. Because of his excellent science his was a delightful and productive stay. We met again at scientific meetings and after a 2003 meeting on emerging viruses in Annecy, he invited me to visit the Pasteur Institute in Lyon, of which he was Director. His gracious hospitality and good humor made that visit a memorable one for me, with a drive through gorgeous wine country, a visit to the home of the great French physiologist Claude Bernard, and partaking of excellent foods and wines.

When I misunderstood my departure date from Lyon, Deubel had to hurriedly stuff me on a train to Geneva from where my plane was to take me to Brussels, then home early the next morning. When I arrived in Geneva about midnight the last plane had departed and I was not about to pay an inordinate sum to sleep in a hotel for two hours, so I decided to sleep in the airport. Swiss police, with machine guns, told me the airport was closing. I told them that was fine, so long as I could sleep there. They wished me well, turned off the lights and locked the doors. I read, took food from unlocked kiosks, left some money to pay for my thefts, and slept until the lights came on. I caught my flight to Brussels. When I arrived there I was met by two Belgian soldiers with machine guns who told me they had been ordered by an anonymous virologist to escort me to my connecting flight to be sure I did not become lost. I transferred planes at New York City and arrived in Denver just in time to greet a newly born granddaughter at the hospital. Not all trips go smoothly but all trips go well if one returns home safely.

Duane J. Gubler: A leader in dengue research for more than four decades, Gubler (Figure 141) obtained a B.Sc. degree in entomology and zoology from Utah State University and a M.Sc. degree in parasitology from the University of Hawaii in Honolulu, then enrolled in The Johns Hopkins University School of Hygiene and Public Health, Baltimore, where he studied pathobiology and tropical disease ecology, graduating with an Sc.D. degree. Following these experiences, he obtained a series of positions in places where he could study parasites and virus diseases. Principally, he has studied dengue and the viruses that cause its various manifestations: in Calcutta (now Kolkata), Jakarta, Indonesia, Urbana, Illinois, San Juan, Puerto Rico, and now Singapore, where he is Professor and Director of the Signature Research Program on Emerging Infectious Diseases at the Duke-National University of Singapore Graduate Medical School facility. He has developed techniques to study parasites and viruses, used those techniques to study displacement of mosquitoes of one species by mosquitoes of a closely related species, reproductive mechanisms of mosquitoes, transovarial transmission of viruses, the use of mosquitoes to detect and propagate dengue viruses, and the susceptibility to viruses of variant mosquito strains. He also studied epidemiologic, clinical and virologic characteristics of dengue, as well as details of individual epidemics and overviews of the huge problem of dengue and dengue hemorrhagic fever throughout the world, about which he likely now is the world expert.

Figure 141. Duane J Gubler (1939 -)
(image courtesy of Duane Gubler)

Karl M. Johnson: An excellent example of a brilliant, insightful, experienced and innovative arbovirologist and epidemiologist is Karl Johnson. Like so many arbovirologists, he also is great fun to be with. Johnson was educated at Oberlin College, graduated from the University of Rochester medical school, and did a residency and internship at Columbia-Presbyterian Hospital, in New York City. He spent five years at the United States National Institutes of Health studying the principles of laboratory and field practices of virology. While there Johnson was first to isolate and characterize parainfluenza 4 virus as well as five of the original nine rhinoviruses. He also demonstrated the respiratory disease potential of Coxsackie A-21 virus, studied reinfection by respiratory syncytial virus, and determined the experimental pathogenicities of several rhinoviruses. This broad background provided him an opportunity to expand his interests, which expanded to include just about every infectious disease.

In 1964 Johnson accepted an assignment in the Panama Canal Zone, where the National Institutes of Health had an active and capable laboratory, the Middle America Research Unit. Johnson eventually became its director and remained in that position for the next 12 years. While in Panama, he isolated a Venezuelan equine encephalitis virus from a human. He also investigated, isolated, and named Machupo virus, the cause of Bolivian hemorrhagic fever, and described the clinical disease, elucidated its prominent epidemiologic features and controlled the disease by a rodent control program based on virus-specific splenomegaly in the chronically infected reservoir-vector. Johnson helped establish a proper basis for designation of the family *Arenaviridae*, collaborated with Nathaniel Young in characterizing the various antigenic and pathogenic subtypes of Venezuelan encephalitis virus, and directed clinical trials of the attenuated Venezuelan equine encephalitis virus vaccine in equids in Central America, presaging the advance of that virus into Texas in 1971 and providing data useful in stemming that epidemic.

To provide merely one example of his imaginative thinking, consider a hypothesis that he, Robert Tesh and Pauline Peralta devised regarding the transmission of vesicular stomatitis Indiana virus. They proposed that this virus might be a plant virus, one which is transferred from plants to susceptible vertebrates under certain conditions and which then is amplified by certain arthropods to cause outbreaks or epidemics in vertebrates. The hypothesis is much more complex than this, and I recommend that the reader examine that paper (listed in *Suggested Readings*) for details. This anecdote is included here to demonstrate the innovative nature of Johnson and colleagues, not to imply that the hypothesis is correct. Indeed, those authors themselves asked whether this might not be a fantastic notion, intriguing or not. Ideas are the currency of science.

Johnson's ability to fascinate, recruit and retain a talented team of young investigators provided opportunities for them to gain useful experiences in arbovirology, including the first documentation of transovarial transmission of vesicular stomatitis virus in phlebotomine flies, the demonstration of circulating virus-antibody complexes in severe clinical yellow fever, investigations of Q fever, epidemic investigations of eastern equine encephalitis, and more. Johnson's works were all collaborative efforts, with Douglas F. Antczak, Byron N. Chaniotis, William H. Dietz,

Jr. Peter T. Franck, Pedro Galindo, David H. Martin, Pauline H. Peralta, C. J. Peters, William C. Reeves, Jr., Robert B. Tesh, Thomas E. Walton, and Patricia A. Webb among the principals. In addition to these investigators, who were at the Middle America Research Unit or the Gorgas Memorial Institute, Johnson brought in collaborators from laboratories in the United States, taking advantage of his contacts, his ability to excite people about studies in which he was interested, and the marvelous epidemiologic and other opportunities in the tropics. His associates in Panama were trained well, and all went on to become senior investigators and first-class scientists and administrators in various fields.

After his accomplishments in Panama, Johnson moved to the CDC as Chief of the Special Pathogens Branch (1975-1981), where he designed and established standards for the first maximum containment laboratory based on the principal of positive pressure plastic suits and complete primary containment of aerosols. He established and managed CDC's Lassa research station in Sierra Leone, defined the clinical virology of Lassa fever, and instituted a clinical trials unit that demonstrated the efficacy of ribavirin, an anti-viral drug, in therapy of patients with defined severe disease. He also co-discovered Hantaan virus and isolated Zaire ebolavirus.

In 1981 Johnson moved to the United States Army Medical Research Institute of Infectious Diseases. There he served as program director for hazardous viruses and manager for a program of discovery, disease and epidemiological elucidation, rapid diagnosis, molecular biology, pathogenesis, therapy and prevention of hazardous zoonotic viruses. Johnson developed a special unit to investigate the epidemiology of hantaviruses and the disease potential in *Rattus* species worldwide. From 1984 to 1992, Johnson advised various commercial biological companies and now considers himself "retired", though he continues to serve as a consultant to industry, governments, and academia on topics such as hantaviruses, ebolaviruses and other infectious diseases, on the design and use of maximum containment laboratories for medical and animal disease research, and on epidemiology and emergent diseases. Johnson also has served as President of the American Society for Tropical Medicine and Hygiene.

Dennis LeRoy Knudson: Born in Wolf Point, Montana, Knudson received his undergraduate education in biology at the University of Illinois, Urbana and a doctorate at the University of Oxford, in England (thesis entitled "Replication of Nuclear Polyhedrosis Viruses in Cell Cultures"). Knudson was a post-doctoral fellow at Yale University, working with Robert Shope and others and always was a productive and meticulous investigator. Because of his expertise in viral genomics, he served the International Committee for Taxonomy of Viruses in many important capacities, mostly regarding baculoviruses, orbiviruses and rhabdoviruses. Rejoining Beaty at Colorado State University, but in the Department of Entomology, College of Agricultural Sciences, Knudson applied his knowledge and intellect to studies of the application of molecular technologies to entomological disciplines, the use of baculoviruses as agents for integrated insect pest management, viral evolution, molecular epidemiology and the genetics of orbiviruses and baculoviruses. Knudson conducted physical mapping of the *Aedes aegypti* and *Culicoides variipennis* genomes and of barley (*Hordeum* species) and of the bacterial ring rot pathogen, *Clavibacter michiganensis,* all using fluorescent in situ hybridization. Truly a microbiologic renaissance man, Knudson's wide-ranging interests and expertise served both his universities and the virology and greater communities for many years.

Laura D. Kramer: Wanting to study the competence of mosquitoes to transmit viruses, Kramer worked with William C. Reeves, James L. Hardy, Sally B. Presser, Bruce F. Eldridge, Michael D. Bowen and others at the Department of Biomedical and Environmental Health Sciences, School of Public Health, University of California at Berkeley. Her work focused on the effects of vector competence on persistence and transmission of California serogroup and Bunyamwera serogroup viruses and studied entomological aspects of mosquito vectors of West Nile virus and California serogroup viruses with William K. Reisen, John Edman, and others at the Arbovirus Research Unit of the School of Veterinary Medicine, University California at Davis. Kramer now heads the Arbovirus Laboratory of the New York State Health Department laboratory. She has accumulated a remarkable body of information regarding human, bird, and mosquito infections with West Nile virus there and has been invaluable in working out some of the bases of the epidemiology of that virus.

Frederick A. Murphy: Murphy obtained his B.S. in bacteriology and D.V.M. degrees from Cornell University, served in the military, and attended University of California, School of Veterinary Medicine at Davis, where he obtained a Ph.D. in comparative pathology with emphasis in immunology. From 1964 to 1970 he honed his skills in electron microscopy in the Arbovirus Unit at CDC/Atlanta, then spent a year at the John Curtin School of Medical Research in Canberra, investigating the pathogenesis of viral diseases with Cedric A. Mims. He returned to CDC in 1972, remaining there until 1978, when he became Associate Dean of the College of Veterinary Medicine at Colorado State University. In 1983 he returned to CDC until 1991, when he became Dean of the School of Veterinary Medicine at the University of California at Davis. After stepping down from that post, Murphy served as Professor of Virology until 2005, when he moved to the University of Texas Medical Branch at Galveston. He continues to serve national and international public health by editing journals, sharing his wisdom and insights with other scientists and government boards, post-doctoral and other students, as well as with visiting scientists. Over the years these included Ernest Borden, Bernard Fields (Figure 142), Pekka Halonen, Brian Henderson, Martin Hirsch, Thomas Monath, Oyewale Tomori, David Walker, and Washington C. Winn. All went on to accomplished professional careers.

Figure 142. Bernard Nathan Fields (1938 - 1995)
(image courtesy of Frederick Murphy)

Murphy was a principal contributor in establishing virus families *Bunyaviridae, Rhabdoviridae, Filoviridae,* and *Arenaviridae* and the virus genus *Orbivirus* (family *Reoviridae*); he collaborated with others in naming them. Viruses of these families variously cause diseases of humans, livestock, and wild animals, diseases such as La Crosse encephalitis, rabies, vesicular stomatitis, Marburg disease, Ebola hemorrhagic fever, Bolivian and Argentine hemorrhagic fevers, and bluetongue, each a severe, serious and life-threatening disease.

Murphy was first to use antilymphocyte and antimacrophage globulins to study cell-mediated immunity in viral pathogenesis and chaired the International Committee on Taxonomy of Viruses and the Virology

Division of that committee. As Director of the National Center for Infectious Diseases at CDC, Murphy involved himself with programs concerning child health care, hepatitis B control, prevention and control of human immunodeficiency virus and Acquired Immune Deficiency Syndrome, Lyme disease, and food-borne diseases. Murphy also participated in the first identifications of hepatitis C virus and herpesvirus 6 and in programs to improve laboratory safety, laboratory design, and more. Murphy has been a meeting organizer, program chair, advisor to the United States National Academy of Sciences on International Security and Arms Control, to the Institute of Medicine Board on International Health, to the United States-Russian Program to convert former Soviet Biological Warfare Personnel and Facilities, and so on. Nonetheless, he remains true to his scientific roots, remains a believer in the importance and effectiveness of the American Committee on Arthropod-borne Viruses, and is a member of that group.

Stuart Thomas Nichol: After obtaining his undergraduate degree in the Department of Microbiology, University of Liverpool, Nichol attended Wolfson College, University of Cambridge for his Ph.D. and then was a postgraduate research biologist in the Department of Biology, University of California, San Diego. Moving to the University of Nevada at Reno, he rose through the ranks and then moved to the U.S. Centers for Disease Control in Atlanta. Nichol now is Chief of the Viral Special Pathogens Branch, Division of High-Consequence Pathogens and Pathology, Centers for Disease Control and Prevention. Along the way he has been a major player in the identification of many of the most hazardous and life-threatening viruses and entrusted with oversight of laboratory and field investigations of many of these viruses, including Crimean-Congo hemorrhagic fever, Marburg virus, many ebolaviruses, and Rift Valley fever virus, and has published on other viruses, including pathogenic reassortants. His contributions to molecular studies of viruses have set a high standard for innovation and usefulness and his pleasant demeanor has facilitated collaborative efforts with investigators world-wide.

Clarence J. Peters: C.J. Peters is another to have made enormous contributions to arbovirology and to hemorrhagic fever research. Born in Midland, Texas, Peters obtained a degree in chemistry from Rice University in Houston, then an M.D. degree from Johns Hopkins University in Baltimore. After first serving as medical intern and resident at Parkland Memorial Hospital, Dallas, he was a research associate in the United States Public Health Service (NIH), Middle America Research Unit, in the Panama Canal Zone, working with Karl Johnson and his hardy band of infectious disease investigators. In 1977, after another medical residency, this one at the University of California, San Diego, and a research fellowship in the Department of Immunopathology, Scripps Clinic and Research Foundation, La Jolla, he moved to the Virology Division, USAMRIID, Fort Detrick, in Frederick, Maryland, where he was a research scientist, then Chief of the Department of Viral Pathogenesis and Immunology in the Virology Division, becoming Chief of the Medical Division in 1982, Deputy Commander of USAMRIID, and Chief of the Disease Assessment Division. Fortunately for CDC, he left military service in 1991 and became Chief of the Special Pathogens Branch, Division of Viral and Rickettsial Diseases, National Center for Infectious Diseases in Atlanta, Georgia. His book, *Virus Hunter,* a personal and professional summary of his experiences with hazardous viruses, is dramatic but, unlike many other books dramatizing epidemic events, is not contrived.

In 2000 he moved again, this time to Galveston, Texas, to the University of Texas Medical Branch, where he has a number of titles and responsibilities, most importantly as Director for Biodefense, Center for Biodefense and Emerging Infectious Diseases, Professor, Departments of Microbiology and Immunology and Pathology, and John Sealy Distinguished University Chair in Tropical and Emerging Virology. His interests focus on diseases of humans, livestock and wildlife and the clear interrelationships among and pathogenetic mechanisms of those diseases.

Beginning with studies of the antigenic relationships of Tacaribe complex viruses and lymphocytic choriomeningitis virus with Wallace Rowe and Patricia Webb, Peters conducted in-depth investigations of the biology of arenaviruses and the diseases they cause. He studied various aspects of hepatitis (with William Reeves, Jr., Robert H. Purcell, Karl Johnson, and others). He participated in the initial investigations of Bolivian hemorrhagic fever (Machupo virus) in Cochabamba, conducted and evaluated results of serosurveys of various human pathogenic viruses; and conducted laboratory studies of the replication of dengue viruses and of Junin virus. Peters began a more than 30-year, wide-ranging effort to study Rift Valley fever in the Middle East and elsewhere and to develop a useable vaccine against Rift Valley fever virus infection. He led the team that discovered hantavirus pulmonary syndrome and the causative virus, Sin Nombre virus, in the Southwestern United States in 1993 and oversaw the public health response at the national level. He planned and led the CDC response to the ebolavirus outbreak in Zaire in 1995, investigated the Rift Valley fever outbreak in Kenya in 1997 and spearheaded a remote sensing approach to prediction of the occurrence of this disease, and managed the discovery and investigation of Nipah virus emergence in Malaysia in 1999. In general, he pursued studies of viral immunology, vaccines, epidemiology, the pathogenesis of viral diseases, and the genetic basis of host resistance. Peters' insightful and intellectual approach to a wide range of medical problems and their solutions is demonstrated most clearly when he teaches and lectures. He is, if not a national treasure, at least a national and international resource, and his more than 400 publications attest to his productivity. A former Chair of the American Committee on Arthropod-borne Viruses, his long and close association with arbovirology and arbovirologists demonstrates his continuing interest in the field.

William C. Reeves: Born in 1916 in Riverside, California, he became interested in insects at a young age, hence his childhood nickname, "Billy Bugs Reeves". That interest increased when he worked on a summer project while attending Riverside Junior College. He then obtained an undergraduate degree in entomology (1938) and a Ph.D. degree in medical entomology and parasitology (1943) at the University of California at Berkeley, where he focused on mosquito research. He went on to become the pre-eminent entomologist-epidemiologist of his time.

During World War II, Reeves worked as a civilian advisor to the United States military, investigating arboviruses in the United States and elsewhere. In due course, because he was the recognized expert in such matters and particularly because of his good humor, lack of patience, ability to write one word after another properly and to succinctly summarize multi-day meetings, he became a member of numerous national and international boards, committees, advisory panels, study groups, and the like. Reeves was one of a kind, and everyone who met him immediately recognized that. His tours through Australia, searching for clues to the natural history of Murray Valley encephalitis were classics, especially when he told the stories. He was the elected President of the American Society for Tropical Medicine and Hygiene, served as Chair of the American Committee on Arthropod-borne Viruses and was honored with the Richard M. Taylor Award of that group. As its long-time Treasurer he always complained when someone even suggested spending any of the small amount of funds it held, originally consisting of US $10,000, which had been donated by the Rockefeller Foundation, which is why that Committee did not go bankrupt. Thomas Yuill succeeded him as Treasurer and now Scott Weaver has succeeded Yuill. Thanks to them and their diligent supervision of the bank account, with very small annual voluntary dues and the sale of some special neckties there is now more than three times as much money in the account than was there when the Committee was established more than 50 years ago.

In 1949 Reeves earned an additional Master's degree, this one in epidemiology, and became professor of epidemiology at the University of California-Berkeley, then headed the school's epidemiology program, advising scores of students in his inimitable fashion, and served as Dean of the School of Public Health. He stepped down as Dean and retired in 1987, having spent 41 years as a faculty member at the University of California-Berkeley. He continued to work in his campus office four days a week.

When West Nile virus was discovered to be causing serious, sometimes fatal, human and bird illnesses in New York City in 1999, Reeves was coaxed out of "retirement" to join conference calls with workers at the CDC and various state health departments, so that he could provide his invaluable knowledge and insights. He was often the catalyst in such discussions. A serious, humorous, and insightful interview with Reeves can be found in his oral history at the web site of the Bancroft Library University of California – Berkeley, School of Public Health.

Rebeca Rico-Hesse: Born in Los Angeles, California, and raised in Saltillo, Coahuila, Mexico, Rico-Hesse obtained an undergraduate degree at the University of Nebraska at Lincoln; a Master of Public Health degree at the University of Minnesota, Minneapolis; and a Ph.D. at Cornell University Medical College in New York City under the tutelage of William Scherer. At the time of Scherer's sudden and unexpected death, Rico-Hesse was his student. She finished her laboratory studies with Dennis W. Trent at CDC in Fort Collins but obtained her degree from Cornell University. After serving as a Postdoctoral Fellow at the CDC in Atlanta, she became an Associate Professor in the Department of Epidemiology and Public

Health at Yale University and now works in the Department of Virology and Immunology at the Southwest Foundation for Biomedical Research in San Antonio, Texas. Having received many honors, Rico-Hesse serves or has served on NIH and CDC committees and is a member of national and international professional associations. She plays an active role in the American Society of Tropical Medicine and Hygiene and the American Committee on Arthropod-borne Viruses, where she has served as Chair of the Executive Committee.

Rico-Hesse began her publishing career with papers on Venezuelan equine encephalitis virus, then on poliomyelitis viruses (at CDC), then back to Venezuelan equine encephalitis virus, then to molecular epidemiology of Japanese encephalitis virus and other viruses, and, most recently and significantly, the molecular epidemiology, molecular evolution and pathogenesis of dengue viruses. Through her work, and of course the work of others, we now have a greater understanding of these viruses, so that production and application of acceptable vaccines against them is nearer realization.

Rico-Hesse collaborated with Rosa Alba Salas, Nuris de Manzione, Hector Paredes and others in Guanare and Caracas, Venezuela, Charles F. Fulhorst and Robert B. Tesh at the University of Texas Medical Branch at Galveston, and Thomas G. Ksiazek, James N. Mills, Barbara A Ellis, and C.J. Peters at the CDC in Atlanta on the discovery of Guanarito arenavirus, the etiologic agent of Venezuelan hemorrhagic fever. She further documented the emergence of epidemic Venezuelan equine encephalitis virus in Venezuela with Scott C. Weaver, Julieta de Siger, Gladys Medina, and Rosa Alba Salas.

Among other notable contributions she made, Rico-Hesse used nucleic acid sequence data to predict the evolutionary and functional relationships of arenaviruses of the Western Hemisphere. The results indicate that these New World arenaviruses have been evolving independently of one another for a very long time and that this has led to divergent virus complexes that do not correlate with geography, rodent host, or human epidemic potential. After the discovery of Sabia arenavirus, the etiologic agent of Brazilian hemorrhagic fever, described by T. Lisieux Moraes Coimbra, Amelia P. Travassos da Rosa, Pedro Vasconcelos, Francisco de Paulo Pinheiro, James Leduc, Jean-Paul Gonzalez, Peter Jahrling, and Robert Tesh, as well as others in Brazil and the United States, she worked with Michael D. Bowen, Stuart T. Nichol and others to genetically characterized that virus. Clearly, the professional interactions and collaborations among arbovirologists are essential to accomplishments in arbovirology and all of science.

Leon Rosen: As mentioned previously, one brilliant and stubborn investigator who opposed universal acceptance of Halstead's hypothesis was Leon Rosen. While working at NIH, Rosen initially and principally studied hepatitis viruses and enteroviruses. Recognizing that one of the many viruses classified as an enterovirus was, in fact, not an enterovirus, he showed that this virus, and two others related to it were members of a different family, the reoviruses (family *Reoviridae*). Although involved in many other investigations of virus diseases, Rosen came to focus his efforts on dengue and the viruses that cause it. He postulated that DHF could be caused by particularly virulent strains of dengue viruses or that human genetics, parasitic or other infections, or other associated factors might be involved. Halstead and Rosen, both brilliant physician-scientists, argued long, and sometimes loudly, at scientific meetings. They likely both were correct, with Halstead's hypothesis now more generally accepted as the common cause of DHF.

Phillip K. Russell: Not the last in a long line of talented and devoted military professionals in the United States Army (George Sternberg, Walter Reed, William Gorgas, Joseph Smadel, Edwin Lennette, Edward Buescher, Albert Sabin among them), Phillip K. Russell made and led others who made significant contributions to arbovirology. A native of Syracuse, New York, Russell received an A.B. in Biology from Johns Hopkins University and an M.D. from the University of Rochester. After an internship at North Carolina Memorial Hospital in Chapel Hill he entered the United States Army Medical Corps and completed his residency training in internal medicine at University Hospital (University of Maryland), Baltimore. During his military career, Russell conducted and directed research on a variety of infectious diseases and managed several vaccine development programs. At one time or another, he was Chief of the Department of Virus Diseases; Director of the Division of Communicable Diseases; and Deputy Director, Institute Director and Commandant at Walter Reed Army Institute of Research. His overseas medical research assignments included the Pakistan Medical Research Center in Lahore, Chief of Virology at the Southeast Asia Treaty Organization Medical Research Laboratory in Bangkok, and Commander of the United States Army Medical

Research Team in Vietnam. Russell served as Commander of Fitzsimons Army Medical Center in Aurora, Colorado, and Commander of the United States Army Medical Research and Development Command. He retired from the Army as a Major General with many awards and was then appointed Professor in the Department of International Health at the Johns Hopkins University School of Hygiene and Public Health, serving on many national and international advisory groups, including the Institute of Medicine Committee on Microbial Threats to Health and the President's Advisory Committee on Human Radiation Experiments. Russell also served as a member of the Board of Scientific Counselors of CDC's National Center for Infectious Diseases. In addition, Russell served as Special Advisor to, and member of the Board of Directors of, the International Children's Vaccine Initiative – a global coalition of organizations from the public, non-governmental and private sectors, including the vaccine industry. He served as Founding President of the Albert B. Sabin Vaccine Institute, where he currently serves as Trustee, and is a member of the Board of Directors of the Aeras Foundation. His more than 40 years' interest in and focus on dengue have resulted in substantial programs to study and control this disease.

I first met Russell in 1969 in Puerto Rico. I had been sent there by the CDC to help investigate what eventually was recognized as a huge epidemic of dengue virus 2. Russell had traveled there to see what he could do to lessen the rate of acquisition of this virus and disease by United States military personnel and civilian employees. We spent considerable time discussing what I knew to that point and Russell told me some of what he knew about dengue and dengue viruses. He invited me to have dinner at the Officer's Club at a military base and I accepted.

After dinner, Russell introduced me to a pilot who, with his crew, was scheduled to overfly San Juan and spray insecticide on the city in an attempt to reduce its mosquito population. As it was by now 1 AM, the flight was to leave at 5 AM, and the pilot appeared to me to have had at least one too many drinks, I passed on the opportunity. I never regretted that decision.

Toby D. St. George: St. George was born in Wynnum, near Brisbane and obtained Bachelor's, Master's and Doctorate of Veterinary Science at the University of Queensland. Sitting on the examining board for the latter were Ralph Doherty, Robert Shope and Frederick Murphy. After six years with the Department of Agriculture of South Australia and two years as a veterinary inspector in the United States working for the U.S.D.A., he accumulated considerable experience in diagnosis and control of infectious and nutritional diseases of farm animals. He spent useful time at Cornell University in Ithaca, New York, Mukteswar, India, Pando, Uruguay, Harbin, China and other places, his perspective widening at each stop. After serving as a Major in the Australian Army in Vietnam in 1971, he returned to Australia in research positions with the Commonwealth Scientific and Industrial Research Organization in Melbourne and Brisbane, where he became Chief Research Scientist. St. George's continuing interest in assisting developing countries with their livestock disease problems supplemented his primary work to diagnose and control livestock problems in Australia. In 1974, after a visit to the United States Centers for Disease Control and Prevention in Fort Collins, St. George began to focus more intensely on the arboviruses of Australia. Although these certainly were known to occur by the score, St. George established study sites and sentinel cattle herds near Darwin and elsewhere in the Northern Territory, sites that were remarkably productive in terms of viruses, vectors, disease and publications. To this day, some of those many viruses are being identified and further characterized. Having had a wide-ranging career in veterinary virology, St. George retired but, as do so many "retired" arbovirologists, he continues to take an active interest in these fascinating viruses and to follow the ever-continuing story of bovine ephemeral fever in Australia and elsewhere.

William F. Scherer: A person of gentlemanly manner and wide-ranging interests, Scherer graduated from the University of Rochester (New York) School of Medicine and Dentistry in 1947, interned in medicine at Barnes Hospital in St. Louis, served an internship in pathology at Strong Memorial Hospital in Rochester, and completed a residency in medicine at Vanderbilt Hospital from 1949 to 1950. At the University of Minnesota medical school from 1950 to 1962, he became Professor of Microbiology. In 1962 he was appointed Professor and Chairman of the Department of Microbiology at Cornell Medical College, where he continued to make scientific contributions of lasting importance. While in Minnesota he worked with George O. Gey and Jerome T. Syverton to propagate poliomyelitis viruses in cell cultures. Following the lead of Enders, Weller, and Robbins, who had accomplished that a few years previously, Scherer and his co-workers made additional fundamental findings regarding the replication of viruses in cells grown in vitro and were first to demonstrate that poliomyelitis viruses replicate in HeLa cells.

At the Department of Virus and Rickettsial Diseases, 406th Medical General Laboratory, United States Army, Japan, in the 1950s, Scherer and many colleagues, including Buescher, Jack M. McCown, James L. Hardy and John Scanlon, conducted classic investigations of Japanese encephalitis virus and the disease it causes in humans. Given his background, he naturally studied the replication of that virus in cell cultures but also considered the immune responses of both humans and wild birds (a natural vertebrate host of that virus) and, transmission of the virus by its vector mosquito, *Culex tritaeniorhynchus.* Scherer conducted experimental infections of a principal vertebrate host, the black crowned night heron (*Nycticorax nycticorax*), at the Sagiyama heronry. This body of work provided fascinating conclusions, including observations that *Cx. tritaeniorhynchus* mosquitoes tend to feed on pigs, which explained the high frequency of virus infection in pigs detected during an outbreak of Japanese encephalitis near Sagiyama a few years earlier. Scherer and colleagues further concluded that pigs may serve as hosts for this virus. Today we recognize the natural epidemic cycle of this virus to include pig to mosquito to birds (herons) and only incidentally to humans. Scherer and his entomological co-workers went as far as to determine the flight paths of *Cx. tritaeniorhynchus* mosquitoes, which helped to explain the spread of Japanese encephalitis virus among birds nesting in tree tops.

Were all these findings a fortuitous coincidence because Scherer was the right person in the right place at the right time? Or were they the result of brilliant insight? Here was a physician, trained in human medicine, who turned his interests towards understanding the essentials of the natural history of a virus and, therefore, the basis of a disease. After receiving many awards and appointments to NIH and United States Army boards, Scherer served as Director of the Armed Forces Epidemiology Board's Commission on Viral Infections for eight years. As a bonus, he discovered a newly recognized virus, Sagiyama alphavirus. Motivated by this discovery, he became interested in virus identification. Through the rest of his career until his untimely death, Scherer supported and contributed to virus discovery and classification. His arbovirological studies in El Salvador, Guatemala, Mexico, Nicaragua, Panama, Peru, and Trinidad provided essential information regarding the presence of these viruses. With collaborators from each country and his students (C. Campillo-Saenz, A. Diaz-Najera, Pedro Galindo, Herbert Hurlbut, Julio de Mucha Macias, Jose Madalengoitia, Bette A. Pancake, Rebecca Rico-Hesse, Sunthorn Srihongse, Arnoldo Ventura, Michael Wiebe, Cesar Wong-Chia, Maria Luisa Zarate, and many more), he discovered and partially characterized many arboviruses, established the use of sentinel hamsters to measure the rates of mosquito exposure and virus prevalence and to discover even more viruses, and reported the discovery of Nodamura virus. Scherer isolated the latter from mosquitoes, finding it both ether- and chloroform-resistant and otherwise unlike most other arboviruses. Nodamura virus is now recognized as the prototype of an entirely new family of viruses, the *Nodaviridae*.

Figure 143. Peter Becker Jahrling (1946 -)
(image courtesy of Peter Jahrling)

Because he enjoyed teaching and was an excellent teacher, Scherer welcomed graduate students, planning to pass the torch when the time came. One of his students was Peter B. Jahrling (Figure 143), formerly with the U. S. Army Medical Research Institute of Infectious Diseases, now the principal scientific advisor to the NIH on issues related to medical defense against infectious disease threats. Jahrling, one of the top national defense and public health experts, has devised animal models for diseases caused by exotic and hazardous viruses, work that has led to improved vaccines, antiviral drugs, and improved diagnostics. Among others trained by Scherer and his long-time colleague Robert Dickerman, the expert ornithologist, were Laura D. Kramer, Rebeca Rico-Hesse, Scott C. Weaver, Eddie W. Cupp and Charles Seymour.

> In 1970 I was privileged to be appointed to the Armed Forces Epidemiology Board Commission on Viral Infections' Dengue Task Force as the CDC representative; the Chair was William Scherer. The night before attending my first meeting, I was registering at a motel near the Walter Reed Army Institute of Research near Washington, D.C. when Scherer, Jordi Casals, and other scientists on the Commission entered the lobby and tried to register. Scherer was just off a plane, returning from a field study in Latin America and was wearing a ruana, a poncho-like blanket. As he tried to register, the manager of the motel told him that he "and his hippie friends" were not welcome to stay. I explained to the manager who these fine gentlemen were, but to no avail. We found shelter elsewhere. Thereafter, Scherer was known to some of us as "the hippie".

Figure 144. Robert Swanepoel (1936 -)
(image courtesy of Robert Swanepoel)

Robert Swanepoel: Born in Lichtenburg, South Africa, Swanepoel (Figure 144) obtained veterinary degrees at the University of Pretoria and the University of Edinburgh and a Ph.D. degree at the University of Edinburgh. A member of the Royal College of Veterinary Surgeons, he has worked in veterinary medicine and taught in Zimbabwe and Malawi, and in 1980 became Chief Specialist Scientist, Special Pathogens Unit, National Institute for Virology (now National Institute for Communicable Diseases), Johannesburg. He retired from that post in 2001 but immediately was reappointed there. He has had many joint appointments in medical schools, headed a W.H.O. Regional Collaborating Centre for Reference and Research on Viral Haemorrhagic Fevers and Arboviruses, has had many honors, committee and advisory board memberships, editorial positions and advisory posts. When investigators around the world want information about a veterinary or human disease problem in Africa, particularly emerging and otherwise dangerous diseases, they sensibly contact Swanepoel.

Figure 145. Jelka Vesenjak-Hirjan (1913 - 1992)
(image courtesy of Deanka Hirjan)

Jelka Vesenjak-Hirjan: A physician, Vesenjak-Hirjan (Figure 145) began her scientific career by investigating poliomyelitis cases in 1960, then turned to the study of tick-borne encephalitis in Slovenia (where she was born), influenzavirus infections, adenovirus infections, rickettsial diseases and Q fever. She spent a sabbatical year in Ceylon (now Sri Lanka); conducted surveys for antibody to arboviruses in humans; and renewed her interests in arboviruses and rodent-borne viruses. After returning to Yugoslavia, she discovered a focus of the hantaviral-caused hemorrhagic fever with renal syndrome in Plitvice Lakes National Park, Croatia. Working with collaborators from her Andrija Štampar School of Public Health in Zagreb (Zvonimir Brudnjak, Josip Fališevac, Volga Punda-Polić, Vlasta Vince, Marija Galinović-Weisglass), as well as with Danica Tovornik, (an entomologist working at the Institute of Public Health, Ljubljana, Slovenia), she investigated tick-borne encephalitis in northern (near Slovenia) and southern (Adriatic coastal) Croatia. Vesenjak-Hirjan and her colleagues showed that many fewer encephalitis cases and fewer deaths occurred on the coastal islands than in heavily wooded areas of the north but that the prevalence of infection with this virus was higher in the south than in the north. They later showed that repasturing sheep from north to south "seeded" the paths with ticks infected with tick-borne encephalitis virus, thereby spreading the virus.

Their investigations of hemorrhagic fever with renal syndrome in enlisted military personnel indicated an epidemiologic association between sleeping on the ground without ground sheets and infection in enlisted personnel but not in officers, who were housed in tents with flooring. Once the enlisted men were provided with adequate housing, no more cases occurred.

As a dividend of their work, Vesenjak-Hirjan led a team that isolated Bhanja virus from ticks collected in Croatia, a virus that had been isolated previously only in India. Bhanja virus was shown to cause both laboratory and natural infections, some fatal. Studies elsewhere, by others, have now demonstrated that Bhanja virus occurs in Italy, Bulgaria, Slovakia, Romania, Portugal, southern and central Asia, and Africa. Vesenjak-Hirjan's persistence with less than optimum funding and logistical support and under difficult political conditions made her an unsung heroine to many.

Scott C. Weaver: An exceptional member of this generation of viral molecular biologists, Weaver is Professor and Vice Chair for Research, Department of Pathology, and Director of Tropical and Emerging Infectious Diseases, Center for Biodefense and Emerging Infectious Diseases, University of Texas Medical Branch at Galveston, and Director of the Galveston National Laboratory.

Weaver attended The College of William and Mary, where he obtained a Bachelor of Science degree in biology and music, and Cornell University, where he earned a Master of Science degree in medical entomology (advisors Eddie W. Cupp and William F. Scherer). After obtaining a Ph.D. in molecular biology and virology at the University of California, San Diego (advisor, John Holland), Weaver served as a postdoctoral fellow at Yale University School of Medicine (advisor, Robert Tesh) and collaborated with Rebeca Rico-Hesse while both were there. Moving to the University of Texas Medical Branch at Galveston in 1994, Weaver's studies have emphasized basic research on the genetics, ecology, evolution, and pathogenesis of arboviruses; virus-mosquito interactions; and vaccine development. Studies of viral phylogenesis, mosquito vector competence, experimental infections, molecular epidemiology, taxonomy and evolution, as well as collaborative immunologic studies of AIDS patients and HIV, and of the biology of bats attest to his wide interests.

His devotion to academic responsibilities accompanies a parallel devotion to and energetic activities for the American Committee on

Arthropod-borne Viruses and the American Society for Tropical Medicine and Hygiene, where Weaver participates in the work of committees and subcommittees. A member of grant review panels and study sections, manuscript reviewer par excellence, journal editor and patent holder, and by now heaped with honors and awards, Weaver is still relatively young and it is expected that through his energy and intellectual approach to virological problems he will accomplish even more in the future.

Thomas M. Yuill: Involved in the recognition of overwintering of La Crosse virus in mosquitoes since the early days of those studies, Yuill was born in California and obtained his B.S. degree in wildlife management from Utah State University and M.S. and Ph.D. degrees in veterinary science and wildlife ecology from the University of Wisconsin at Madison, focusing on epizoology of infectious diseases of domestic and wild animals. He held research positions in the Department of Virus Diseases, Walter Reed Army Institute of Research, and in the Virology Department of the South East Asia Treaty Organization Medical Research Laboratory in Bangkok, Thailand. In 1968 he returned to the University of Wisconsin at Madison as an assistant professor with joint appointments in other departments, developing research and graduate training programs in epizoology of infectious diseases of wildlife and domestic animals in Wisconsin and Latin America. In 1979 he became professor and chairman of the Department of Veterinary Science and a few years later was appointed Associate Dean for Research and Graduate Training in the University of Wisconsin's School of Veterinary Medicine and assistant director in the university's Agricultural Experiment Station. Yuill subsequently served for a year as the Chief of Party for a University of Wisconsin-led team advising the Bolivian Government on restructuring their national agricultural research and extension agency. Upon his return from Bolivia in 1993, he became director of the Institute for Environmental Studies, where he served until his retirement from the University. After retiring in 2003, Yuill was appointed to various emeritus positions, has been given many awards for his excellent work with and effective administration of the Organization for Tropical Studies (president), the Wildlife Disease Association (treasurer and president), and the United States-Japan Biomedical Sciences Program. He has served as consultant on wildlife diseases to the states of Wisconsin and North Dakota, and to the United States Environmental Protection Agency, on arbovirus-caused diseases to the United States National Institutes of Health, and on higher education in the agricultural sciences to the United States Agency for International Development, mainly in India. Author of many scores of scientific papers and book chapters, Yuill is an outstanding example of a scientist-administrator whose comprehensive interests, fostered by the study of arboviruses, have led him down an exceedingly productive path. An active and enthusiastic member of the American Committee on Arthropod-borne Viruses in whatever there was of his spare time, Yuill served as a knowledgeable resource, common sense advisor, and treasurer of that group for decades. He continues to apply his expertise and vast knowledge as a Moderator of ProMED.

ACKNOWLEDGMENTS

During fits of writing I received considerable assistance from colleagues who critiqued individual sections (Barry Beaty, Scott Halstead, Stephen Higgs, Marian Horzinek, Karl Johnson, James Leduc, Donald McLean, James Mills, Thomas Monath, David Morens, Frederick Murphy, Robert Tesh, and Scott Weaver). They were helpful to me and I am grateful to them for their frank comments, particularly Murphy and Monath; this book could not have been written without their suggestions and contributions.

I could have dedicated the book principally to the people who taught me what was what, and otherwise nurtured me over more than 50 years of studying viruses in general and arboviruses and rodent-borne virus in particular. These include my family, of course, without whom I might have been a beer-drinking baseball fanatic, single, and alone; thanks to them, I am only one of these. In the 1960s, while I was a graduate student at Georgetown University in Washington, D.C. and also an employee at what was then Microbiological Associates, Inc. (now Bioreliance Corp.) in Bethesda, Maryland, my mentors pointed out many of the fascinating and important peculiarities of viruses: Thomas G. Ward, M.D., of Microbiological Associates, Inc., and Bernice E. Eddy, Ph.D., M.D., Sarah E. Stewart, Ph.D., Janet W. Hartlcy, M.D., Robert J. Huebner, M.D., Karl M. Johnson, M.D., Leon Rosen, M.D., and Wallace P. Rowe, M.D. of the United States National Institutes of Health (NIH). Each gave me a hint or a gentle shove to get me started in my career in virology. It was the late Robert Huebner who sent me to the Library of Congress in 1963 to find the first mention of "mouse" in the Hebrew scriptures! The fun never stopped after that. Willie Warfield, my friend and informal mentor at the University of Notre Dame and at Microbiological Associates, Inc., without whom I would have been sunk, contributed more than he ever knew.

I thank Arthur E. Greene, Ph.D., my college microbiology teacher, who guided me ever so gently away from bacteriology towards virology and Roy E. Ritts, Jr., M.D., Chair of the Department of Microbiology at Georgetown University Medical School, whose support and good humor kept me afloat long enough to swim away.

Were it not for hundreds of people, active participants in the writing of this book, people who encouraged me, who provided references, insights, stories, photos, leads, and clues, putting all this in one place would have been impossible. Over a decade or longer, Fred Murphy, my empathetic, long time, and good friend, a great pathologist, virologist, and administrator, a true believer in all things arbovirus and disease, and a huge Bob Cousy fan, urged me to write this. Without his frank comments and unwavering support (and very gentle reminders), nothing would have gotten done. A passel of arbovirologists and others encouraged, prodded, cajoled, and wheedled me, and eventually won. It was not that I did not want to put this together, it just appeared to be too onerous a task to try to describe, in anything like a chronological order, the tangled history of arbovirology and the contributions of people that I respected, admired, and loved. Some of these people are no longer with us in body but they certainly are in spirit and in what they left us.

Thomas Monath, who was and still is my Best Man, my longtime friend, supervisor, encouraging leader, hard-nosed editor, knowledgeable medical historian, and provider of numerous photos, tidbits, suggestions and laughs, always turned me in the right direction when I headed in the wrong one. He never said "No" to anything I wanted to do and has always been there when personal or professional difficulties arose.

Of others who provided the most encouragement and sent papers, photos, and memories, provided historical perspectives, or who at one time or another provided access to historic files or insights, the following stand out: Harvey Artsob, Barry Beaty, John Booss, Walter Brandt, Donald Burke, Joel Breman, Alexander Butenko, Donald Carey, Stanton Cope, Judy De Acetis, Xavier de Lamballerie, Robert Dickerman, Bruce Eldridge, Durland Fish, Ernesto Gutierrez, Andrew Haddow, Scott Halstead, Marian Horzinek, Karl Johnson, Laura Kramer, Louis LaMotte, James Leduc, Rexford Lord, Dmitri Lvov, John Mackenzie, Terry Maguire, Robert McLean, Donald McLean, Loredana Nicoletti, Ananda Nisalak, Malik Peiris, Francisco Pinheiro, Betty Porterfield, William Reisen, Charles Rice, José Rigau, Phillip Russell, Richard Russell, Toby St. George, Jean-Francois Saluzzo, Alexis Shelokov, Leslie Spence, Robert Swanepoel, Robert Tesh, Gregory Tignor, Elisha Tikasingh, Oyewale Tomori, Amelia Travassos da Rosa, Guido van der Groen, Pedro Vasconcelos, Daan Verwoerd, Thomas Walton, Douglas Watts, Scott Weaver, John Woodall, Martine Jozan Work, Betty Young, and Thomas Yuill. I hope I have not overlooked someone; if I have, I apologize sincerely.

Many of those named above have made significant contributions to our knowledge of arboviruses. The fact that I did not use them as examples of investigators whose accomplishments were pivotal does not in any way lessen the significance of their contributions. If readers will search Pubmed, they can see for themselves.

For providing DVD copies of the Workers in Tropical Medicine series, I am grateful to Thomas Monath and to the American Society of Tropical Medicine and Hygiene. It was enjoyable to see old friends again, even if only by video; simply seeing them stirred marvelous memories. For his excellent work to improve old, yellowed, or damaged photos, I thank Rusty Gruppo, Front Range DVD Solutions, Loveland, Colorado.

Invited by Durland Fish to present a seminar at Yale University School of Public Health some years ago, I was asked if I would be willing to take a look at many boxes of stored files, and to advise whether any of the contents were worth retaining. Knowing that when Robert Shope and Robert Tesh left Yale University to go to Galveston, they had taken with them all the files they thought were useful and meaningful, I expected that nothing I would come across would be useful to me in writing this book; I was wrong. The contents of those boxes included sheets containing data that had been summarized and published and therefore were of no tangible value to anyone. Still, as I more carefully went through those boxes, I came across pieces of paper that had been carefully handled and often completed by hand by some of the people mentioned above, including Jordi Casals-Ariet and Robert E. Shope. Though they no longer had scientific value, they certainly had sentimental value. These were read, tears dropped, and then the documents were shredded.

Not enough can be said about the members of the American Committee on Arthropod-borne Viruses, an unusually intelligent, caring, sensitive, and eclectic group of people, the heart and soul of arbovirology. Without the continuing support and joy they provided, this book would not have been written because there would not have been anything to write. When I arrived at the annual meetings of this group and of the American Society of Tropical Medicine and Hygiene, wherever it was held, I always had the feeling that "the clan" was gathering from far and wide and knew that the next few days would be enjoyable, informative, and, usually, amazing.

From 1965-1973 I had the opportunity to work for or with Telford H. Work, Roy W. Chamberlain, Leo E. Chester, Philip H. Coleman, Paul M. Feorino, Brian W. Henderson, John C. Hierholzer, Helen Lindsay-Regnery, Rexford D. Lord, Kathryn S. Carruthers Maness, Frederick A. Murphy, Donna Sasso, W. Daniel Sudia, and many, many others who comprised the marvelous staff at the United States Centers for Disease Control in Atlanta. It continues to amaze me that I was encouraged to take on so many interesting and enjoyable tasks, to meet so many great scientists, to have adventures throughout the world and, as well, to get paid.

I find it impossible to adequately acknowledge all who contributed to this book. Does one thank and mention hundreds of people? One or two or twenty of the most key people? Funding institutions? The many who influenced me and helped make me who I am (in addition to my parents)? Scores of scientists and others made contributions small or large to this book and to me personally, but it was their individual and collective contributions to arbovirology in particular and to virology in general that remain important. Among a host of giants in the field, people with whom I have had the pleasure and honor to collaborate over many decades and of whom I remain in awe include the following: Thomas H.G. Aitken, Ph.D., Barry J. Beaty, Ph.D., Jordi Casals-Ariet, M.D., Mikhail Petrovich Chumakov, M.D., Joel M. Dalrymple, Ph.D., Wilbur G. Downs, M.D., Richard W. Emmons, M.D., Clarence Joseph ("Joe") Gibbs, Jr., Ph.D., Ernest A. Gould, Ph.D., Scott B. Halstead, M.D., Harry Hoogstraal, Ph.D., John S. Mackenzie, M.D., Julio Maiztegui, M.D., Thomas P. Monath, M.D., Frederick A. Murphy, D.V.M., Ph.D., Neal Nathanson, M.D., C.J. Peters, M.D., Vanda V. Pogodina, M.D., James S. Porterfield, M.D., William C. Reeves, Ph.D., Leon Rosen, M.D., Robert E. Shope, M.D., Robert B. Tesh, M.D., Amelia P.A. Travassos da Rosa, Ph.D., Toby D. St. George, D.V.M. and lastly, but certainly not leastly, Gilberta Bensabath, M.D., David H.L. Bishop,Ph.D., Walter Brandt, Ph.D., Carol Blair, Ph.D., Charles Fulhorst, Dr. P.H., D.V.M., Duane Gubler, D.Sc., James Hardy, Ph.D., Nick Karabatsos, Ph.D., Robert Kokernot, M.D., John Austin Kerr, M.D., Edwin Lennette, M.D., Rexford Lord, Ph.D., Ian Marshall, Ph.D., Ronald Mackenzie, M.D., Donald McLean, M.D., James Meegan, Ph.D., Stuart Nichol, Ph.D., Fu-Xi Qiu, M.D., William Reisen, Ph.D., Pierre Rollin, M.D., Albert Rudnick, M.D., Gladys Sather, M.S., Donald Stamm, Ph.D., Walter Tabachnick, Ph.D., Thomas E. Walton, D.V.M., Ned Wiebenga, M.D., John P. Woodall, Ph.D., and many others far too numerous to mention made major contributions to arbovirology and hemorrhagic fever research.

I had opportunities to work with and to guide students at both CDC and at Colorado State University. Some were short-term visitors from domestic or foreign laboratories, others were employed elsewhere and did their research work with me or were CDC employees attempting to add research experience to their resumes and to gain an additional degree. These included Ying Bai, M.D., Ph.D., Gerald L.

Brooks, Dr. P.H.; Kathryn S.C. Maness, M.S.; Helen S. Lindsey, M.S.; Richard M. Kinney, M.S.; Ann R. Hunt, M.S.; Volga Punda, Ph.D.; Jon Jeffery Root, Ph.D.; Brooke A. Roeper, M.S.; and a post-doctoral fellow, Irene V. Wesley.

Without the expert and devoted assistance of numerous technicians, the results achieved in the laboratory and in the field would have been significantly less. These included Kathryn S.C. Maness, who died at an early age and whose loss shattered dreams and lives, Leo E. Chester, David J. Muth, John S. Lazuick, Jon Jeffery Root, Jeffrey B. Doty and Katherine L. Wolff.

Shelley Calisher, my wife, soul mate, and primary editor did a great job organizing or re-organizing the text I had given her in the hope that she would do what she has done many times before: turn a sow's ear into a silk purse. If this book contains factual, spelling, grammatical or organizational errors they are mine and such errors likely were introduced due to my refusal to accept the good advice given to me in an attempt to save me from myself.

Finally, I thank my family: Shelley as well as our children, Jennifer, Daniel, Sarah and Sean, all of whom think I am interesting, but a bit wacky and difficult.

SUGGESTED READINGS

It is impossible to list here all the many thousands of publications pertaining to arboviruses and hemorrhagic fever viruses. Therefore, following are some of the many key publications that relate to the contents of this book. The reader is urged to search for other publications to gain an even better appreciation of the superb work that has been done.

Agramonte, A. 1908. An account of Dr. Louis-Daniel Beauperthuy — a pioneer in yellow fever research. *Boston Med. Surg. J.* 158:927-930.

Agüero, M., J. Fernández-Pinero, D. Buitrago, A. Sánchez, M. Elizalde, E. San Miguel, R. Villalba, F. Llorente, and M.A. Jiménez-Clavero. 2011. Bagaza virus in partridges and pheasants, Spain, 2010. *Emerg. Infect. Dis.* 17:1498-1501.

Aitken, T.H. 1957. Virus transmission studies with Trinidadian mosquitoes. *West Indian Med. J.* 6:229-32.

Aitken, T.H.G., R.B. Tesh, B.J. Beaty, and L. Rosen. 1979. Transovarial transmission of yellow fever virus by mosquitoes (*Aedes aegypti*). *Am. J. Trop. Med. Hyg.* 28:119-121.

American Society of Tropical Medicine and Hygiene. 1965. Proceedings of a symposium on some aspects of hemorrhagic fevers in the Americas. *Am. J. Trop. Med. Hyg.* 14:790-818.

Anderson, C.R., and G. Wattley. 1955. The isolation of yellow fever virus from human liver obtained at autopsy. *Trans. Roy. Soc. Trop. Med. Hyg.* 49:580-581.

Anderson, C.R., L. Spence, and W.G. Downs. 1954. Report of a case of yellow fever in Trinidad, B.W.I. *Carib. Med, J.* 16:68-70.

Anderson, C.R., and W.G. Downs. 1955. The isolation of yellow fever virus from the livers of naturally infected red howler monkeys. *Am. J. Trop. Med. Hyg.* 4:662-664.

Anderson, S.G. 1954. Murray Valley encephalitis and Australia X disease. *J. Hyg.* 52:447-468.

Anyamba, A., J.-P. Chretien, J. Small, C.J. Tucker, P.B. Formenty, J.H. Richardson, S.C. Britch, D.C. Schnabel, R.L. Erickson, and K.J. Linthicum. 2009. Prediction of a Rift Valley fever outbreak. *Proc. Natl. Acad. Sci. USA.* 106:955–959.

Arata, A.A., and N.G. Gratz. 1975. The structure and rodent faunas associated with arenaviral infections. *Bull. W.H.O.* 52:621-627.

Arroyo, J., F. Guirakoo, S. Fenner, Z.-X. Zhang, T.P. Monath, and T.J. Chambers. 2001. Molecular basis for attenuation of neurovirulence of a yellow fever virus/Japanese encephalitis virus chimera vaccine (ChimeriVax-JE). *J. Virol.* 75:934-942.

Ashburn, P.M., and C.F. Craig. 1907. Experimental investigations regarding the etiology of dengue fever with a general consideration of the disease. *Philipp. J. Sci.* 2:93–152.

Attoui, H., M.R. Mendez-Lopez, S. Rao, A. Hurtado-Alendes, F. Lizaraso-Caparo, C.L. Hice, A.R. Samuel, L.I. Pritchard, L. Melville, R. Weir, S. Davis, R. Lunt, C.H. Calisher, R.B. Tesh, R. Fujita, and P.P.C. Mertens. 2009. Peruvian horsesickness virus and Yunnan orbivirus isolated from equine, bovine, ovine and mosquito species in Peru and Australia. *Virology.* 394:298-310.

Avery, O.T., C.M. MacLeod, and M. McCarty. 1944. Studies on the chemical nature of the substance inducing transformation of pneumococcal types: Induction of transformation by a desoxyribonucleic acid fraction isolated from Pneumococcus Type III. *J. Exp. Med.* 79:137-158.

Balfour, A. 1914. The wild monkey as a reservoir for the virus of yellow fever. *Lancet.* 1:1176-1178.

Ballinger-Crabtree, M.E., and B.R. Miller. 1990. Partial nucleotide sequence of South American yellow fever virus strain 1899/81: Structural proteins and NS1. *J. Gen. Virol.* 71:2115-2121.

Bárdos, V., ed. 1969. *Arboviruses of the California complex and the Bunyamwera group.* Bratislava: Publishing House of the Slovak Academy of Sciences; 412 pages.

Bárdos, V., M. Medek, V. Kania, and Z. Hubálek. 1975. Isolation of Tahyna virus from the blood of sick children. *Acta Virol.* 19:447.

Barrie, H.J. 1997. Diary notes on a trip to West Africa in relation to a yellow fever expedition under the auspices of the Rockefeller Foundation, 1926, by Oskar Klotz. *Canad. Bull. Med. History.* 14:133-163. http://www.cbmh.ca/index.php/cbmh/article/view/399

Bauer, S.P., and F.A. Murphy. 1975. Relationship of two arthropod-borne rhabdoviruses (kotonkan and obodhiang) to the rabies serogroup. *Infect. Immun.* 12:1157-1172.

Baylis, M., P.S. Mellor, and R. Meiswinkel. 1999. Horse sickness and ENSO in South Africa. Nature. 397:574.

Beaty, B.J., and Bishop D.H. (1988) Bunyavirus-vector interactions. *Virus Res.* 10:289-301.

Beaty, B.J., E.J. Rozhon, P. Gensemer, and D.H. Bishop. 1981. Formation of reassortant bunyaviruses in dually infected mosquitoes. *Virology.* 111:662-665.

Beauperthuy, L.D. 1854. Fiebre amarilla. *Gaceta Oficial de Cumana.* 57:1-12.

_______________. 1875. Miasmas. *Escuela Medica. Periodico Medico Quirurgico* (Caracas, Venezuela) 1:10-15.

Beijerinck, M.W. 1898. Ueber ein contagium vivum fluidum als Ursache der Fleckenkrankheit der Tabaksblltter. *Verh. Kon. Akad.Wetensch.* 5:3-21. [English translation published in 1942: Concerning a contagium vivum fluidum as cause of the spot disease of tobacco leaves. *Phytopathol. Classics.* 7:33-52.]

Blake, J.B. 1968. Yellow fever in eighteenth century America. *Bull. N.Y. Acad. Med.* 44:673-686.

Bloom, K.J. 1993. *The Mississippi Valley's great yellow fever epidemic of 1878.* Baton Rouge: Louisiana State University Press, 290 pages.

Boshell-Manrique, J. 1948. The yellow fever reservoir of the Orinoco-Amazon basin. *Am. J. Trop. Med. Hyg.* S1-28:457-467.

Boulger, L.R., and J.S. Porterfield. 1958. Isolation of a virus from Nigerian fruit bats. *Trans. Royal Soc. Trop. Med. Hyg.* 52:421-424.

Bowen, M.D., S.G. Trappier, A.J. Sanchez, R.F. Meyer, C.S. Goldsmith, S.R. Zaki, L.M. Dunster, C.J. Peters, T.G. Ksiazek, S.T. Nichol, and the RVF Task Force, 2001. A reassortant bunyavirus isolated from acute hemorrhagic fever cases in Kenya and Somalia. *Virology.* 291:185-190.

Brandt, W.E., E.L. Buescher, and F.M. Hetrick. 1967. Production and characterization of arbovirus antibody in mouse ascitic fluid. *Am. J. Trop. Med. Hyg.* 16:339–347.

Breinl, A. 1918. Clinical pathological and experimental observations on the "mysterious disease", a clinically abberant form of poliomyelitis. *Med. J. Aust.* 1:209-213.

Briese, T., X.Y. Jia, C. Huang, L.J. Grady, and W.I. Lipkin. 1999. Identification of a Kunjin/West Nile-like flavivirus in brains of patients with New York encephalitis. *Lancet.* 354:1261-1262.

Buckley, A., A. Dawson, S.R. Moss, S.A. Hinsley, P.E. Bellamy, and E.A. Gould. 2003. Serological evidence of West Nile virus, Usutu virus and Sindbis virus infection of birds in the UK. *J Gen. Virol.* 84:2807-2817.

Bugher, J.C. 1941. The use of baby mice in yellow fever studies. *Am. J. Trop. Med.* 21:299-307.

__________. 1955. Jungle yellow fever. in *Yellow fever, a symposium in commemoration of Carlos Juan Finlay.* Paper 8. http://jdc.jefferson.edu/yellow_fever_symposium/8

Bugher, J.C., J. Boshell-Manrique, M. Roca-Garcia, and E. Osorno-Mesa. 1944. Epidemiology of jungle yellow fever in eastern Colombia. *Am. J. Hyg.* 39:16-51.

Burke, D.S., K. Chatiyanonda, S. Anandrik, S. Nakornsri, A. Nisalak, and C.H. Hoke Jr. 1985. Improved surveillance of Japanese encephalitis by detection of virus-specific IgM in desiccated blood specimens. *Bull. World Health Org.* 63:1037-1042.

Burke, D.S., W. Lorsomrudee, C.J. Leake, C.H. Hoke, A. Nisalak, V. Chongswasdi, and T. Laorakpongse. 1985. Fatal outcome in Japanese encephalitis. *Am. J. Trop. Med. Hyg.* 34:1203-1210.

Burton, A.N., J. McLintock, and J.G. Rempel. 1966. Western equine encephalitis virus in Saskatchewan garter snakes and leopard frogs. *Science.* 154:1029-1031.

Calisher, C.H. 1996. Telford H. Work - a tribute. *J. Am. Mosq. Contr. Assoc.* 12:385-395.

Calisher, C.H. 2009. From Adamovec to Dubrovnik: an extended adventure, 1971-1992. *Croatian Med. J.* 50:600-603.

Calisher, C.H. 2009. Scientist in a strange land: a cautionary tale. *Nonproliferation Rev.* 16:509-519.

Calisher, C.H., and H.C. Goodpasture. 1975. Human infection with Bhanja virus. *Am. J. Trop. Med. Hyg.* 24:1040 1042.

Calisher, C.H., J.E. Childs, H.E. Field, K.V. Holmes, and T. Schountz. 2006. Bats: important reservoir hosts of emerging viruses. *Clin. Microbiol. Rev.* 19:531-545.

Calisher, C.H., and M.H. Horzinek, eds. 1999. *Virology: The first 100 years. Arch. Virol.* Vienna: Springer-Verlag; 220 pages.

Calisher, C.H., N. Karabatsos, L. Thompson, and J.S. Smith. 1989. Protection against rabies virus conferred by immunising mice with other rhabdoviruses and preliminary evidence of molecular similarities between bovine ephemeral fever-related and rabies-related viruses. in M.F. Uren, J. Blok, L.H. Manderson, eds., *Arbovirus Research in Australia, Proc. Fifth Symp.*; Indooroopilly, Queensland, Australia: CSIRO; pp: 261-264.

Calisher, C.H., R.E. Shope, W. Brandt, J. Casals, N. Karabatsos, F.A. Murphy, R.B. Tesh, and M.E. Wiebe. 1980. Proposed antigenic classification of registered arboviruses: *I. Togaviridae, Alphavirus. Intervirology.* 14:229 232.

Calisher, C.H., and W.H. Thompson, eds.. 1983. *Proc. Int'l Symp. Calif. Serogr. Viruses.* New York: Alan R. Liss, Inc.; 399 pages.

Calisher, C.H., R.G. McLean, H.G. Zeller, D.B. Francy, N. Karabatsos, and R.A. Bowen. 1990. Isolation of Tete serogroup bunyaviruses from Ceratopogonidae collected in Colorado. *Am. J. Trop. Med. Hyg.* 43:314-318.

Carey, D.E., R. Reuben, K.N. Panicker, R.E. Shope, and R.M. Myers. 1971. Thottapalayam virus: a presumptive arbovirus isolated from a shrew in India. *Indian J. Med. Res.* 59:1758-1760.

Carrel, A. 1912. On the permanent life of tissues outside of the organism. *J. Exper. Med.* 15:516-530.

Carter, H.R. 1901. A note on the spread of yellow fever in houses, extrinsic incubation, *Med. Rec.* 24:937.

Casals, J. 1943. Non-virulent and dried antigens for complement-fixation tests with central nervous system virus infections. *Science.* 97:337-338.

________. 1959. Antigenic classification of arthropod-borne viruses. *Proc. 6th Int'l. Congr. Trop. Med. Malaria* (Lisbon). 5:34-47.

________. 1964. Antigenic variants of eastern equine encephalitis virus. *J. Exp. Med.* 119:547-565.

________. 1975. Arenaviruses. *Yale J. Biol. Med.* 48:115-140.

Casals, J. and G.H. Tignor. 1980. The *Nairovirus* genus: serological relationships. *Intervirol.* 14:144-147.

Casals, J., H. Hoogstraal, K.M. Johnson, A. Shelokov, N.H. Wiebenga, and T.H. Work. 1966. A current appraisal of hemorrhagic fevers in the U.S.S.R. *Am. J. Trop. Med. Hyg.* 15:751-764.

Casals, J. and L.T. Webster. 1943. Close relation between Russian Spring-Summer encephalitis and louping-Ill viruses. *Science.* 97:246-248.

Casals, J. and L.V. Brown. 1954. Hemagglutination with arthropod-borne viruses. *J. Exp. Med.* 99:429-449.

Casals, J. and L. Whitman. 1960. A new antigenic group of arthropod-borne viruses: the Bunyamwera group. *Am. J. Trop. Med. Hyg.* 9:73-77.

Casals, J. and L. Whitman. 1961. Group C, a new serological group of hitherto undescribed arthropod-borne viruses. Immunological studies. *Am. J. Trop. Med. Hyg.* 10:250-258.

Casals, J., P.K. Olitsky, and A.B. Sabin. 1952. Homotypic complement-fixing antibody in monkeys infected with type 2 poliomyelitis virus by the oral route. *J. Exp. Med.* 96:55–58.

Casals, J., P.K. Olitsky, and R.O. Anslow. 1951. Adaptation of a Lansing strain of poliomyelitis virus to newborn mice. *J. Exp. Med.* 94:111–121.

Casals, J., R.O. Anslow, and G. Selzer. 1951. Method for increasing the yield of complement-fixing antigens of certain neurotropic viruses, and the use of newborn mice for their production. *J. Lab. Clin. Med.* 37:663–664.

Causey, O.R., G.E. Kemp, C.E. Causey, and V.H. Lee. 1972. Isolations of Simbu-group viruses in Ibadan, Nigeria 1964-69, including the new types Sango, Shamonda, Sabo and Shuni. *Ann. Trop. Med. Parasitol.* 66:357-362.

Chamberlain, R.W. 1982. Arbovirology – then and now. *Am. J. Trop. Med. Hyg.* 31:430-437.

Chamberlain, R.W., W.D. Sudia, P.H. Coleman, and T.H. Work. 1964. Venezuelan equine encephalitis virus from South Florida. *Science.* 145:272-274.

Chandler, L.J., G. Hogge, M. Endres, D.R. Jacoby, N. Nathanson, and B.J. Beaty. 1991. Reassortment of La Crosse and Tahyna bunyaviruses in *Aedes triseriatus* mosquitoes. *Virus Res.* 20:181-191.

Chanock, R.M., and A.B. Sabin. 1953. The hemagglutinin of St. Louis encephalitis virus. I. Recovery of stable hemagglutinin from the brains of infected mice. *J. Immunol.* 70:271–285.

Chen, W.R., R. Rico-Hesse, and R.B. Tesh. 1992. A new genotype of Japanese encephalitis virus from Indonesia. *Am. J. Trop. Med. Hyg.* 47:61–69.

Chernin, E. 1983. Josiah Clark Nott, insects, and yellow fever. *Bull. NY Acad. Med.* 59:790-802.

Childs, J.E., J.S. Mackenzie, and J.A. Richt, eds. 2007. *Wildlife and emerging zoonotic diseases: the biology, circumstances and consequences of cross-species transmission.* New York: Springer; 521 pages.

Chin, T.D.Y., C.R. Heimlich, R.F. White, D.M. Mason, and M. Furcolow. 1957. An outbreak of St. Louis encephalitis in the lower Rio Grande Valley of Texas in 1954. Epidemiological features. *Pub. Health Rep.* 72:512-518.

Chua, K.B., K.J. Goh, K.T. Wong, A. Kamarulzaman, P.S. Tan, T.G. Ksiazek, S.R. Zaki, G. Paul, S.K. Lam, and C.T. Tan. 1999. Fatal encephalitis due to Nipah virus among pig-farmers in Malaysia. *Lancet.* 354:1257-1259.

Chua, K.B., W.J. Bellini, P.A. Rota, B.H. Harcourt, A. Tamin, S.K. Lam, T.G. Ksiazek, P.E. Rollin, S.R. Zaki, W.-J. Shieh, C.S. Goldsmith, D.J. Gubler, J.T. Roehrig, B. Eaton, A.R. Gould, J. Olson, H. Field, P. Daniels, A.E. Ling, C.J. Peters, L.J. Anderson, and B.W. Mahy. 2000. Nipah virus: a recently emergent deadly paramyxovirus. *Science.* 288:1432-1435.

Clarke, D.H., and J. Casals. 1958. Techniques for hemagglutination and hemagglutination-inhibition with arthropod-borne viruses. *Am. J. Trop. Med. Hyg.* 7:561-573.

Cleland, J.B., B. Bradley, and W. MacDonald. 1919. Further experiments in the etiology of dengue fever. *J. Hyg.* 18:217-254.

Cohen, S.N., A.C.Y. Chang, H.W. Boyer, and R.B. Helling. 1973. Construction of biologically functional bacterial plasmids in vitro. *Proc. Natl. Acad. Sci. USA.* 70:3240-3244.

Craig, G.B., Jr., and W. A. Hickey (1967) Genetics of *Aedes aegypti.* in J. Wright and R. Pal, eds., *Genetics of insect vectors of disease,* Amsterdam: Elsevier; pages 67-131.

Cupp, E.W. 1998. George Brownlee Craig, Jr. July 8, 1930-December 21, 1995. *Biogr. Mem. Natl. Acad. Sci.* 74:77-90.

Daubney, R., J.R. Hudson, and P.C. Garnham. 1931. Enzootic hepatitis or Rift Valley fever. An undescribed virus disease of sheep, cattle and man from East Africa. *J. Path. and Bacteriol.* 34:545-579.

Detinova, T.S., and M.T. Gillies. 1964. Observations on the determination of the age composition and epidemiological importance of populations of *Anopheles gambiae* Giles and *Anopheles funestus* Giles in Tanganyika. *Bull. World Health Org.* 30:23-28.

Doerr, R., K. Franz, and S. Taussig. 1909. Das Pappatacifieber. Leipzig: Franz Deuticke.

Doherty, R.L. 1987. William C. Reeves and arbovirus research in Australia. *Am. J. Trop. Med. Hyg.* 37 (Suppl.):875-893S.

Downs, W.G. 1982. The Rockefeller Foundation virus program: 1951-1971 with update to 1981. *Ann. Rev. Med.* 33:1-29.

Downs, W.G., C.R. Anderson. and L. Spence. 1955. Isolation of yellow fever virus from a human patient on the twelfth day of illness. *Trans. Roy. Soc. Trop. Med. Hyg.* 49:577-579.

Downs, W.G., T.H.G. Aitken, and C.R. Anderson. 1955. Activities of the Trinidad Regional Virus Laboratory in 1953 and 1954 with special reference to the yellow fever outbreak in Trinidad, B.W.I. *Am. J. Trop. Med. Hyg.* 4:837-843.

Duffy, J. 1992. *The Sanitarians. A history of American public health.* Champaign, Illinois: University of Illinois Press; 330 pages.

Duffy, M.R., T.H. Chen, W.T. Hancock, A.M. Powers, J.L. Kool, R.S. Lanciotti, M. Pretrick, M. Marfel, S. Holzbauer, C. Dubray, L. Guillaumot, A. Griggs, M. Bel, A.J. Lambert, J. Laven, O. Kosoy, A. Panella, B.J. Biggerstaff, M. Fischer, E.B. Hayes. 2009. Zika virus outbreak on Yap Island, Federated States of Micronesia. *N. Engl. J. Med.* 360:2536-2543.

Emmons, R.W., L.S. Oshiro, H.N. Johnson, and E.H. Lennette. 1972. Intra-erythrocytic location of Colorado tick fever virus. *J. Gen. Virol.* 17, I85-195.

Enders, J.F., T.H. Weller, and F.C. Robbins. 1949. Cultivation of the Lansing strain of poliomyelitis virus in cultures of various human embryonic tissues. *Science.* 109:85-87.

Etheridge, E.W. 1992. *Sentinel for Health. A history of the Centers for Disease Control.* Berkeley: University of California Press; 414 pages.

Evans, A.S. 1976. Causation and disease: the Henle-Koch postulates revisited. *Yale J. Biol. Med.* 49:175-195.

Feemster, R.F. 1938. Outbreak of encephalitis in man due to the eastern virus of equine encephalomyelitis. *Am. J. Public Health Nations Health* 28: 1403-1410.

Fenner, F., and D.R. Curtis. 2001. *The John Curtin School of Medical Research: the first fifty years, 1948-1998.* Gundaroo, Australia: Brolga Press; 565 pages.

Fenner, F., and F.N. Ratcliffe. 1965. *Myxomatosis.* Cambridge U.K.: Cambridge University Press; 379 pages.

Fergusson, W. 1817. An inquiry into the origin and nature of the yellow fever, as it has lately appeared in the West Indies, with official documents relating to this subject. *Med. Chir. Trans. (Proc. Royal Soc. Med.,* later *J. Royal Soc. Med.)* 8:108-172.

Finlay, C. 1881. El mosquito hipotéticamente considerado como agente de transmission de la fiebre amarilla. *Ann. report Acad. de cien. Méd. de la Habana.* 18:147–169.

Fothergill, LeR., J.H. Dingle, S. Farber, and M.L. Connerly. 1938. Human encephalitis caused by the eastern variety of equine encephalomyelitis. *New Engl. J. Med.* 219:411.

Foy, B.D., K.C. Kobylinski, J.L. Chilson Foy, B.J. Blitvich, A. Travassos da Rosa, A.D. Haddow, R. S. Lanciotti, and R.B. Tesh. 2011. Probable non-vector-borne transmission of Zika virus, Colorado, USA. *Emerg. Infect. Dis.* 17:880-882.

French, E.L. 1952. Murray Valley encephalitis: isolation and characterisation of the aetiological agent. *Med J Aust.* 1:100-103.

Fuller, J.G. 1975. *Fever! The hunt for a new killer virus.* New York: Random House; 288 pages.

Garrett, L. 1994. *The coming plague.* New York: Penguin; 750 pages.

Gentsch, J.R., E.J. Rozhon, R. A. Klimas, L.H. el Said, R.E. Shope, and D.H.L. Bishop. 1980. Evidence from recombinant bunyavirus studies that the M RNA gene products elicit neutralizing antibodies. *Virology.* 102:190-204.

Gerrard, S.R., L. Li, A.D. Barrett, and S.T. Nichol. 2004. Ngari virus is a Bunyamwera virus reassortant that can be associated with large outbreaks of hemorrhagic fever in Africa. *J. Virol.* 78:8922-8926.

Godoy, G.A., and E. Tarradath. 2010. Short biography of Louis Daniel Beauperthuy (1807-1871): Pioneer of microbiology and medical science in Venezuela. *J. Med. Biogr.* 18:38-40.

Gonzalez-Scarano, F., R.E. Shope, C.H. Calisher, and N. Nathanson. 1983. Monoclonal antibodies against the G1 and nucleocapsid proteins of LaCrosse and Tahyna viruses. *Progr. Clin. Biol. Res.* 123:145-156.

Gould, E.A., A. Buckley, P.A. Cane, S. Higgs, and N. Cammack. 1989. Use of a monoclonal antibody specific for wild-type yellow fever virus to identify a wild-type antigenic variant in 17D vaccine pools. *J. Gen. Virol.* 70:1889-1894.

Guirakhoo, F., R. Weltzin, T.J. Chambers, Z.-X. Zhang, K. Soike, M. Ratterree, J. Arroyo, K. Georgakopoulos, J. Catalan, and T.P. Monath. 2000. Recombinant chimeric yellow fever-dengue type 2 virus is immunogenic and protective in nonhuman primates. *J. Virol.* 74:5477-5485.

Hahn, C.S., J.M. Dalrymple, J.H. Strauss, and C.M. Rice. 1987. Comparison of the virulent Asibi strain of yellow fever virus with the 17D vaccine strain derived from it. *Proc. Nat. Acad. Sci., USA.* 84:2019-2023.

Halstead, S.B. 1979. In vivo enhancement of dengue virus infection in rhesus monkeys by passively transferred antibody. *J. Infect. Dis.* 140:527-533.

Halstead, S.B. 1988. Pathogenesis of dengue: challenges to molecular biology. *Science.* 239:476-481.

Halstead, S.B., and E.J. O'Rourke. 1977. Antibody enhanced dengue virus infection in primate leukocytes. *Nature.* 265:739-741.

Halstead, S.B., J.S. Porterfield, and E.J. O'Rourke. 1980. Enhancement of dengue virus infection in monocytes by flavivirus antisera. *Am. J. Trop. Med. Hyg.* 29:638-642.

Hammon, W. McD. 1969. Observations on dengue fever, benign protector and killer: A Dr. Jekyll and Mr. Hyde. *Am. J. Trop. Med. Hyg.* 18:159-165.

Hammon W.M., Rudnick A. and Sather G.E. (1960) Viruses associated with epidemic hemorrhagic fevers of the Philippines and Thailand. *Science.* 131:1102-1103.

Hammon, W.M., and W.C. Reeves. 1952. California encephalitis virus, a newly described agent. I. Evidence of infection in man and other animals. *Calif. Med.* 77:303-309.

Hammon, W.M., W.C. Reeves, and G. Sather. 1952. California encephalitis virus, a newly described agent. II. Isolations and attempts to identify and characterize the agent. *J. Immunol.* 69:493-510.

Hanson, R.P., S.E. Sulkin, E.L. Buescher, W. McD. Hammon, R.W. McKinney, and T.H. Work. 1967. Arbovirus infections of laboratory workers. *Science.* 158:1283-1286.

Hawkes, R.A. 1964. Enhancement of the infectivity of arboviruses by specific antisera produced in domestic fowls. *Austral. J. Exp. Biol. Med. Sci.* 42:465-482.

Hawley, WA, P. Reiter, R.S. Copeland, C.B. Pumpuni, G.B. Craig, Jr. 1987. *Aedes albopictus* in North America: probable introduction in used tires from northern Asia. *Science.* 236:1114-1116.

Hayashi, M. 1933. Übertragung des Virus von Encephalitis epidemica japonica auf Affen. *Psychiatr. Clin. Neurosci.* 1:419-465.

Hayes, R.O., L.C. LaMotte, and P. Holden. 1967 Ecology of arboviruses in Hale County, Texas, during 1965. *Am. J. Trop. Med. Hyg.* 16:675-687.

Hershey, A.D., and M. Chase. 1952. Independent functions of viral protein and nucleic acid in growth of bacteriophage. *J. Gen. Physiol.* 36:39–56.

Hierholzer, J.C., P.G. Bingham, R.A. Coombs, K.H. Johansson, L.J. Anderson, and P.E. Halonen. 1989. Comparison of monoclonal antibody time-resolved fluoroimmunoassay with monoclonal antibody capture-biotinylated detector enzyme immunoassay for respiratory syncytial virus and parainfluenza virus antigen detection. *J. Clin. Microbiol.* 27:1243-1249.

Hirst, G.K. 1941. The agglutination of red cells by allantoic fluid of chick embryos infected with influenza virus. *Science.* 94:22-23.

Hoffman, D.C., and F. Duran-Reynals. 1931. The influence of testicle extract on the intradermal spread of injected fluids and particles. *J. Exp. Med.* 53:387-398.

Hooper, P.T., R.A., Lunt, A.R. Gould, A.D. Hyatt, G.M. Russell, J.A. Kattenbelt, S.D. Blacksell, L.A. Reddacliff, P.D. Kirkland, R.J. Davis, P.J. Durham, A.L. Bishop, and J. Waddington. 1999. Epidemic blindness in kangaroos – evidence of a viral aetiology. *Austral. Vet. J.* 77:529-536.

Hughes, G. 1750. *The natural history of Barbados,* (self-published) London, England; 314 pages.

Huxsoll, D.L. 1992. In memoriam: Joel M. Dalrymple. The microbiologist and biological defense research. R.A. Zilinskas, ed. *Annals of the N.Y. Acad. Sci.* 666: ix-x.

Igarashi, A. 1978. Isolation of a Singh's *Aedes albopictus* cell clone sensitive to dengue and chikungunya viruses. *J. General Virology.* 40:531-544

Institute of Medicine of the National Academies. 2008. Global climate change and extreme weather events. Washington, D.C.: The National Academies Press; 279 pages.

Ivanovsky, D. 1882. Concerning the mosaic disease of the tobacco plant. *St. Petsb. Acad. Imp. Sci. Bul.* 35:67-70.

Jahrling, P.B., T.W. Geisbert, D.W. Dalgard, E.D. Johnson, T.G. Ksiazek, W.C. Hall, and C.J. Peters. 1990. Preliminary report: isolation of Ebola virus from monkeys imported to the USA. *Lancet.* 335:502-505.

Janssen, R., F. Gonzalez-Scarano, and N. Nathanson. 1984. Mechanisms of bunyavirus virulence. Comparative pathogenesis of a virulent strain of La Crosse and an avirulent strain of Tahyna virus. *Lab. Invest.* 50:447-455.

Johnson, H.N. 1991. An oral history, University of California – Berkeley, School of Public Health; http://www.archive.org/stream/virologistnatura00johnrich/virologistnatura00johnrich_djvu.txt

Johnson, K.M. (with M. Emmons-Johnson) The Machupo Story (manuscript in preparation)

Johnson, K.M., N.H. Wiebenga, R.B. Mackenzie, M.L. Kuns, N.M. Tauraso, A. Shelokov, P.A. Webb, G. Justines, and H.K. Beye. 1965. Virus isolations from human cases of hemorrhagic fever in Bolivia. *Proc. Soc. Exp. Biol. Med.* 118:113-118.

Johnson, K.M., R.B. Tesh, and P.H. Peralta. 1969. Epidemiology of vesicular stomatitis virus: some new data and a hypothesis for transmission of the Indiana serotype. *J. Am. Vet. Med. Assoc.* 155:2133-2140.

Johnson, K.M., J.V. Lange, P.A. Webb, and F.A. Murphy. 1977. Isolation and partial characterisation of a new virus causing acute haemorrhagic fever in Zaire. *Lancet.* 1 (8011):569–571.

Jones, L.D., C.R. Davies, G.M. Steele, and P.A. Nuttall. 1987. A novel mode of transmission involving a nonviremic host. *Science.* 237:775-777.

Jonkers, A.H., W.G. Downs, L. Spence, and T.H. Aitken. 1965. Arthropod-borne encephalitis viruses in northeastern South America II. A serological survey of northeastern Venezuela. *Am. J. Trop. Med. Hyg.* 14:304-308.

Kemp, G.E., V.H. Lee, D.L. Moore, R.E. Shope, O.R. Causey, and F.A. Murphy. 1973. Kotonkan, a new rhabdovirus related to Mokola virus of the rabies serogroup. *Am. J. Trop. Med Hyg.* 98:43-49.

Kerr, J.A. 1932. (revised by W.G. Downs) Yellow fever. in F. Tice, ed. *Practice of Medicine.* Vol. 4, 1-31. New York: Harper and Rowe.

Kharitonova, N.N., and Y.A. Leonov. 1985. *Omsk hemorrhagic fever. Ecology of the agent and epizootiology.* New Delhi, India: Amerind Publ.; 230 pages.

Kliks, S.C. 1989. Antibody dependent enhancement of dengue virus growth in human monocytes as a risk factor for dengue hemorrhagic fever. *Am. J. Trop. Med. Hyg.* 40:444-451.

Kliks, S.C., and S.B. Halstead. 1983. Role of antibodies and host cells in plaque enhancement of Murray Valley encephalitis virus. *J. Virol.* 46:394-404.

Köhler, G., and C. Milstein. 1975. Continuous cultures of fused cells secreting antibody of predefined specificity. *Nature.* 256:495-497.

Kubes, V., and F.A. Rios. 1939. The causative agent of infectious equine encephalomyelitis in Venezuela. *Science.* 90:20-21.

Kuhn, J.H. (2008) Filoviruses. A compendium of 40 years of epidemiological, clinical, and laboratory studies. Vienna: Springer; 411 pages.

Kuhn, J.H., S. Becker, H. Ebihara, T.W. Geisbert, K.M. Johnson, Y. Kawaoka, W.I. Lipkin, A.I. Negredo, S.V. Netesov, S.T. Nichol, G. Palacios, C.J. Peters, A. Tenorio, V.E. Volchkov, and P.B. Jahrling. 2010. Proposal for a revised taxonomy of the family *Filoviridae*: classification, names of taxa and virus, and virus abbreviations. *Arch. Virol.* 155:2083-2103.

Labuda, M., and C.H. Calisher, eds. 1980. *Proc. Int'l. Symp. New Aspects in Ecology of Arboviruses.* (Smolenice, Czechoslovakia, June 11-15, 1979) Bratislava: Slovak Acad. Sci.; 567 pages.

Lanciotti, R.S., J.T. Roehrig, V. Deubel, J. Smith, M. Parker, K. Steele, B. Crise, K.E. Volpe, M.B. Crabtree, J.H. Scherret, R.A. Hall, J.S. MacKenzie, C.B. Cropp, B. Panigrahy, E. Ostlund, B. Schmitt, M. Malkinson, C. Banet, J. Weissman, N. Komar, H.M. Savage, W. Stone, T. McNamara, D.J. Gubler. 1999. Origin of the West Nile virus responsible for an outbreak of encephalitis in the northeastern United States. *Science.* 286:2333-2337.

Landsteiner, K., and E. Popper. 1909. Übertragung der Poliomyelitis acuta auf Affen. Z. *Immunitätsforsch.* 2:377-390.

Laveran, A. 1891. *Traite des fievres palustres.* Masson, Paris.

Lederberg, J., R.E. Shope, and S.C Oaks, Jr, eds. 1992. *Emerging infections: microbial threats to health in the United States.* Washington: National Academy Press; 312 pages.

Lee, H.-W. 2004. *Hantavirus hunting: Forty years of battling hantaviruses around the world.* Seoul: Sigongsa; 415 pages.

Lee, H.W., P.W. Lee, and K.M. Johnson. 1978. Isolation of the etiologic agent of Korean hemorrhagic fever. *J. Infect. Dis.* 137:298-308.

Lennette, E., and H. Koprowski. 1946. Antigenic relationships of the West Nile, Japanese B encephalitis, and St. Louis encephalitis viruses. *J. Immunol.* 52:235-246.

Lewis, P.A. 1930. The survival of yellow fever virus in cultures. *J. Exp. Med.* 52:113-119.

Loeffler, F., and P. Frosch. 1897. Summarischer Bericht über die Ergebnisse der Untersuchungen der Kommission zur Erforschung der Maul- und Klauenseuche bei dem Institut für Infektionskrankheiten in Berlin. *Centrbl. Bakt. Parasitenk.* 22:257-259.

Maiztegui, J.I., K.T. McKee, Jr., J.G. Barrera Oro, L.H. Harrison, P.H. Gibbs, M.R. Feuillade, D.A. Enria, A.M. Briggiler, S.C. Levis, A.M. Ambrosio, N.A. Halsey, and C.J. Peters. 1998. Protective efficacy of a live attenuated vaccine against Argentine hemorrhagic fever. AHF Study Group. *J. Infect. Dis.* 177:277-283.

Manson, P. 1878. Further observations on filaria sanguinis hominis. Medical reports for the half-year ended 30th September, 1877. *Shanghai Statistical Department of the Inspectorate General.* 14:1-27.

Marchette, N.J., J.S. Sung Chow, S.B. Halstead, S. Lolekha, and B. Pongpanich. 1975. Dengue virus replication in cultures of peripheral blood leukocytes during the course of dengue hemorrhagic fever. *Southeast Asian J. Trop. Med. Public Health.* 6:316-321.

Marchette, N.J., and S.B. Halstead. 1974. Immunopathogenesis of dengue infection in the rhesus monkey. *Transplant Proc.* 6:197-201.

Marchette, N.J., S.B. Halstead, and J.S. Chow. 1976. Replication of dengue viruses in cultures of peripheral blood leukocytes from dengue-immune rhesus monkeys. *J. Infect. Dis.* 133:274-282.

Marquardt, W.C., Kondratieff, B., Moore, C.G., Freier, J., Hagedorn, H.H., Black, W. III, James, A.A., Hemingway, J. and Higgs, S., eds. 2004. *The Biology of Disease Vectors.* 2nd edition. Elsevier Academic Press, San Diego, California; 816 pages.

Marsh, G.A., C. de Jong, J.A. Barr, M. Tachedjian, C. Smith, D. Middleton, M. Yu, S. Todd, A.J. Foord, V. Haring, J. Payne, R. Robinson, I. Broz, G. Crameri, H.E. Field. and L.F. Wang. 2012. Cedar virus: a novel henipavirus isolated from Australian bats. *PLoS Pathog.* 8(8):e1002836.

Marshall, I.D., G.M. Woodroofe, and S. Hirsch. 1982. Viruses recovered from mosquitoes and wildlife serum collected in the Murray Valley of south-eastern Australia, February 1974, during an epidemic of encephalitis. *Austral. J. Exp. Biol. Med. Sci.* 60:457-470.

McKinney, R.W., T.O. Berge, W.D. Sawyer, W.D. Tigertt, and D. Crozier. 1963. Use of an attenuated strain of Venezuelan equine encephalomyelitis virus for immunization in man. *Am. J. Trop. Med. Hyg.* 12:597-603.

Melnick, J.L., N. Ledinko, A.S. Kaplan, and L.M. Kraft. 1950. Ohio strains of a virus pathogenic for infant mice (Coxsackie group). Simultaneous occurrence with poliomyelitis virus in patients with "Summer grippe". *J. Exp. Med.* 91:185-195.

Meselson, M., and F.W. Stahl. 1958. The replication of DNA in *Escherichia coli. Proc. Nat. Acad. Sci.* 44:671–682.

Meyer, K.F., C.M. Haring, and B. Howitt. 1931. The etiology of epizootic encephalomyelitis of horses in the San Joaquin Valley, 1930. *Science.* 74:227-228.

Mitamura, T., S. Yamada, H. Hagato, R. Mori, T. Hosoi, M. Kitaoka, S. Watanabi, K. Okudo, and S. Tenjuri. 1937. Über den infektionsmodus der epidemischen enzephalitis. experimentelle untersuchungen über ihre austeckung durch mucken. *Tr. Soc. Path. Jap.* 27:573-580.

Monath, T.P. 1975. Lassa fever: review of epidemiology and epizootiology. *Bull. World Health Org.* 52:577-592.

Monath, T.P., (ed.) 1980. *St. Louis encephalitis.* Washington, D.C.: *Am. Publ. Hlth. Assoc.*; 680 pages.

Monath, T.P. 1991. Yellow fever: Victor, Victoria? Conqueror, conquest? Epidemics and research in the last forty years and prospects for the future. *Am. J. Trop. Med. Hyg.* 45:1-43.

Monath, T.P., C.B. Cropp, and A.K. Harrison. 1983. Mode of entry of a neurotropic arbovirus into the central nervous system. Reinvestigation of an old controversy. *Lab. Invest.* 48:399-410.

Monath, T.P., K.R. Brinker, F.W. Chandler, G.E. Kemp, and C.B. Cropp. 1981. Pathophysiologic correlations in a rhesus monkey model of yellow fever with special observations on the acute necrosis of B cell areas of lymphoid tissues. *Am. J. Trop. Med. Hyg.* 30:431-443.

Monath, T.P., K. Soike, I. Levenbook, Z.-X. Zhang, J. Arroyo, S. Delagrave, G. Myers, A.D.T. Barrett, R.E. Shope, T.J. Chambers, and F. Guirakhoo. 1999. Recombinant, chimeric live, attenuated vaccine (ChimeriVax) incorporating the envelope genes of Japanese encephalitis (SA14–14-2) and the capsid and nonstructural genes of yellow fever (17D) is safe, immunogenic and protective in non-human primates. *Vaccine.* 17:1869–1882.

Monath, T.P., V.F. Newhouse, G.E. Kemp, H.W. Setzer, and A. Cacciapuoti. 1974. Lassa virus isolation from *Mastomys natalensis* rodents during an epidemic in Sierra Leone. *Science.* 185:263-265.

Montgomery, E. 1917. On a tick borne gastro-enteritis of sheep and goats occurring in East Africa. *J. Comp. Path.* 30:28-57.

Mora, C., D.P. Tittensor, S. Adl, A.G.B. Simpson, and B. Worm. 2011. How many species are there on earth and in the ocean? *PLoS Biol.* 9(8): e1001127. doi:10.1371/journal.pbio.1001127

Morens, D.M., N.J. Marchette, M.C. Chu, and S.B. Halstead. 1991. Growth of dengue type 2 virus isolates in human peripheral blood leukocytes correlates with severe and mild dengue disease. *Am. J. Trop. Med. Hyg.* 45:644-651.

Muckenfuss, R.S., C. Armstrong, and H.A. McCordock. 1933. Encephalitis: studies on experimental transmission. *Pub. Health Rep.* 48:1341-1343.

Mullan, F. 1989. *Plagues and politics.* New York: Basic Books; 223 pages.

Mullis, K., F. Faloona, S. Scharf, R. Saiki, G. Horn, and H. Erlich. 1986. Specific enzymatic amplification of DNA in vitro: The polymerase chain reaction. *Cold Spring Harbor Symp. Quant. Biol.* 51:263-273.

Murphy, F.A., A.K. Harrison, and S.G. Whitfield. 1973. *Bunyaviridae*: morphologic and morphogenetic similarities of Bunyamwera serologic supergroup viruses and several other arthropod-borne viruses. *Intervirology.* 1:297–316.

Murphy, F.A., A.K. Harrison, and T. Tzianabos. 1968. Electron microscopic observations of mouse brain infected with Bunyamwera group arboviruses. *J. Virol.* 2:1315-1325.

Nderitu, L., J.S. Lee, J. Omolo, S. Omulo, M.L. O'Guinn, A. Hightower, F. Mosha, M. Mohamed, P. Munyua, Z. Nganga, K. Hiett, B. Seal, D.R. Feikin, R.F. Breiman, M.K. Njenga. 2011. Sequential Rift Valley fever outbreaks in eastern Africa caused by multiple lineages of the virus. *J. Infect. Dis.* 203:655-665.

Nott, J. C. 1848. Yellow fever contrasted with bilious fever: Reasons for believing it a disease sui generis – its mode of propagation – remote cause – probable insect of animalcular origin, etc. *New Orleans Med. Surg. J.* 4:563-601.

Nunes, M.R., A.P. Travassos da Rosa, S.C. Weaver, R.B. Tesh, and P.F. Vasconcelos. 2005. Molecular epidemiology of group C viruses (*Bunyaviridae, Orthobunyavirus*) isolated in the Americas. *J. Virol.* 79:10561-10570.

Parrish, C.R., E.C. Holmes, D.M. Morens, E.-C. Park, D.S. Burke, C.H. Calisher, C.A. Laughlin, L.J. Saif, and P. Daszak. 2008. Cross-species viral transmission and the emergence of new epidemic diseases. *Microbiol. Mol. Biol. Rev.* 72:457-470.

Pasteur, L. 1878. The germ theory and its applications to medicine and surgery [read before the French Academy of Sciences, April 29th, 1878.] *Comptes Rendus de l' Academie des Sciences.* 86:1037-1043.

Pavlovsky, E. 1965. *Natural nidality of transmissible diseases.* Moscow: Peace Publishers; 249 pages.

Peiris, J.S., and J.S. Porterfield. 1979. Antibody-mediated enhancement of flavivirus replication in macrophage-like cell lines. *Nature.* 282:509-511.

Peiris, J.S., S. Gordon, J.C. Unkelless, and J.S. Porterfield. 1981. Monoclonal anti-Fc receptor IgG blocks antibody enhancement of viral replication in macrophages. *Nature.* 289:189-191.

Peters, C.J., and M. Olshaker. 1997. *Virus hunter: Thirty years of battling hot viruses around the world.* New York: Anchor Books; 323 pages.

Petri, W.A. Jr. 2004. America in the world: 100 years of tropical medicine and hygiene. *Am. J. Trop. Med. Hyg.* 71:2-16.

Poland, J.D., C.H. Calisher, T.P. Monath, W.G. Downs, and K. Murphy. 1981. Persistence of neutralizing antibody 30-35 years after immunization with 17D yellow fever vaccine. *Bull. World Health Org.* 59:895-900.

Porterfield, J.S. 1989. Yellow fever in west Africa: a retrospective glance. *Brit. Med. J.* 299:1555-1957.

Powers, A.M., A.C. Brault, R.B. Tesh, and S.C. Weaver. 2000. Re-emergence of chikungunya and o'nyong-nyong viruses: evidence for distinct geographical lineages and distant evolutionary relationships. *J. Gen. Virol.* 81:471-479.

Powers, A.M., A.C. Brault, Y. Shirako, E.G. Strauss, W. Kang, J.H. Strauss, and S.C. Weaver. 2001. Evolutionary relationships and systematics of the alphaviruses. *J. Virol.* 75:10118-10131.

Preston, R. 1994. *The Hot Zone: a terrifying true story.* New York: Anchor Books (Random House); 323 pages.

Quammen, D. 1996. *The song of the dodo. Island biogeography in the age of extinctions.* New York: Scribner; 702 pages.

Quevedo V., E., Manosalva R., C., Tafur A., M., Matiz, G., and Morales L., E. 2008. Knowledge and power: the asymmetry of interests of Colombian and Rockefeller doctors in the construction of the concept of "Jungle yellow fever", 1907-1938. *Canad. Bull. Med. Hist.* 25:71-109.

Rambhia, K.J., A.S. Ribner, and G.K. Gronvall. 2011. Everywhere you look: select agent pathogens. *Biosecur. Bioterror.* 9:69-71.

Reed, L.J., and H. Muench. 1938.. A simple method of estimating fifty percent endpoints. *Am. J. Hyg.* 27:493–497.

Reed, W., J. Carroll, A. Agramonte, J.W. Lazear. 1900. The etiology of yellow fever—a preliminary note. *Public Health Pap Rep.* 26:37–53. [and *Philadelphia Med. J.* 6:790-796, 1900]

Reeves, W.C. 1990. *Epidemiology and control of mosquito-borne arboviruses in California, 1943-1987.* Sacramento, California: California Mosquito and Vector Control Assoc.; 508 pages.

Reeves W.C.1991. An oral history, University of California – Berkeley, School of Public Health <http://content.cdlib.org/view?docId=kt3j49n66k&query=&brand=calisphere>

Reeves, W.C., and W. McD. Hammon. 1944. Feeding habits of the proven and possible mosquito vectors of western equine and St. Louis encephalitis in the Yakima Valley, Washington. *Am. J. Trop. Med.* 24:131-134.

Rice, C.M., E.M. Lenches, S.R. Eddy, S.J. Shin, R.L. Sheets, and J.H. Strauss. 1985. Nucleotide sequence of yellow fever virus: implications for flavivirus gene expression and evolution. *Science.* 229:726–733.

Rico-Hesse, R. 1990. Molecular evolution and distribution of dengue viruses type 1 and 2 in nature. *Virology.* 174:479-493.

Rosen, G. 1993. *A history of public health.* Baltimore: Johns Hopkins University Press; 535 pages.

Rosen, L., and D. Gubler. 1974. The use of mosquitoes to detect and propagate dengue viruses. *Am. J. Trop. Med. Hyg.* 23:1153-1160.

Ross, R. 1897. On some peculiar pigmented cells found in two mosquitoes fed on malarial blood. *Brit. Med. J.* 18:1786-1788.

Ross, R.W. 1956. The Newala epidemic: III. The virus: isolation, pathogenic properties and relationship to the epidemic. *J. Hyg.* 54:177-191.

Sabin, A.B. 1951. Hemagglutination by viruses affecting the human nervous system. *Fed. Proc.* 10:573–578.

________. 1952. Research on dengue during World War II. *Am. J. Trop. Med. Hyg.* 1:30-50.

________. 1980. Karl Friedrich Meyer, a biographical memoir. Washington, D.C.: National Academy of Sciences, USA; pages 267-332.

Sabin, A.B., and E.L. Buescher. 1950. Unique physico-chemical properties of Japanese B encephalitis virus hemagglutinin. *Proc. Soc. Exp. Biol. Med.* 74:222–230.

Sabin, A.B., and P.K. Olitsky. 1936. Cultivation of poliovirus in vitro in human embryonic tissue. *Proc. Soc. Exper. Biol. Med.* 34:357-359.

Sanarelli, G. 1898. Das myxomatogene virus. Beitrag zum studium der krankheitserreger ausserhalb des sichtbaren. *Zentr. Bakt. Parasitenk.* 23:865-873.

Scherer, W.F., J. Madalengoitia, W. Flores, and M. Acosta. 1975. The first isolations of eastern encephalitis, Group C, and Guama group arboviruses from the Peruvian Amazon region of western South America. *Bull. Pan-Am. Health Org.* 9:19-26.

Scherer, W. F., G.A. Eddy, T.P. Monath, T.E. Walton, and J.H. Richardson. 1980. Laboratory safety for arboviruses and certain other viruses of vertebrates. *Am. J. Trop. Med. Hyg.* 29:1359-1381.

Schuffenecker, I., I. Iteman, A. Michault, S. Murri, L. Frangeul, M.-C. Vaney, R. Lavenir, N. Pardigon, J.-M. Reynes, F. Pettinelli, L. Biscornet, L. Diancourt, S. Michel, S. Duquerroy, G. Guigon, M.-P. Frenkiel, A.-C. Bréhin, N. Cubito, P. Desprès, F. Kunst, F.A. Rey, H. Zeller, and S. Brisse. 2006. Genome microevolution of chikungunya viruses causing the Indian Ocean outbreak. *PLoS Med.* 3:e263. doi: 10.1371/journal.pmed.0030263

Schuh, A.J., L. Li, R.B. Tesh, B.L. Innis, and A.D.T. Barrett. 2010. Genetic characterization of early isolates of Japanese encephalitis virus: genotype II has been circulating since at least 1951. *J. Gen. Virol.* 91:95-102.

Sciple, G.W., C.G. Ray, P. Holden, L.C. LaMotte, J.V. Irons, and T.D. Chin. 1968. Encephalitis in the high plains of Texas. *Am. J. Epidemiol.* 87:87-98.

Shoemaker, T., C. Boulianne, M.J. Vincent, L. Pezzanite, M.M. Al-Qahtani, Y. Al-Mazrou, A.S. Khan, P.E. Rollin, R. Swanepoel, T.G. Ksiazek, and S.T. Nichol. 2002. Genetic analysis of viruses associated with emergence of Rift Valley fever in Saudi Arabia and Yemen, 2000-01. *Emerg. Infect. Dis.* 8:1415-1420.

Shope, R.E. 1982. Rabies-related viruses. *Yale J. Biol. Med.* 55:271-275.

__________. 1998. A history of arbovirology in Brazil: Belém 1954-1965. in A.P.A. Travassos da Rosa, P.F.C. Vasconcelos, and J.F.S. Travassos da Rosa, eds., *Arbovirology in Brazil and neighboring countries.* Pages 12-17. Belém, Brazil: Instituto Evandro Chagas.

Shope, R.E., and O.R. Causey. 1962. Further studies on the serological relationships of group C arthropod-borne viruses and the application of these relationships to rapid identification of types. *Am. J. Trop. Med. Hyg.* 11:283-290.

Siegert, R., H.L. Shu, and W. Slenczka. 1968. Isolation and identification of the "Marburg virus". *Dtsch. Med. Wochenschr.* 93:604-612.

Siler, J.F., M.W. Hall, and A.P. Hitchens. 1926. Dengue: Its history, epidemiology, mechanism of transmission, etiology, clinical manifestations, immunity, and prevention. *Philipp. J. Sci.* 29:1-302.

Simmons, J.S., J.H. St. John, and F.H.K. Reynolds. 1931. Experimental studies of dengue. *Philipp. J. Sci.* 44:1-247.

Singh, K.R.P. 1967. Cell cultures derived from larvae of *Aedes albopictus* (Skuse) and *Aedes aegypti* (L.). *Current Science.* 36:506-508.

Smith, T., and F.L. Kilborne. 1893. *Investigations into the nature, causation, and prevention of Texas or Southern cattle fever.* U. S. Bureau of Animal Industry, Bulletin No. 1, Washington, D.C.: Government Printing Office. [reprinted in *Medical Classics*, 1936–1937, 1:372–597].

Smithburn, K.C., T.P. Hughes, A.W. Burke, and J.H. Paul. 1940. A neurotropic virus isolated from the blood of a native of Uganda. *Am. J. Trop. Med. Hyg.* 20:471-492.

Smithburn, K.C., A.J. Haddow, and W.H.R. Lumsden. 1949. An outbreak of sylvan yellow fever in Uganda with *Aedes (Stegomyia) africanus* Theobald as principal vector and insect host of the virus. *Ann. Trop. Med. Parasitol.* 43:74-89.

Smorodintseff, A.A. 1940. The spring-summer tick-borne encephalitis. *Arch. fur Ges. Virusforsch.* 1:468-480.

Spreull, J. 1905. Malarial catarrhal fever (bluetongue) of sheep in South Africa. *J. Comp. Pathol. Therap.* 18:321–337.

Strode, G.K., ed. 1951. *Yellow fever.* New York: McGraw-Hill; 710 pages.

Su, J., S. Li, X. Hu, X. Yu, Y. Wang, P. Liu, X. Lu, G. Zhang, X. Hu, D. Liu, X. Li, W. Su, H. Lu, N.S. Mok, P. Wang, M. Wang, K. Tian, and G.F. Gao. 2011. Duck egg-drop syndrome caused by BYD virus, a new Tembusu-related flavivirus. *PLoS One.* 6(3):e18106.

Sudia, W.D., and V. F. Newhouse. 1975. Epidemic Venezuelan equine encephalitis in North America: a summary of virus-vector-host relationships. *Amer. J. Epidemiol.* 101:1-13.

Sundin, D.R., B.J. Beaty, N. Nathanson, and F. Gonzalez-Scarano. 1987. A G1 glycoprotein epitope of La Crosse virus: a determinant of infection of *Aedes triseriatus. Science.* 235:591-593.

Syverton, J.T., and W.F. Scherer. 1953. Applications of strains of mammalian cells to the study of animal viruses. *Cold Spring Harb Symp Quant Biol.* 18:285-289.

Taylor, R.M. 1962. Purpose and progress in cataloguing and exchanging information on arthropod-borne viruses. *Am. J. Trop. Med. Hyg.* 11:169-174.

Taylor, R.M., and H.S. Hurlbut. 1953. Isolation of West Nile virus from *Culex* mosquitoes. *J. Royal Egypt. Med. Assoc.* 36:199-206.

Taylor, R.M., M.A. Haseeb, and T.H. Work. 1955. A regional reconnaissance on yellow fever in the Sudan, with special reference to primate hosts. *Bull. World Health Org.* 12:711-725.

Ten Broeck, C., E.W. Hurst, and E. Traub. 1935. Epidemiology of equine encephalomyelitis in the eastern United States. *J. Exper. Med.* 62:677-685.

Ten Broeck, C., and M.H. Merrill. 1934. A serological difference between eastern and western equine encephalomyelitis virus. *Proc. Soc. Exp. Biol. and Med.* 31:217-220.

Theiler, A. 1906. Bluetongue in sheep. *Ann. Rep. Dir. Agric. Transvaal,* 1904-1905, 110-121.

________. 1921. African horse sickness (pestis equorum). *S. Afr. Dept. Agr. Sci. Bull.* 19:1-29.

Theiler, M. 1930. Studies on the action of yellow fever virus in mice. *Ann. Trop. Med. Parasit.* 24:249-272.

________. 1957. Action of sodium desoxycholate on arthropod-borne viruses. *Proc. Soc. Exper. Biol. Med.* 96:380-382.

Theiler, M., and W.G. Downs. 1973. *The arthropod-borne viruses of vertebrates: an account of the Rockefeller Foundation virus program, 1951-1970.* New Haven: Yale University Press; 578 pages.

Thompson W.H. and Beaty B.J. (1978) Venereal transmission of La Crosse virus from male to female *Aedes triseriatus. Am. J. Trop. Med. Hyg.* 27:187-196.

Thompson, W.H., B. Kalfayan, and R.O. Anslow. 1965. Isolation of California encephalitis group virus from a fatal human illness. *Am. J. Epidemiol.* 81:245-253.

Tikasingh, E.S. 2000. *The hunt for Caribbean viruses. A history of the Trinidad Regional Virus Laboratory.* Port of Spain, Trinidad : Caribbean Epidemiology Centre: 156 pages.

Tikasingh, E.S., L. Spence, and W.G. Downs. 1966. The use of adjuvant and sarcoma 180 cells in the production of mouse hyperimmune ascetic fluids to arboviruses. *Am. J. Trop. Med. Hyg.* 15:219-226.

Towner, J.S., X. Pourrut, C.G. Albariño, C.N. Nkogue, B.H. Bird, G. Grard, T.G. Ksiazek, J.-P. Gonzalez, S.T. Nichol, and E.M. Leroy. 2007. Marburg virus infection detected in a common African bat. *PLoS One.* 2:e764.

Trent, D.W., J.A. Grant, L. Rosen, and T.P. Monath. 1983. Genetic variation among dengue 2 viruses of different geographic origin. *Virology.* 128:271-284.

Tsetsarkin, K.A., D.L. Vanlandingham, C.E. McGee, and S. Higgs. 2007. A single mutation in chikungunya virus affects vector specificity and epidemic potential. *PLoS Pathog.* 3(12):e201.

Tsetsarkin, K.A., R. Chen, G. Leal, N. Forrester, S. Higgs, J. Huang, and S. Weaver. 2011. Chikungunya virus emergence is constrained in Asia by lineage-specific adaptive landscapes. *Proc. Natl. Acad. Sci. USA.* 108:7872-7877.

Turell, M.J., K.J. Linthicum, L.A. Patrican, F.G. Davies, A. Kairo, and C.L. Bailey. 2008. Vector competence of selected African mosquito (Diptera: Culicidae) species for Rift Valley fever virus. *J. Med. Entomol.* 45:102–108.

van Regenmortel, M.H.V. 1989. Applying the species concept to plant viruses. *Arch. Virol.* 104:1-17.

van Regenmortel, M.H.V. 2005 The nature and classification of viruses, in B.W.J. Mahy and V. ter Meulen, eds., Topley & Wilson's Microbiology & Microbial Infections, vol. 1, London, England: Hodder Arnold; pages 24-25.

Virus Taxonomy, Eighth Report of the International Committee on Taxonomy of Viruses, C.M. Fauquet, M.A. Mayo, J. Maniloff, U. Desselberger and L.A. Ball, eds., London, England: Elsevier/Academic Press; 1259 pages.

Wallace, A.R. 1855. On the law which has regulated the introduction of new species. *Annals and Magazine of Natural History.* 16:184-196.

Watson, J.D., and F.H. Crick. 1953. A structure for deoxyribose nucleic acids. *Nature.* 171:737-738.

Watts, D.M., W.H. Thompson, T.M. Yuill, G.R. De Foliart, and R.P. Hanson. 1974. Overwintering of La Crosse virus in *Aedes triseriatus. Am. J. Trop. Med. Hyg.* 23:694-700.

Weaver, S.C., W. Kang, Y. Shirako, T. Rumenapf, E.G. Strauss, and J.H. Strauss. 1997. Recombinational history and molecular evolution of western equine encephalomyelitis complex alphaviruses. *J. Virol.* 71:613-623.

Webster, L.T. 1938. Japanese B encephalitis virus: its differentiation from St. Louis encephalitis virus and relationship to louping ill virus. *J. Exp. Med.* 67:609-621.

Webster, L.T., and G.L. Fite. 1933. A virus encountered in the study of material from cases of encephalitis in the St. Louis and Kansas City epidemics of 1933. *Science.* 78:463-475.

Weigand, H. and J Hotchin. 1961. Studies of lymphocytic choriomeningitis in mice. II. A comparison of the immune status of newborn and adult mice surviving inoculation. *J Immunol.* 86:401-406.

Weissenböck, H., J. Kolodziejek, A. Url, H. Lussy, B. Rebel-Bauder, and N. Nowotny. 2002. Emergence of Usutu virus, an African mosquito-borne flavivirus of the Japanese encephalitis virus group, central Europe. *Emerg. Infect. Dis.* 8:652-656.

Whitman, L., and J. Casals. 1961. The Guama group: a new serological group of hitherto undescribed viruses. Immunological studies. *Am. J. Trop. Med. Hyg.* 10:259-263.

Whitman, L., and R.E. Shope. 1962. The California complex of arthropod-borne viruses and its relationship to the Bunyamwera group through Guaroa virus. *Am. J. Trop. Med. Hyg.* 11:691-696.

Williams, M.C., and J.P. Woodall. 1961. O'nyong-nyong fever: an epidemic virus disease in East Africa. II. Isolation and some properties of the virus. *Trans. Royal Soc. Trop. Med. Hyg.* 55:135-141.

Wong, S., S. Lau, P. Woo, and K.Y. Yuen. 2007. Bats as a continuing source of emerging infections in humans. *Rev. Med. Virol.* 17:67-91.

Woodall, J.P., M.C. Williams. and D.I. Simpson. 1967. Congo virus: a hitherto undescribed virus occurring in Africa. II. Identification studies. *East Afr. Med. J.* 44:93-98.

Woodruff, A.M., and E.W. Goodpasture. 1931. The susceptibility of chorio-allantoic membrane of chick embryos to infection with the fowl-pox virus. *Am. J. Pathol.* 7:209-222.

Work, T.H. 1961. The expanding role of arthropod-borne viruses in tropical medicine. *Industry and Tropical Health: IV.* Industrial Council of tropical Health. Boston: Massachusetts: Harvard School of Public Health; 21 pages.

Work, T.H. 1964. Serological evidence of arbovirus infection in the Seminole Indians of south Florida. *Science.* 145:270-272.

Work T.H. 1971. On the Japanese B – West Nile virus complex or an arbovirus problem of six continents. *Am. J. Trop. Med. Hyg.* 20:169-186.

Work, T.H., H.S. Hurlbut, and R.M. Taylor. 1953. Isolation of West Nile virus from hooded crow and rock pigeon in the Nile delta. *Proc Soc Exp Biol Med.* 84:719-722

Work, T.H., H.S. Hurlbut, and R.M. Taylor. (1955) Indigenous wild birds of the Nile Delta as potential West Nile virus circulating reservoirs. *Am. J. Trop. Med. Hyg.* 4:872-888.

Work, T.H., and H. Trapido. 1957. Kyasanur Forest disease. A new virus disease in India. *Ind. J. Med. Sci.* 11:1-2.

Yanase, T., K. Maeda, T. Kato, S. Nyuta, H. Kamata, M. Yamakawa, and T. Tsuda. 2005. The resurgence of Shamonda virus, an African Simbu group virus of the genus *Orthobunyavirus*, in Japan. *Arch. Virol.* 150:361-369.

Yates, T.L., J.N. Mills, C.A. Parmenter, T.G. Ksiazek, R.R. Parmenter, J.R. Vande Castle, C.H. Calisher, S.T. Nichol, K.D. Abbott, J.C. Young, M.L. Morrison, B.J. Beaty, J.L. Dunnum, R.J. Baker, J. Salazar-Bravo, and C.J. Peters. 2002. The ecology and evolutionary history of an emergent disease: hantavirus pulmonary syndrome. *BioScience.* 52:989-998.

Young, N.A., and K.M. Johnson. 1969. Antigenic variants of Venezuelan equine encephalitis virus: their geographic distribution and epidemiologic significance. *Am. J. Epidemiol.* 89:286–307.

Yu, X.J., M.F. Liang, S.Y. Zhang, Y. Liu, J.D. Li, Y.L. Sun, L. Zhang, Q.F. Zhang, V.L. Popov, C. Li, J. Qu, Q. Li , Y.P. Zhang, R. Hai, W. Wu, Q. Wang, F.X. Zhan, X.J. Wang, B. Kan, S.W. Wang, K.L. Wan, H. Q. Jing, J.X. Lu, W.W. Yin, H. Zhou, X.H. Guan, J.F. Liu, Z.Q. Bi, G.H. Liu, J. Ren, H. Wang, Z. Zhao, J.D. Song, J.R. He, T. Wan, J.S. Zhang, X.P. Fu, L.N. Sun, X.P. Dong, Z.J. Feng, W.Z. Yang, T. Hong, Y. Zhang, D.H. Walker, Y. Wang, D.X. Li. 2011. Fever with thrombocytopenia associated with a novel bunyavirus in China. *N. Engl. J. Med.* 364:1523-1532.

Zeller, H.G., N. Karabatsos, C.H. Calisher, J.-P. Digoutte, C.B. Cropp, F.A. Murphy, and R.E. Shope. 1989. Electron microscopic and antigenic studies of uncharacterized viruses. II. Evidence suggesting the placement of viruses in the family *Bunyaviridae. Arch. Virol.* 108:211 227.

Zilber, L.A., E.N. Levkovich, A.K. Shubladze, M.P. Chumakov, V.D. Solov'ev, and A.D. Sheboldaeva. 1938. Etiology of spring-summer epidemic encephalitis. *Arch. Biol. Sci.* 52:162–183.

Useful web sites:

American Society for Tropical Medicine and Hygiene: http://www.astmh.org/AM/Template.cfm?Section=Meeting_Archives&Template=/CM/ContentDisplay.cfm&ContentID=1501

ProMED-mail: http://www.isid.org/promedmail/promedmail.shtml

Pubmed: http://www.ncbi.nlm.nih.gov/sites/entrez?db=pubmed

Rockefeller Archives Center: http://www.rockarch.org/

University of Texas Medical Branch at Galveston: http://www.utmb.edu/pathology/

University of Virginia web site: (http://yellowfever.lib.virginia.edu/reed/ and http://etext.virginia.edu/healthsci/reed/commission.html)

United States Army Medical Research Institute of Infectious Diseases: http://www.usamriid.army.mil/

United States Centers for Disease Control and Prevention: http://www.cdc.gov/

United States National Institutes of Health, National Institutes of Allergy and Infectious Diseases: http://www.niaid.nih.gov/Pages/default.aspx

Walter Reed Army Institute of Research: http://wrair-www.army.mil/

Index of Investigators

Made in the USA
Middletown, DE
14 May 2015